Teaching

Vocational Agriculture

E. W. GARRIS

Head of the Department of Agricultural Education
College of Education and College of Agriculture
University of Florida

McGRAW-HILL BOOK COMPANY, INC.

NEW YORK   TORONTO   LONDON

TEACHING VOCATIONAL AGRICULTURE

Library of Congress Catalog Card Number: 53-5162

THE MAPLE PRESS COMPANY, YORK, PA.

Preface

VOCATIONAL AGRICULTURE had become important in many states in the Union before the passage of the Smith-Hughes Act in 1917. Since that date, the Smith-Hughes and the George-Barden Acts have had certain basic requirements for states to meet that have given a thread of unity to the total program in the United States. On the other hand, each state has much latitude in designing an educational program that will best serve its own needs.

A teacher of vocational agriculture has a variety of teaching opportunities in the classroom, in the farm-mechanics shop, and on the farms of the community. He is called upon to give instruction to farm youth, young farmers, and adult farmers. His course of study must be so designed that it will fill the educational need of farm people as they try to become established in farming or try to make progress in farming after they are established. In short, a teacher of vocational agriculture should be proficient in group and in individualized instruction, have a working knowledge of public relations, be a skilled mechanic, and be able to meet all other problems common to public-school teachers.

Having had experience as a teacher of vocational agriculture and as an Assistant State Supervisor of Agricultural Education in South Carolina, as State Supervisor of Agricultural Education in Florida, and, for the past twenty-six years, as head of the Department of Agricultural Education at the University of Florida, the author hopes that he is offering practical help to students who are planning to teach and to employed teachers who desire to make professional growth. Some theory and philosophy are included to give an understanding of the problems, but practical suggestions form the core of the text.

The author wishes to express his appreciation to leaders in his field for many helpful suggestions, to students who often gave insight into problems, and to a number of individuals who were generous in furnishing suitable illustrations.

E. W. GARRIS

Contents

x   CONTENTS

Editor's Foreword

SINCE 1917, the teaching of vocational agriculture has developed as a distinct phase of vocational education. Operating within the framework of America's vast public school system, such teaching has become unique in many respects. Teachers of vocational agriculture hold an enviable position with reference to prospective and present farmers, the school in which they are located, and the rural community of which they are an important part. No other teacher has the opportunity to become so closely acquainted with the home and family life of farmer citizens as does the teacher of vocational agriculture.

The teaching of vocational agriculture is a many-sided occupation. It calls for first-hand basic technical knowledge of farming as an occupation and a business. It requires fundamental and specialized knowledge and skill in how to train others in the many jobs which occur in the daily life and work of agricultural citizens. Such teaching calls for a high degree of leadership and public relations ability. Over a long period of years specific training of this kind has been done by capable teacher trainers in land-grant colleges of the nation.

From the ranks of these teacher trainers comes the author of "Teaching Vocational Agriculture," Dr. E. W. Garris, who holds B.S. and D.Sc. degrees from Clemson College, an M.A. from the University of South Carolina, and a Ph.D. from George Peabody College.

The author has been successively a high school principal, teacher of vocational agriculture, Supervisor of Agricultural Education in South Carolina and Florida, and Head of the Department of Agricultural Education at the University of Florida where he has served continuously since 1927.

"Teaching Vocational Agriculture" represents the best in experience of many teachers of vocational agriculture in all parts of the country over a period of years. It is a guide and source of valuable information for the trainee preparing to teach, the new teacher on the job, and the experienced teacher of vocational agriculture.

W. A. Ross

FIG. 1. Future Farmer today, established farmer and rural leader tomorrow. Such young men typify the American spirit of faith in farming. (*Courtesy of J. K. Coggin, North Carolina.*)

from 83% to 5%

1. Tracing the Development of Agricultural Education

S IGNIFICANT and far-reaching changes have modified the work and the lives of farm people since the early days of Colonial America. Because of the influence of these changes, the public became interested in an educational program that would aid farmers in adjusting to the new demands.

Changes in Rural Population. In 1820, 83 percent of the working population in the United States was engaged in farming. Today between 15 and 20 percent is so engaged. Various improvements in the use of farm machinery have made it possible today for one man, using power equipment, to produce as much food as 28 to 30 men did in 1820. It is doubtful whether people today consume less food: far greater quantities are exported, and a much greater volume of agricultural products is used in industry.

In 1950 there were approximately 54 million people in America living on farms and in villages not exceeding 2,500 in population. These two groups comprised our rural population, which was 36 percent of the total.

From the 1950 census one can see that rural families have more children than urban families. Few cities would be able to maintain their present population levels if no rural people were allowed to migrate there.

The Rural School. Many changes have been made since the era of the one-teacher "little red school house." Consolidation has had a marked effect upon rural schools, but even today about 20 percent of the rural pupils are enrolled in schools having one or two teachers. It is estimated that in 1944 there were approximately 108,000 one-teacher schools.[1] In 1953 there were only about 60,000 one-teacher schools.

It is probably true that many of the best and most of the poorest schools to be found in America are in the rural areas. In many states, however, rural-school consolidation is making it possible for all pupils to have the advantages of high school. School laws have been changed to provide a minimum term of nine months for nearly all schools. Also, many states now require teachers of rural schools to meet the same qualifications as teachers for city

[1] The White House Conference on Rural Education, p. 30, National Education Association, Washington, D.C., 1944.

1

FIG. 2. Small one-teacher school in a sparsely settled rural community.   Far too many of these schools still exist in the United States.   (*Alabama State Department of Education.*)

FIG. 3. A substantial building for a one-teacher school in Chester County, Pennsylvania. (*Courtesy of H. A. Dawson, National Education Association.*)

schools meet.   The same salary scale is often paid to a teacher regardless of where his assignment may happen to be.

The rural schools are gradually being improved from the standpoint of buildings, equipment, and reference materials.   In these larger rural schools, it is possible to offer elective subjects in the high school.   It is from the rural population that the majority of our farmers of the future come, and the rural high school is an excellent place to offer vocational agriculture.

The Need for Agricultural Training. In the early Colonial period of America, the members of a farm family did much of the work now commonly done in industrial plants. On such a farm the boys learned how to make furniture, shoes, harness, and other equipment. They also acquired many of the skills involved in the repair of farm buildings and equipment. Today, however, farm boys spend nine, rather than three, months of each year in school and have less opportunity to learn skills from their parents. The use of farm machinery now demands that the farm operator be skilled in performing many mechanical jobs. The standard of living in progressive rural communities is far higher than it was a century ago. With the coming of

FIG. 4. Four-teacher school in a rural area. (*Alabama State Department of Education.*)

improved highways, better communication facilities, the radio, television, and rural electrification, a farm family now can enjoy practically any of the modern conveniences available to the city dweller. In such an age a successful farm operator must be a good businessman as well as one skilled in farm technology and management. He must know how to conserve and improve the soil, how to manage water, how to combat insect and disease pests, how to manage labor, how to use farm capital wisely, how to anticipate price changes, how to market farm products properly, and how to perform the necessary jobs in growing crops and raising animals.

The present age has brought about keen competition. Nothing less than the best training is required to meet the needs of a successful farmer. However, it is true that different levels of training are needed for the various responsibilities on a farm. A farm laborer who expects to remain one needs to know little more than how to perform certain skills, but these needed skills are getting more complicated with the increased use of modern equipment.

The farm manager needs to possess the skills and have all the facts necessary in making the business decisions he must face.

The average operating period for a farmer has been estimated by the U.S. Department of Agriculture to be twenty years. Individuals have estimated it to be as much as thirty years. To fill the places of farmers and ranchers who must retire annually, there should be a large number of boys and young men in training. Since new and improved methods of farming are constantly being introduced, adults also need instruction from time to time after they have entered the business of farming.

FIG. 5. East Whiteland Consolidated School, Chester County, Pennsylvania. (*Courtesy of H. A. Dawson, National Education Association.*)

Some Early Developments in Agricultural Education. Prior to the passage of the Smith-Hughes Act in 1917, a number of different plans were being followed in certain states for teaching agriculture in secondary schools. Examples of these plans and some states that used them are as follows:

1. State agricultural schools (Minnesota, Nebraska, California)
2. Congressional district agricultural schools (Georgia, Alabama, Virginia)
3. Judicial district agricultural schools (Oklahoma)
4. County agricultural schools (Wisconsin, Michigan, Mississippi)
5. Departments in high schools (Massachusetts, New York, Louisiana, South Carolina)

The first state to begin its program of a state school for secondary agriculture was Minnesota. The school was organized in 1888 in connection with the agricultural college of the State University at St. Anthony Park. The school used the same buildings, equipment, and faculty as the agricultural college.[2]

[2] Development of Agricultural Instruction in Secondary Schools, U.S. Office of Education, *Bulletin* 85, 1919.

Fig. 6. An excellent place to teach vocational agriculture, Unionville Joint Consolidated School, Pennsylvania. (*Courtesy of H. A. Dawson, National Education Association.*)

Fig. 7. Problems in raising hogs form the basis of this young man's agricultural instruction at school. (*Courtesy of D. C. Aebischer, Wisconsin.*)

Any citizen of the state could register who had completed the work of the rural school.

In Georgia there were established 11 congressional district schools.[3] Each of the districts had to provide a minimum of 200 acres of land, the necessary buildings, dormitories, livestock, and equipment. The first state appropria-

[3] Georgia Statutes, Act 448, p. 72, 1906.

tion was $6,000 per district.   In all, the state of Georgia received 3,044 acres of land and cash donations of $470,000 to help the various districts qualify for the appropriation.[4]

The minimum age for entrance in the congressional district schools in Georgia was fourteen for boys and thirteen for girls.   Pupils studying agriculture had to do practical jobs on the school farm.   The course of study extended through four years.   Of the total school day at least three hours had to be devoted to the teaching of agriculture and related sciences.   The course of study included farm crops the first year, horticulture the second year, animal husbandry the third year, and farm management the fourth year.

Oklahoma provided judicial district agricultural schools.   They were very similar in organization to the congressional district schools.   Each school was required to provide a minimum of 80 acres of land.   Citizens over fifteen years of age were admitted without entrance examinations or fees.[5]

Wisconsin was probably the first state to start a program of county agricultural schools.[6]   The state law provided that each county maintaining an agricultural school would receive one-half of the cost per year, not to exceed $2,500, from the state.   The law was later changed so that the state would pay two-thirds of the cost, not to exceed $4,000.   At least three acres of land had to be available.   The course of study was for a period of two years. Pupils were admitted who had a common school education as then obtained in the rural schools.

States organizing the instruction in departments in high schools usually followed the home-project plan.   The home projects formed the core of instruction.   Such high schools were reimbursed on several different bases. Massachusetts paid two-thirds of the salary of the teacher,[7] whereas South Carolina paid $1,500 of each teacher's salary, leaving the balance to the school or county.[8]

Practically every state in the Union had adopted some plan of teaching agriculture on a secondary level prior to the passage of the Smith-Hughes Act of 1917.   Since the passage of the act, comparable programs of instruction have been developed in all the states.

The Project Method of Teaching.   The project method of teaching is often used by teachers of general high school subjects.[9]   Both Massachusetts

[4] Report of the Office of Experiment Stations, U.S. Department of Agriculture, 1907–1908.

[5] Oklahoma Senate Bill 109, chap. 3, 1908.

[6] Wisconsin Laws of 1901, chap. 188, sec. 10.

[7] STIMSON, R. W., "Vocational Agricultural Education," p. 24, The Macmillan Company, New York, 1919.

[8] Smoak-Rector Bill, South Carolina, 1916.

[9] KILPATRICK, W. H., "Foundations of Method," The Macmillan Company, New York, 1925.

and New York are credited with first using the project method of teaching for vocational agriculture. Records indicated that home projects were used as the basis for teaching agriculture in Massachusetts as early as 1908.[10]

In conducting productive farming projects on the home farms, educational processes become immediately effective. The problems, skills, and decisions necessary in conducting the home projects form the basis for the course of study to be followed by the learners.

FIG. 8. Using the project method of teaching in the school farm-mechanics shop. (*Courtesy of T. L. Faulkner, Alabama.*)

The pattern of home projects established by Massachusetts and New York was later followed, after the passage of the Smith-Hughes Act, by other states.

SELECTED REFERENCES

Development of Agricultural Instruction in Secondary Schools, U.S. Office of Education, *Bulletin* 85, 1919.

Georgia Statutes, Act 448, 1906.

HAWKINS, L. S., C. A. PROSSER, and J. C. WRIGHT, "Development of Vocational Education," American Technical Society, Chicago, 1951.

[10] STIMSON, R. W., "Vocational Agricultural Education," The Macmillan Company, New York, 1919.

History of Agricultural Education of Less Than College Grade in the
      United States, U.S. Office of Education, Division of Vocational Edu-
      cation, *Bulletin* 217, Agricultural Series 55, 1942.

The Massachusetts Home Project Plan for Vocational Agricultural Edu-
      cation, U.S. Office of Education, *Bulletin* 8, 1914.

Oklahoma Senate Bill 109, chap. 3, 1908.

Report of the Office of Experiment Stations, U.S. Department of Agri-
      culture, 1907–1908.

Smoak-Rector Bill, South Carolina, 1916.

STIMSON, R. W., "Vocational Agricultural Education," The Macmillan
      Company, New York, 1919.

The White House Conference on Rural Education, National Education
      Association, Washington, D.C., 1944.

Wisconsin Laws of 1901, chap. 188, sec. 10.

2. Tracing the Development of Vocational Education

IN 1914, PRESIDENT WILSON appointed a committee, known as the "Commission on National Aid to Vocational Education," for the purpose of studying the need for a program of vocational education of less than college grade. In the report of the commission to Congress, 12 reasons were given in favor of Federal participation in such a program.[1] It must be remembered that the arguments were presented at a time when Europe was in the early stages of the First World War and that certain conditions change over a period of years. The reasons stated at that time are summarized as follows:

1. Vocational education is needed to conserve and develop our natural resources.
2. Vocational education is needed to prevent the waste of human labor.
3. Vocational education is needed to provide a supplement to apprenticeship.
4. Vocational education is needed to increase wage-earning power.
5. Vocational education is needed to meet the increasing demand for trained workers.
6. Vocational education is needed to offset the increased cost of living.
7. Vocational education is a wise business investment.
8. Vocational education is needed because our national prosperity is at stake.
9. Vocational education is needed to democratize the education in our public schools.
10. Vocational education is needed for its direct and positive effect on the aims and methods of general education.
11. Industrial and social unrest is due in a large measure to the lack of vocational training.
12. Higher standards of living are a direct result of better vocational education and general education.

[1] Report of the Commission on National Aid to Vocational Education, *House Document* 1004, vol. 1, pp. 16–39, 1914.

There was some opposition to the report of the commission to Congress. Strange as it may seem, the chief opposition came from the people themselves, many of whom at that time were opposed to the principle of Federal aid for any form of education. The work of the commission bore fruit, however, in the drafting and in the passage of the National Vocational Education Act, commonly called the "Smith-Hughes Act" after the two authors, Senator

FIG. 9. The late Senator Hoke Smith of Georgia, coauthor of the Smith-Hughes Act.

FIG. 10. The late Dudley M. Hughes, congressman from Georgia, coauthor of the Smith-Hughes Act.

Hoke Smith of Georgia and Representative Dudley M. Hughes of Georgia, who were members of the commission.

Purposes of the National Vocational Education Acts.   As stated in the first paragraph of the Smith-Hughes Act of 1917, the main purpose of this act is to promote a program of vocational education of less than college grade. The act provides for a plan of cooperation between the Federal government and the various states in the task of promoting such a program.   This cooperation is based upon four fundamental factors:

1. Vocational education is essential to our national welfare; therefore, it is a function of the Federal government to assist in the program.
2. Federal funds are needed to equalize the burden among the states in providing such a program.
3. The Federal government is vitally interested in the program for vocational education and should, so to speak, purchase a degree of participation.
4. By maintaining a plan of cooperation between the Federal and local governments, better and more uniform standards may be obtained.

Between 1926 and 1946 other national vocational education acts were passed which contributed further financially to the promotion of vocational

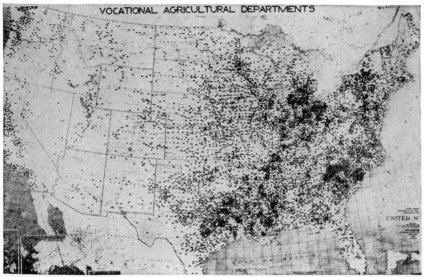

Fig. 11. Locations of departments of vocational agriculture in the United States. (*Vocational Division, U.S. Office of Education.*)

education, including vocational agriculture.   Important among them were the George-Reed Act of 1926 and the George-Ellzey Act of 1934.   These two temporary acts resulted in increased vocational offerings but neither of them assured continuing aid.   The George-Deen Act of 1937, however, authorized funds for apportionment to the states and territories, including Alaska and the District of Columbia.   With the exception of the matching plan and an actual continuing appropriation in the Smith-Hughes Act, the purposes and provisions of this act that pertained to agriculture were the same as in the Smith-Hughes Act.   The George-Barden Act of 1946 replaced the George-Deen Act with increased continuing authorization and liberalization of policies governing vocational education expenditures.   As stated in this act, it is designed "to provide for the further development of vocational education in the several states and territories."

Funds Provided for Agricultural Education.   The Smith-Hughes Act now provides for a sum of 3 million dollars appropriated annually for vocational agriculture.   The money is apportioned to a state on the basis of its rural population as compared with the total rural population of the United States.   No state can receive less than $10,000.

The George-Barden Act authorizes a sum of 10 million dollars annually for vocational agriculture.   The money is apportioned to a state based on its farm population as compared with the farm population of the United States. No state can receive less than $40,000.

Money from the agricultural fund of the Smith-Hughes Act can be expended only for the reimbursement of the salaries of teachers and super-

Fig. 12. Teaching some fine points in the selection of dairy cows to an all-day group. Participating experience in actual selection will follow.   (*Courtesy of C. D. Watson, Vermont.*)

visors.   If so stated in the state plans, money from the agricultural fund from the George-Barden Act may be expended for the following purposes:

1. For supervision
2. For training teachers
3. For approved travel
4. For equipment and supplies
5. For the salaries of regular and special teachers
6. For administration

How the Acts Are Administered.   The Smith-Hughes Act, as passed in 1917, provided for a Federal Board for Vocational Education in Washington and for a state board for vocational education in each state. The Federal Board for Vocational Education was then composed of the following personnel:

The Secretary of Agriculture
The Secretary of Labor
The Secretary of Commerce
The United States Commissioner of Education
Three members appointed by the President
    (One representing agriculture, one rep-
    resenting labor, and one representing
    manufacture and commerce.)

Fig. 13. An all-day class in forestry in a natural setting for practical instruction.

The Federal Board for Vocational Education met monthly at first and transacted all business with the various state boards for vocational education.

In 1933 Congress gave the President authority to consolidate many independent agencies. By Executive order all functions of the Federal Board for Vocational Education were transferred to the Department of the Interior. On October 10, 1933, the Secretary of Interior assigned the functions of the Federal Board for Vocational Education to the U.S. Office of Education through the United States Commissioner of Education. This board was retained in an advisory capacity until 1946, when it was abolished by order of the President.

The United States Commissioner of Education appointed an Assistant Commissioner for Vocational Education to be in direct charge of all types of vocational education. Under him were a Chief of the Agricultural Education Branch and various specialists.

The Smith-Hughes Act required each state to either create or designate a state board for vocational education, a board through which the Vocational Division of the U.S. Office of Education legally deals. Among other things, a state board for vocational education has the following duties:

1. Designates colleges to train teachers.
2. Submits state plans to the Office of Education for approval.
3. Appoints state supervisors.
4. Approves new vocational schools or departments.
5. Approves annual budgets.
6. Makes annual reports to the Office of Education.

The state plans for vocational education submitted by the state board must show the following:

1. The kind of vocational education for which it is proposed that the money shall be used.
2. The kinds of schools and the types of equipment.
3. The course of study to be followed.
4. The qualifications of teachers.
5. The methods of instruction to be used.
6. The qualifications of supervisors and teacher-trainers.
7. The plan for training teachers.
8. The plan for supervising teachers.
9. The plan for paying the salaries of vocational teachers.

Types of Vocational Agriculture Classes. The program of vocational agriculture is designed to give further training to people who are farming as well as to prepare those who plan to enter the vocation of farming. To meet these two objectives, the states organize three types of classes:

1. Day classes
   a. All-day
   b. Day-unit
2. Young-farmer classes
3. Adult-farmer classes

The All-day Class. This class is designed for boys who are in school, usually high school, and who are at least fourteen years of age. Classes meet 60 to 90 minutes or more daily according to one of four time schedules recommended by the Vocational Division of the U.S. Office of Education.

The Day-unit Class. This class, a modification of the all-day class, is designed for farm boys enrolled in rural schools where a regular all-day department of vocational agriculture has not been established.   Classes must

FIG. 14. Students of vocational agriculture discussing their problems in a class conducted by the teacher of vocational agriculture.   (*Courtesy of C. D. Watson, Vermont.*)

meet for a minimum of 90 consecutive minutes each week during the school term.

The Young-farmer Class. This class is designed to assist young men and boys who have left school, helping them become satisfactorily established in

FIG. 15. Young-farmer group discussions are a feature of vocational teaching.   (*U.S. Office of Education.*)

farming.   The length of the class periods usually varies from 90 to 120 minutes and the number of class meetings from 15 to 30.   The class may meet daily for several weeks, or it may meet periodically throughout the year.

The number of class meetings and the frequency of meetings should be based upon a year-round program of instruction.

The Adult-farmer Class. This class, often called an "evening class," is conducted to give farmers assistance in improving specific phases of their farm business, frequently of a managerial nature. The class meets for a minimum of 90 to 120 minutes at needed intervals for a total of 10 or more meetings throughout the year.

Aims of Secondary Education. A major part of the teaching time in vocational agriculture is done in all-day classes in the high school. It is

FIG. 16. Adult farmers discuss the principles of terracing in a vocational agriculture adult evening class. (*Courtesy of J. K. Coggin, North Carolina.*)

advisable, therefore, for the teacher of agriculture to keep clearly in mind the aims or objectives of the secondary school. The Committee on the Reorganization of Secondary Education in its report gave the following objectives:[2]

1. A better command of the fundamental processes
2. Health
3. Citizenship
4. Worthy home membership
5. Vocational efficiency
6. Worthy use of leisure time
7. Ethical character

[2] Cardinal Principles of Secondary Education, U.S. Office of Education, *Bulletin* 25, 1918.

Foster[3] has suggested that the aim of leadership-followship should be added.

In the report of the Educational Policies Commission, four groups of objectives for education in a democracy were emphasized:[4]

1. The objectives of self-realization
2. The objectives of human relationships
3. The objectives of economic efficiency
4. The objectives of civic responsibilities

From a report of the Department of Secondary School Principals in 1937,[5] a person may find listed 10 functions of secondary education:

1. Integration. To continue by a definite program, though in a diminishing degree, the integration of pupils. This should be on an increasingly intellectual level until the desired common knowledge, appreciation, ideals, attitudes, and practices are firmly fixed.
2. Satisfaction of needs. To satisfy the important immediate and probable future needs of pupils in so far as the maturity of the learner permits.
3. Revaluation of the racial heritage.
4. Exploration of interests, aptitudes, and capacities.
5. Systematization and application of knowledge, especially laws and principles.
6. Establishment and direction of interests.
7. Guidance.
8. Methods of teaching and learning involving the elementary principles of research.
9. Differentiation.
10. Retention and direction of pupils.

Aims of Agricultural Education. In teaching vocational agriculture, the teacher is trying to meet the vocational efficiency objective of the establishment of farm youth and out-of-school young men in farming and the improvement in the economic and farming status of persons already engaged in farming. As stated in the text of the Smith-Hughes Act, the chief aims of agricultural education of less than college grade are[6]

[3] FOSTER, H. H., "High School Administration," Appleton-Century-Crofts, Inc., New York, 1928.

[4] Educational Policies Commission, The Purposes of Education in American Democracy, National Education Association, Washington, D.C., 1937.

[5] Committee on Orientation, Functions of Secondary Education, *Bulletin* 64, National Education Association, Washington, D.C., 1937.

[6] Smith-Hughes Act, sec. 10, 1917.

1. That controlling purpose of such education shall be to fit for useful employment.
2. That such education shall be designed to meet the needs of persons over fourteen years of age who have entered upon or who are preparing to enter upon the work of the farm.

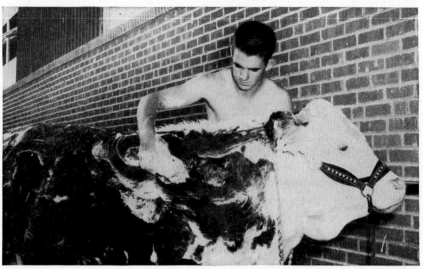

Fig. 17. Producing high-quality animals is a part of producing agricultural products efficiently.

Dr. Eaton once stated that the course of study in vocational agriculture should have two functions:[7]

1. To prepare pupils to meet their immediate agricultural needs.
2. To prepare pupils to meet with growing efficiency and happiness the demands of a progressive vocation of farming.

In 1929 a committee was appointed to list the aims of agricultural education of less than college grade. The objectives listed were as follows:[8]

1. To produce agricultural products efficiently.
2. To market agricultural products commercially.
3. To select and purchase suitable farm equipment and supplies.
4. To cooperate intelligently in economic activities.
5. To manage the farm business effectively.

[7] U.S. Office of Education, Division of Vocational Education, *Bulletin* 98, Agricultural Series, 1934.

[8] Objectives for a Program in Vocational Agriculture, U.S. Office of Education, Division of Vocational Education, *Miscellaneous Publication* 1046, 1929.

6. To maintain a satisfactory farm home.
7. To perform appropriate and economic farm-mechanics activities.
8. To participate in worthy rural social activities.
9. To use scientific knowledge and procedure in a farming occupation.
10. To exercise constructive leadership.
11. To grow vocationally.
12. To get successfully established in farming.

FIG. 18. To get farm boys successfully established in farming is the primary objective of vocational education in agriculture.

Other objectives often quoted are from *Monograph* 21.   Stated in terms of abilities, the following are given:[9]

1. To make a beginning and advance in farming.
2. To produce farm commodities efficiently.
3. To market farm products advantageously.
4. To conserve soil and other natural resources.
5. To manage a farm business.
6. To maintain a favorable environment.

In 1931 the Southern Regional Conference at Tulsa, Oklahoma, adopted a list of 27 abilities which a farmer should possess after he has been properly trained.[10]   The development of these abilities should be the aim of each agricultural teacher.

[9] Educational Objectives in Vocational Agriculture, U.S. Office of Education, Division of Vocational Education, *Monograph* 21, 1940.

[10] Report of Southern Regional Conference, Tulsa, Okla., 1931, U.S. Office of Education, Division of Vocational Education.

TWENTY-SEVEN ABILITIES

I. *Soils*

1. Ability to determine the adaptation of particular types of soils for particular crops, pastures, and timber.
2. Ability to utilize particular types of soils for the largest economic return for the farm as a whole.
3. Ability to adapt tillage practices to different types of soils.
4. Ability to select and use appropriate methods of building up and maintaining soil productivity.

II. *Production*

5. Ability to select and use the most economical practices in crop and livestock production.
6. Ability to economically produce and handle livestock.
7. Ability to select, produce, and utilize suitable food crops for the farm families.
8. Ability to produce crops of desired quality according to market demands.
9. Ability to produce livestock and livestock products of desired quality according to market demands.
10. Ability to use and keep up machinery and power equipment best suited to market demands.

III. *Farm Organization*

11. Ability to combine the farm enterprises which will make the farm organization as a whole most productive as to maximum economic returns, both present and long-time.
12. Ability to organize and manage the farm business so as to provide economic security.
13. Ability to select the farming practices, machinery, and power equipment best suited to the farm organization.
14. Ability to make the maximum utilization of labor, capital, and land resources.
15. Ability to make adjustments in production of farm products on the basis of:
    a. Probable market conditions when the product is ready for the market.
    b. Relationship between the supply and price of major farm products grown in the community.
    c. Business conditions (local, domestic, and foreign) and prices of farm products.
    d. Competition between producing regions.
16. Ability to make practical adjustments in production, taking into consideration the limitations of the individual farm business.
17. Ability to determine the most economical size of farm for any given type.

IV. *Marketing*

18. Ability to evaluate the marketing opportunities and the advantages and limitations of the marketing agencies accessible to the farmer for the existing and potential products of the farm.
19. Ability to adapt profitable production to market demands as to quality.
20. Ability to determine buying and selling programs in keeping with probable price trends for a season.

V. *Capital and Investment*

21. Ability to determine an actual need for credit.
22. Ability to establish and maintain a good credit rating.

23. Ability to conserve farming credit.
24. Ability to rent or buy a farm.
25. Ability to create reserve capital.

VI. *Sociological*

26. Ability to utilize the economic returns of farming for satisfactory standards of living through:
    a. Farm and home conveniences.
    b. Beautification of farmstead.
    c. Recreation.
    d. Civic relationships.
27. Ability to recognize and appreciate the aesthetic values of life.

SELECTED REFERENCES

COOK, G. C., and L. J. PHIPPS, "A Handbook on Teaching Vocational Agriculture," The Interstate, Danville, Ill., 1952.

George-Barden Act, Public Law 586, Seventy-ninth Congress, Senate Bill 619.

HAMLIN, H. M., "Agricultural Education in Community Schools," The Interstate, Danville, Ill., 1949.

HAWKINS, L. S., C. A. PROSSER, and J. C. WRIGHT, "Development of Vocational Education," American Technical Society, Chicago, 1951.

National Vocational Education Act (Smith-Hughes), Public Law 347, Sixty-fourth Congress, Senate Bill 703, 1917.

Report of the Commission on National Aid to Vocational Education, *House Document* 1004, Sixty-third Congress, 1914.

State Plans for Vocational Education of the various states.

Statement of Policies for Vocational Education, U.S. Office of Education, Division of Vocational Education, *Bulletin* 1, rev. 1948.

STRUCK, F. T., "Vocational Education for a Changing World," John Wiley & Sons, Inc., New York, 1945.

3. Analyzing the Duties and Responsibilities of Teachers

A TEACHER of vocational agriculture must be able to develop an educational program to meet the specific needs of the people in his community. It is necessary for him to understand what is expected of him and to be able to use the best techniques for designing a sound program—one that will be accepted by the people who must pay taxes to support this work as well as other work in the public interest.

Fig. 19. Classroom instruction for an all-day group in soil conservation. (*Courtesy of J. K. Coggin, North Carolina.*)

What Is Expected of the Teacher of Vocational Agriculture. The duties and responsibilities of a teacher of vocational agriculture have been increased from time to time since the passage of the Smith-Hughes Act. His chief duty has always been to teach and train farm people, including present as well as prospective farmers. The needs of farm people change with economic conditions and with scientific developments in agriculture. In many rural communities the teacher of vocational agriculture assists with special community programs for improved farm-family living which may include the operation of a school canning plant, a freezer locker, a meat-

22

curing plant, a feed-mixing plant, a post-treating plant, a fertilizer-mixing plant, a sawmill, and a community farm-mechanics shop.

In the text of the Smith-Hughes Act, a teacher is charged with the responsibility of seeing that each student in his classes has a program of supervised farming. This means that the teacher must have some form of transportation in order that he may make service calls to the various farms in the area. It is also a well-understood fact that he is expected to sponsor and serve as adviser for the local chapter of Future Farmers of America (F.F.A.) or New Farmers of America (N.F.A.).

The teacher of vocational agriculture usually has to make all reports required of other high school teachers since he is definitely a part of the local school system. In addition, certain reports and information relative to the vocational program and progress are required by the state and by the U.S. Office of Education.

Since the program in vocational agriculture is financed by Federal, state, and local funds, it is necessary for the teacher to keep various groups of people informed of his plans and accomplishments. This can be done largely by means of well-organized publicity released from time to time through appropriate channels.

All teachers are expected to participate in the extracurricular activities of the school and to accept places of leadership in many community movements for social, educational, and recreational improvement. Every teacher is also expected to grow both technically and professionally from year to year. The following outline of some of the duties of a teacher of vocational agriculture should be helpful:

A. Getting acquainted with people in the community
   1. By visiting farm homes.
   2. By meeting businessmen and bankers.
   3. By meeting people engaged in other types of agricultural work.
   4. By affiliating with social, civic, fraternal, and religious organizations.
B. Preparing the course of study
   1. By obtaining local farming information from:
      a. Census reports.
      b. Farm surveys.
      c. Land-use surveys.
      d. Records of supervised farming kept by students in former years.
      e. Conferences with representatives of agricultural agencies that keep desirable facts.
      f. Conferences with farmers, businessmen, and the advisory council.
   2. By summarizing local farming facts.
   3. By visiting students and prospective students of vocational agriculture.

  4. By analyzing locally important agricultural enterprises into jobs for
     teaching.
  5. By arranging the jobs to be taught into years, months, and periods.
C. Getting ready for teaching
     1. By securing needed equipment.
     2. By securing necessary supplies.
     3. By securing reference books and bulletins.

Fig. 20. Individual instruction in forestry on the wood lot. (*Courtesy of R. W. Roberts,
Arkansas.*)

     4. By filing bulletins and books.
     5. By subscribing for agricultural periodicals.
     6. By securing needed illustrative materials.
     7. By preparing illustrative materials.
     8. By providing a magazine rack, bulletin boards, and bulletin cases for
        the classroom and for the farm shop.
     9. By checking the list of prospective students and visiting them before
        school opens in the fall.

10. By assisting the high school principal in preparing the teaching schedule.
11. By assisting with the registration of pupils.
12. By preparing teaching plans for each job to be taught.
13. By securing an automobile for necessary travel if not provided by the school.
14. By setting up an annual and a long-time plan of instruction.

D. Teaching and training farm people
   1. By teaching all-day classes in the high school.
   2. By teaching day-unit classes in rural schools.

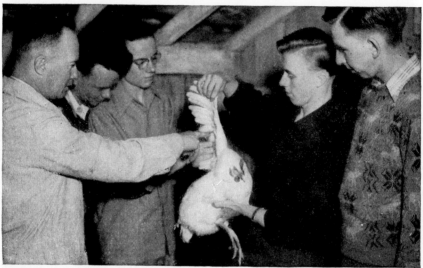

FIG. 21. Using the farms in the community to teach young students of vocational agriculture how to cull poultry.   (*Courtesy of D. W. Dalgleish, Michigan.*)

   3. By organizing and teaching young-farmer classes for young men who have dropped out of school or former students of vocational agriculture striving to become better established in farming.
   4. By organizing and teaching evening classes for adult farmers.
   5. By organizing and supervising institutional farm-training classes in vocational agriculture for veterans.

E. Helping with supervised farming programs
   1. By assisting students in selecting and developing the right projects as units in their farming programs.
   2. By teaching on the job the skills or making decisions that are needed.
   3. By assisting students in keeping cost-account records and in analyzing the results.

Fig. 22. Instructing students in the school farm shop how to build a feeder for cattle. (*New Mexico State Department of Vocational Education.*)

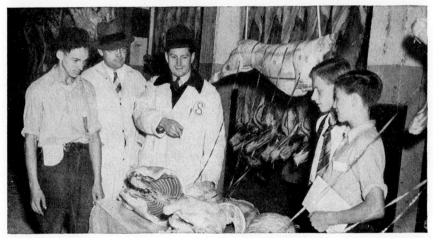

Fig. 23. Training in judging meats with the aid of experts at a packing plant.   (*Courtesy of M. J. Peterson, Minnesota.*)

    4. By maintaining a land laboratory for supplementing the experience and practice obtained on the home farm.

F. Performing community service
    1. By assisting farmers and other rural patrons in groups or individually.
    2. By teaching the principles of agricultural cooperative organization.
    3. By cooperating with other agricultural organizations in their programs.
    4. By helping in educational campaigns of an agricultural nature.

Fig. 24. The progress and final results of home projects included in the student's farming program must be checked by the teacher of vocational agriculture. (*Minnesota Association of Future Farmers of America.*)

Fig. 25. A school canning plant under the direction of the teacher of vocational agriculture is a teaching laboratory for both youth and adults. Well-canned wholesome foods mean much to the health of the citizens of any community. (*Courtesy of H. C. Fetterolf, Pennsylvania.*)

    5. By making the facilities of the farm-mechanics shop and canning plant available to farm families.

G. Supervising the F.F.A. or N.F.A. Chapter
    1. By assisting in the organization of a chapter.
    2. By assisting in building the program of work.
    3. By maintaining good morale and ideals.
    4. By training boys to compete in appropriate contests.
    5. By helping plan a parent-and-son banquet.

6. By organizing a suitable recreational program.
7. By seeing that proper chapter equipment is provided.
8. By seeing that organization standards are met.
9. By seeing that the necessary records are kept and reports made.

H. Promoting the agricultural program
  1. By writing articles for the press.
  2. By giving talks to organizations.
  3. By planning programs for radio and television.
  4. By preparing exhibits for store windows and for fairs.
  5. By having pupils give demonstrations at community meetings or at fairs.

Fig. 26. This cooperative order of fruit trees was used to improve the orchards on the home farms of these students.   (*Courtesy of T. L. Faulkner, Alabama.*)

  6. By maintaining a bulletin board.
  7. By conducting project tours.
  8. By conducting camping trips.
  9. By participating in judging contests.
  10. By conducting demonstrations on farms.
  11. By conducting summer tours.

I. Assisting with school activities
  1. By attending faculty meetings.
  2. By helping in chapel or assembly programs.
  3. By helping in Parent-Teacher Association (P.T.A.) meetings.
  4. By helping determine the high school curriculum based on community needs.
  5. By cooperating with school officials and other teachers in maintaining desirable school standards.

FIG. 27.   Logs cut and hauled to the sawmill produce lumber to be used in the repair and construction of instructional buildings.   (*Courtesy of J. A. Taft, Massachusetts.*)

FIG. 28. A committee of F.F.A. members, under the direction of the teacher as adviser, working on items to be included in the chapter's annual program of work.   (*Courtesy of M. J. Peterson, Minnesota.*)

J. Keeping proper records and making reports
1. By making attendance and grade reports required by the local school.
2. By making reports required by the state office.
3. By filing a copy of all reports.
4. By keeping follow-up records of former students.

    5. By keeping on file a copy of the course of study, agricultural community program, and teaching plans.

    6. By keeping an inventory of all equipment and supplies.

    7. By keeping a copy of all official correspondence received and sent.

K. Growing technically and professionally

    1. By maintaining membership in educational organizations.

    2. By subscribing for and reading professional magazines.

    3. By reading professional books and bulletins.

    4. By visiting the departments of other agricultural teachers.

    5. By taking graduate work.

    6. By reading technical publications.

    7. By writing for publications.

    8. By visiting, when possible, other agricultural areas of the United States.

    9. By attending district and state conferences for teachers.

Qualifications of Teachers of Vocational Agriculture. In reviewing the duties of a teacher of vocational agriculture, as just outlined, it is apparent

Fig. 29. Vocational livestock judging at the Florida State Fair.

that his training program must include a number of technical and professional subjects. It will also be observed that the program demands more complete training than can be given in four years of college training.

In order to understand properly the field of agriculture, a student needs a good background of agricultural science and technical subjects. In general, most states require at least a minimum of thirty semester hours in the field of science. The requirement may vary from thirty to forty semester hours.

Such subjects as botany, biology, chemistry, entomology, bacteriology, plant pathology, physics, and geology are considered important.

There are many essential courses in technical agriculture needed by a teacher. Unfortunately, he is often regarded as a specialist and authority in all branches of agriculture in the community where he is located. Naturally, his training in agriculture should have breadth. He will usually need some instruction in the following subject areas: agronomy and soils, fruit crops, vegetable crops, food conservation, ornamental planting, animal husbandry, dairy husbandry, poultry, farm management, marketing, forestry,

Fig. 30. Some localities provide a home for the teacher of vocational agriculture and his family. This one is in Wilson County, North Carolina. (*Courtesy of J. K. Coggin, North Carolina.*)

and agricultural engineering. Courses in technical agriculture will vary from one state to another. As a general rule, students are required to have at least fifty semester hours of work in technical agriculture. Many states require as many as sixty hours.

The professional requirements vary from 16 to 24 semester credits. Professional courses usually include the following: educational psychology, principles of secondary education or problems of curriculum development, methods of teaching agriculture, F.F.A. program development, and student teaching. In some states a course in general psychology is required and also a course in school administration or in the introduction to vocational education. The professional courses have to be presented on a practical basis in order for the prospective teacher to learn how to actually "do" the various jobs expected of him. Student teaching may be done in a center near the institution where the prospective teacher participates for a part of the day during the regular school year, or, better yet, he may spend all his time for two to five months in a department of vocational agriculture located anywhere in the state, preferably beyond commuting distance from the training institution.

An individual desiring to become a teacher of vocational agriculture should have been reared on a farm. It is difficult for him to properly appreciate problems facing farm people if he has not experienced them himself. The associations, actual experiences, and skills learned at an early age on a farm are invaluable to him in many of his teaching problems. They help him understand the thinking and reactions of rural people and give them confidence in his ability to assist them in solving their problems.

There are many desirable personal characteristics in a prospective teacher, some of which are brought out and developed through training and practical experience. Among them are the following:

1. A love of rural life.
2. A feeling that the teaching of vocational agriculture is the best vocation.
3. A willingness to cooperate with others.
4. The ability to lead.
5. Good health and a willingness to work.
6. A voice of the proper tone and pitch.
7. Unquestionable character.
8. Good tact and judgment.
9. Patience, courage, and enthusiasm.
10. Neatness in dress at all times.
11. The willingness to follow the professional ethics of a teacher.
12. The willingness to study continuously in order to grow both technically and professionally.

The Advisory Council. In carrying out his duties and responsibilities, the teacher will need the help and sound advice of many other people. Considerable thought has been given to this matter in recent years. The following splendid suggestions on local advisory councils come from the Division of Vocational Education of the U.S. Office of Education.[1]

> The use of advisory councils in agricultural education preceded the passage, by the United States Congress in 1917, of the Organic Act (Smith-Hughes) for vocational education. As early as 1911, it was mandatory in Massachusetts to have advisory committees for local departments of agriculture. In other states similar requirements were attempted by some school officials, but in many cases their use was not continued success-

[1] Selected from The Advisory Council for a Department of Vocational Agriculture, U.S. Office of Education, Division of Vocational Education, *Bulletin* 243, 1947.

fully for a long period.   The discontinuance or relative inactivity of advisory committees where once started cannot be attributed to a lack of need for a council, but can probably be charged more appropriately to other factors such as lack of experience in proper selection, organization, and operation of a local advisory council.

. . . An advisory council concerns itself with the over-all activities of the local department of vocational agriculture.   An active advisory council provides an exceptional opportunity for broadening and improving the agricultural instruction offered.   Such councils have been used in some states for many years by local departments of vocational agriculture, but on the whole their use has been rather limited.   In some instances this may be due to a lack of participating experience with such councils by state staff members.

FIG. 31. The teacher and his students are expected to keep the public informed on vocational activities and accomplishments.   (*Georgia State Department of Education.*)

This fact has been partially attested to by the number of inquiries received from them for further information and assistance on this subject.   Probably the greatest use of advisory groups has been in connection with young farmer, adult farmer, and veterans Institutional on-Farm classes.   Usually, the number of persons serving in an advisory capacity with such classes has been rather limited; therefore, they might be more appropriately called an advisory committee rather than a council.

. . . It is important for boards of education that have departments of vocational agriculture in their schools to maintain good working relationships with farmers and agricultural organizations because vocational education in agriculture often directly affects the well-being of all individuals and groups in the community.   One good way for a local board of education to maintain sound contacts with the farmers in the community is to establish and utilize an advisory council that will represent the views of all interested groups.   Through such a procedure, it will be more nearly possible to attain satisfactorily the over-all objective of vocational education in agriculture which is recognized as the training of present and prospective farmers for proficiency in farming.   Proficiency includes the ability to think reflectively through the many problems confronting them. An essential is for communities to authorize the establishment of advisory councils through their boards of education and school administrators in order for them to function effectively.

Advisory councils are comprised of laymen who represent all community interests and have been named to assist with the development of school policies and programs affecting agriculture. This may be termed a reciprocal policy in that the laymen inform the schools of the educational needs of farm groups in the community, and the school officials inform the laymen of their needs, facilities, and possibilities for conducting such a program. Through such an exchange of ideas, as well as lessons learned from the experiences of those who have worked with advisory councils over a period of years, sound progress will be made through the effective use of advisory councils.

Fig. 32. Taking part in community activities is an important responsibility of the teacher of vocational agriculture. (*Courtesy of J. K. Coggin, North Carolina.*)

. . . The purposes of an advisory council are numerous, and these purposes affect the extent to which the major objectives of vocational education in agriculture are achieved. The work of the teacher of vocational agriculture, school administrators, board of education, civic organizations, and agricultural agencies in the community will be affected by a program of agricultural education planned in cooperation with the advisory council. However, the program planned in cooperation with the advisory council will affect the extent to which the major objectives in vocational education in agriculture are attained. The purposes of an advisory council as they pertain to a department of vocational agriculture can be listed under four logical headings or phases of the program, namely: educational, operational, informational, and organizational.

It is suggested that a council be composed of at least five persons and that it meet at regular intervals. Individuals serving on this council may well be drawn from the occupational groups indicated as represented in the community:

1. Key farmers of the locality
2. Leading businessmen, bankers, and professional men
3. The high school principal

4. The county superintendent of schools
5. The county agricultural agent

School officials, including the superintendent of schools and members of the local board of education, should be invited to attend sessions of the council.

The Teacher's Annual Program of Work. Each year the teacher of vocational agriculture is expected to prepare a definite program of work. In some states he is also expected to prepare a five-year agricultural improvement program for the community. The exact form of a teacher's annual program of work will vary from state to state. As a rule, however, these programs include such items as the following:

A. Types of instruction
    Classes to be taught: all-day, day-unit, young-farmer, and adult farmer.
B. Preparation for and methods of instruction
    1. Facts upon which the course of study is based.
    2. The type of course of study to be used.
    3. Plans to be used in teaching.
    4. Use to be made of classroom notebooks.
    5. Teaching aids to be used.
C. Supervised farming
    1. Standard to be followed.
    2. Steps to be followed in making each program.
    3. Records to be kept.
    4. Plans for local supervision.
D. Physical plant and equipment
    1. Furniture to be used in the classroom.
    2. Equipment to be purchased.
    3. Arrangement of the equipment.
    4. The farm-mechanics shop.
    5. The school cannery and freezer locker.
    6. The land laboratory or school farm.
    7. Miscellaneous equipment.
E. Future Farmers of America or New Farmers of America
    1. Supervise the preparation of the program of work.
    2. See that an annual report is made.
    3. Act as adviser at meetings.
    4. Assist pupils to compete in F.F.A. and N.F.A. contests.
    5. Develop leadership and character training.
F. Participation in the state program of work
    1. Reports to be made to the state office.
    2. Attendance at the state and district conferences.

    3. Attendance at other professional meetings.

    4. Performance of the activities suggested by the supervisory staff.

G. Publicity

    1. Newspaper articles.

    2. Magazine articles.

    3. Talks before groups.

    4. Radio and television programs.

    5. Project tours.

    6. Exhibits.

    7. Demonstrations.

H. Community service

    1. Individual service calls.

    2. Cooperative agricultural activities.

    3. Recreational activities.

    4. Social activities.

    5. Religious activities.

    6. Miscellaneous activities.

I. School activities (other than teaching)

    1. Assist in preparing the schedule.

    2. Assist in preparing the course of study.

    3. Plan the landscaping of school grounds.

    4. Supervise the school farm and school garden.

    5. Attend faculty meetings.

J. Professional improvement

    1. Reading program to be followed.

    2. Conferences to attend.

    3. Membership to be maintained in organizations.

    4. Graduate courses.

K. Summer activities

    1. Attending conferences.

    2. Making tours or camping trips with students.

    3. Teaching classes.

    4. Supervising the farming programs of students.

    5. Visiting prospective students.

    6. Checking equipment and supplies.

    7. Revising the reference-library classroom and shop.

    8. Revising the teaching program.

    9. Preparing teaching plans.

   10. Preparing visual aids.

   11. Supervising the F.F.A. or N.F.A. chapters.

   12. Maintaining publicity.

   13. Supervising the land laboratory.

14. Supervising the school cannery or freezer locker.
15. Making reports to the state office.
16. Revising the office files.
17. Attending summer school.

In order to give a more complete picture of what advance planning in an annual program of work for the teacher will include, an example of how the outline was applied to a specific local community is presented here:

A. Types of instruction and supervision
    Classes to have a minimum of 10 and maximum of 25 students, the total enrollment to be at least 75.

FIG. 33. Well-organized and well-directed recreational and camp programs are a teacher responsibility.   (*Courtesy of J. K. Coggin, North Carolina.*)

    1. Teach two all-day classes in the high school.
    2. Teach one day-unit class.
    3. Teach one young-farmer class.
    4. Teach one adult-farmer class.
    5. Supervise two veteran-on-the-farm classes.
B. Preparation for and methods of instruction
    1. The course of study is designed to train students to become successfully established in farming.
    2. In all teaching programs, the individual farm will be considered as a unit. The teaching program will be based on developing three primary abilities:
        a. To make a living and develop a good home.
        b. To secure and conserve an economic income.

  c. To assist, through group participation in social activities, each person toward a more complete rural living.

3. The course of study for the first year will be based on fundamental principles and skills in agriculture and farm mechanics. Time will be given to production problems in the supervised farming program.

4. Advanced students will spend more time on management jobs, individualized study, budgeting, etc.

5. Each student will spend a minimum of one double period each week in the farm-mechanics shop.

6. The land laboratory will be used for demonstrating the value of cover crops and for growing an acre of tomatoes as a cooperative chapter project.

7. Teaching plans to be followed after an analysis of the job has been made will include:
  a. Name of the job.
  b. Objectives of the teacher.
  c. Preparation step.
  d. Presentation step, including questions for discussion.
  e. Supervision of practice step.
  f. Testing step.
  g. List of equipment and supplies needed.
  h. References to be used.

8. Each all-day student will be required to keep a classroom notebook under the following main headings or under farm enterprises:
  a. Group jobs on principles and skills.
  b. Supervised farming jobs.
  c. Farm-mechanics jobs.
  d. Forestry jobs.
  e. F.F.A. jobs.
  f. Conservation jobs.
  g. Farm-management jobs.
  h. Miscellaneous jobs.

9. The course of study for the day-unit class will involve general principles and skills in agriculture and the production jobs on at least one enterprise.

10. The course of study for the young-farmer class will be based upon the needs of the members, stressing the problems of assisting them to become established in farming.

11. The course of study for the adult-farmer class will be based on the individual needs of members. Special stress will be given to assist them in adopting improved farm practices.

12. A daily diary of all jobs taught will be kept to aid in the revision of the course of study.

C. Supervised farming

1. Standards for each student:

   a. A practical supervised farming program adapted to the home farm will be developed from the ideal.

   b. Productive projects in a program will be of sufficient scope to enable the student to make a labor income of at least $150 and to require a minimum of 250 hours of self-labor.

   c. Each student is to have some type of continuation project.

   d. The supervised farming program for each all-day student will include:

      1) At least two productive projects.

      2) Two or more improvement projects.

      3) Six or more supplementary farm practices.

   e. Boys in all-day classes are to have complete ownership of their projects.

   f. Day-unit students are to have the following minimum program:

      1) One productive project.

      2) One improvement project.

      3) Three supplementary farm practices.

   g. Young-farmer class members are to use their farms as a whole for record keeping, skills, and management problems.

   h. Adult-farmer class members will put into operation on their farms at least two improved practices.

   i. All students are to learn how to perform skills. Attention will also be given to practice in the supervision of farm labor and other farm-management problems.

2. Supervisory plans of the teacher:

   a. A diary is to be kept, showing for each student:

      1) The student's complete program.

      2) The size and type of the farm.

      3) A summary of the student's records.

      4) The record of the future needs of the student.

      5) The date and purpose of each visit.

      6) A copy of recommendations made.

   b. Visits are to be made at least monthly to each student for the purpose of:

      1) Checking the situation or condition of the projects.

      2) Teaching the students facts and skills.

      3) Inspiring the students to do better work.

      4) Getting better acquainted with the parents and with the needs of the farm.

   c. Make a minimum of 30 service calls per month to supervise the farming programs of students.

   d. Additional visits will be made to students who need assistance.

   e. Special stress will be given to the cooperation of parents in letting the student have complete management of his farming program.

   f. Checking maintenance needs of farm machinery.

  3. Record keeping:

   a. Each all-day and day-unit student will keep records in the adopted project record book. Records will be analyzed at the end of the year to show efficiency factors.

   b. Young-farmer class members will keep complete farm records.

   c. Adult-farmer class members will keep records on the improved farm practices which they agree to adopt.

D. Physical plant and equipment

  1. Laboratory tables and chairs are to be used in the classroom.

  2. A farm level, pruning tools, and a soil-testing kit must be purchased.

  3. The farm shop is to have the floor painted with safety-zone lines about power equipment, all machinery painted, all safety devices checked, and all tools stored in cabinets.

  4. The cannery is to be operated one day each week (Friday) during the fall and winter and daily during the vegetable and fruit season.

  5. A 3-acre land laboratory is to be operated. One acre will be planted in tomatoes as a cooperative chapter project, 1 acre in cover crops for a demonstration, and 1 acre for general teaching purposes.

  6. A request from the county board of education for $250 to purchase additional shop tools is approved.

E. Future Farmers of America

  1. An active chapter will be maintained.

  2. The chapter will enter the state and the national chapter contests.

  3. The chapter will hold a parent-and-son banquet.

  4. Chapter members will make a 10-day out-of-state tour during the summer.

  5. The chapter will have all standard paraphernalia.

  6. Delegates will be sent to the state convention.

  7. The chapter will have representation in all F.F.A. state contests.

  8. The chapter will meet at least twice each month.

  9. Accepted parliamentary procedure will be followed at all meetings.

 10. The chapter will strive to get one member ready to meet the qualifications for the American Farmer degree and three members for the State Farmer degree.

11. The chapter programs for the year will stress good citizenship and rural leadership.

F. Participation in the state program
    1. Submit all reports required by the state department of education on time.
    2. Plan to attend all state and district conferences called by the state supervisor of agricultural education.
    3. Plan to attend the annual meeting of the state education association.
    4. Plan to cooperate with district and state supervisors in trying to stress whatever phases of the program they may suggest from time to time.

FIG. 34. The F.F.A. chapter in session at Barnardsville, North Carolina. Note the excellent facilities. (*Courtesy of J. K. Coggin, North Carolina.*)

G. Publicity
    1. An average of one article each month should be submitted to the local newspaper.
    2. Four articles are to be prepared for agricultural magazines.
    3. Talks are to be made before the Lions Club, Rotary Club, and P.T.A.
    4. A monthly radio program is to be given over the local station.
    5. A project tour is to be conducted in May.
    6. Livestock exhibits of beef cattle are to be made at the feed-stock show, and an exhibit of products from boys' projects is to be made at the chamber of commerce building.
    7. A demonstration of cover crops is to be given on the land laboratory.

H. Community service
    1. Individual service calls in the field of agriculture are to be made as the need arises.
    2. Cooperation is to be given to the farmer's auction market that has just been operating a few months.

3. Assistance is to be given in helping the city complete two playgrounds for children's summer recreation.
4. Parties are to be sponsored for the F.F.A. members.
5. Active participation is to be taken in Sunday school and church work.
6. Active participation is to be made in the local Rotary Club, other civic clubs, and fraternal organizations.

I. School activities
1. Time is to be spent in assisting the high school principal in preparing the schedule of classes.

Fig. 35. Farm-machinery repair in the school farm shop is often done in connection with adult evening-class instruction and also as a general community service. (*U.S. Office of Education.*)

2. Assistance is to be given to a committee of the high school faculty charged with the responsibility of enriching the curriculum.
3. Supervision is to be given to the preparation of a landscape plan for the school grounds and to putting the plan in operation.
4. A vegetable garden for the lunchroom is to be produced.
5. Cut flowers are to be produced for the principal's office and for special school programs.
6. Active participation is to be given to faculty meetings and to faculty committee work.

J. Professional improvement
1. Regular attention is to be given to the reading of the following professional magazines:
   a. The Agricultural Education Magazine.

    b. American Vocational Journal.

    c. State education association journals.

2. The state conference for agricultural teachers and two or three (depending upon the number called) district conferences are to be attended. Also, the state education association meeting is to be attended.

3. Membership is to be maintained in the following professional and honorary education organizations:

    a. The National Education Association.

    b. The American Vocational Association.

    c. The State Education Association.

    d. The State and National Agricultural Teachers Association.

    e. Alpha Tau Alpha.

    f. Phi Delta Kappa.

4. A graduate extension course is to be taken each semester at the state university.

K. Summer activities

1. Educational conferences are to be attended, as already listed.

2. A tour of 10 days is to be made to take members of the F.F.A. chapter to Washington, D.C., and New York City.

3. A class is to be taught during the summer months for adult farmers on the canning of fruits and vegetables.

4. Supervision of student farming programs is to be continued.

5. All prospective farm boys from the eighth grade are to be visited.

6. All equipment and supplies are to be checked. Additional items and supplies will be purchased.

7. The agricultural reference materials are to be checked and new ones ordered.

8. The course of study is to be revised.

9. Teaching plans for all group jobs are to be revised.

10. Charts, graphs, and maps for use in teaching are to be made.

11. The work of supervising the F.F.A. chapter is to be continued.

12. The regular publicity program will be continued.

13. Supervision will be given to the land laboratory.

14. Special attention will be given to the operation of the school cannery.

15. Regular reports are to be made as required.

16. The office files are to be revised.

17. A three weeks' special summer school is to be attended to learn the latest facts concerning the quick-freezing of fruits and vegetables.

Most states require agricultural teachers to submit an accomplishment report covering the items in the program of work at the close of the fiscal year. Good planning includes such provision whether or not required.

The Community Agricultural Program.   The teacher with the help of his advisory council should determine perhaps ten or fifteen major agricultural problems that need to be stressed.   After these problems are selected, this procedure is suggested:

1. Set up annual objectives.
2. Set up objectives for each year of a five-year period.
3. List the accomplishments at the end of each year.
4. Incorporate these problems in the teacher's program of work.

EXAMPLE OF A FIVE-YEAR COMMUNITY AGRICULTURAL PROGRAM IN A SOUTHERN STATE

Items to be accomplished	Objective (scope, number)	Goals (G) and accomplishments (A)									
		1st year		2d year		3d year		4th year		5th year	
		G	A	G	A	G	A	G	A	G	A
1. Ratproof corncribs..........	25 cribs	5	3	5	*	5	*	5	*	5	*
2. Winter cover crops..........	1,250 acres	250	135	250		250		250		250	
3. Improved pasture..........	100 acres	20	45	20		20		20		20	
4. R.E.A.† lights.............	50 homes	10	50	10		10		10		10	
5. Cooperative hog sales.......	10 sales	2	3	2		2		2		2	
6. Screens in homes..........	200 homes	40	8	40		40		40		40	
7. Purebred bulls.............	100 farms	20	5	20		20		20		20	
8. Fruit (12 varieties).........	50 farms	10	7	10		10		10		10	
9. Milk cows (two 3-gal. cows per farm).................	250 farms	50	23	50		50		50		50	
10. Landscape home grounds....	25 farms	5	3	5		5		5		5	
11. Keep farm records.........	200 farms	40	11	40		40		40		40	
12. Running water............	100 homes	20	19	20		20		20		20	

* These columns are to be filled in at the close of the year.
† Rural Electrification Administration.

Opportunities for Advancement.   The successful teacher, if he desires to do so, can usually find employment in other fields.   There are many positions in the teaching of vocational agriculture, however, where the local school authorities desire an outstanding man and are willing to pay a salary high enough to secure one.   Promotions in the field of agricultural education include the following positions:

1. Supervising teachers in departments where teachers are trained
2. Teacher-training positions
3. State supervisory positions
4. Subject-matter specialists
5. Executive secretaries for the F.F.A. or N.F.A.
6. Research specialists

Other related work for which the training and experience as a teacher of vocational agriculture are assets includes:

1. County agricultural agents
2. Soil conservation workers
3. Work with the Farmers Home Administration
4. Farm Credit Administration positions
5. Production and Marketing Administration services
6. Agricultural development work for railroads
7. Agricultural work for chambers of commerce
8. Educational services to commercial firms selling products to farmers or purchasing products from the farm
9. Agricultural magazine writing
10. Agents to sell products to farmers
11. Principals of rural high schools
12. County superintendents of education in rural counties

As in most fields of service, a person can advance if he has the proper qualifications and is willing to work hard. In order to do his best work, however, a teacher of vocational agriculture needs to remain in the same community for a number of years.

SELECTED REFERENCES

The Advisory Council for Department of Vocational Agriculture, U.S. Office of Education, Division of Vocational Education, *Bulletin* 243, 1947.

Cook, G. C., and L. J. Phipps, "A Handbook on Teaching Vocational Agriculture," The Interstate, Danville, Ill., 1952.

Galpin, C. J., "Rural Social Problems," Appleton-Century-Crofts, Inc., New York, 1924.

Pre-employment Records and Activities of Teachers of Vocational Agriculture, *Bulletin* 333, Pennsylvania State College, State College, Pa.

The Teacher of Vocational Agriculture and His Work, *Bulletin* 3, North Carolina State College, Raleigh, N.C.

Teaching Agriculture as a Career, *Bulletin*, Division of Agricultural Education, University of Illinois, Urbana, Ill.

Teaching Vocational Agriculture—An Opportunity, *Bulletin*, University of Nebraska, Lincoln, Neb.

Teaching Vocational Agriculture as a Career, *Bulletin* 14, vol. 39, Michigan State College, East Lansing, Mich.

The Virginia Plan for Training Teachers of Vocational Agriculture, *Bulletin* 2, Virginia Polytechnic Institute, Blacksburg, Va.

4. Planning Buildings

THE CHANGING objectives of the agricultural education program demand increased and more appropriate physical facilities. Although the needs in a classroom have changed very little during the past 10 years, the equipment in the farm-mechanics shops has been increased to include various types of power equipment. The needs in the community for repairing farm machinery have increased because fewer and fewer hand

FIG. 36. The Honey Brook Vocational School, Chester County, Pennsylvania, where vocational agriculture is one of the subjects taught. (*Courtesy of H. A. Dawson, National Education Association.*)

tools are being used on farms. The community program of food conservation may demand the use of a canning plant and quick-freezing unit. The school may also be called upon to provide a post-treating plant, a feed-mixing plant, a fertilizer-mixing plant, and still other cooperative ventures, depending on times and conditions.

Types of Buildings. In the beginning of the vocational program, the agricultural department was often located in the main high school building wherever a vacant classroom could be found, usually in the basement. That situation has long since passed. The department of vocational agriculture needs facilities on the ground floor. Because of the nature of various activities, the noise from the farm-mechanics shop, and the increased

46

cost of fire insurace to the main building, most school people today favor a separate building for the department.

The type of materials used and the style of architecture should match the main high school building if located nearby and on the same plot of

FIG. 37. The one-teacher department of vocational agriculture at Hilmar, California. The classroom is at the right and the shop to the left. (*Courtesy of G. P. Couper, California.*)

ground. The local teacher and the community should decide in general what building facilities they need and then secure the services of a competent architect. Many states have a school architecture service through their state departments of education, and such services are available either to design buildings or to check building plans. It is advisable to secure the

FIG. 38. This Chickasha, Oklahoma, building utilizes natural sunlight and has indirect lighting. (*Department of Agricultural Education, Oklahoma Agricultural and Mechanical College.*)

services of a local architect to assist in making the plans and specifications and in supervising the building while it is under construction.

Location of the Agricultural Building. The vocational agricultural building should, if possible, be located on the high school campus to lessen the loss of time for students going to and from the main building. Because of the noise and fire hazards that exist if this building is adjacent to the high school structure, it is recommended that the vocational agriculture building be located on a corner of the school campus and at some distance from the other buildings. Easy access to a street, alley, or road is very important. It is also important for the building to be located on soil that can be properly drained and where the grounds can be neatly landscaped. The location affects the interior arrangements of the building in such matters as the placing of windows.

Size of Classrooms. The size of a classroom depends upon the number of students to be taught in each section. The maximum number thought

FIG. 39. This vocational agriculture building of native stone is located at Barnardsville, North Carolina. It contains a classroom, a farm shop, and an F.F.A. chapter room. (*Courtesy of J. K. Coggin, North Carolina.*)

to be advisable for a subject like vocational agriculture is 24. To meet the needs of 24 students in each section, the classroom should be at least 24 by 36 feet. With fewer students in each section, the classroom may be as small as 22 by 30 feet. Future as well as present needs, however, deserve careful consideration. The size will also depend upon whether or not a separate library room and a supply room are included.

In a number of local communities where the consolidation of rural schools has been completed, it is often necessary to have several teachers of vocational agriculture. Each teacher in such schools will need to be provided with classroom facilities.

Size of the School Farm-mechanics Shop. Because of the addition of power tools to the equipment of the average farm shop and the necessity of repairing many types of rather large farm machinery, space in the shop has had to be considerably increased. The best opinion today, based upon the experience of the past several years, is that a farm-mechanics instructor needs approximately 100 square feet per student. For 24 students in each section, that would mean a floor space of 2,400 square feet, or a shop about 30 by 80 feet or 40 by 60 feet. Space must also be allowed for farmers to leave machinery they may be repairing in evening classes as well as for the proper storage of tools, materials, and supplies. A patio or strongly fenced machinery court area with an all-weather floor is needed to provide space for holding farm machines to be reconditioned and for those that are ready to be returned to the owner.

Fig. 40. Students of vocational agriculture helping to enlarge the school farm-mechanics shop. (*Georgia State Department of Education.*)

Since the teacher is not using the farm-mechanics shop when he is teaching in the classroom, it is possible for one shop to be used by two vocational agriculture teachers working in the same department.

The Agricultural Library. It is possible to keep reference books and bulletins in the agricultural classroom. However, where individual instruction is given to certain students at the same time that the teacher has group instruction, a separate reference or library room is very desirable. The agricultural library has many advantages for former students and interested farmers, giving them a place to seek agricultural information freely at any time.

The agricultural library should be a room where books, bulletins, and periodicals can be properly indexed and filed in shelves against the walls

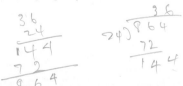

of three sides, the fourth side being left for windows. Space is needed also for reading tables and for a desk in which to keep a record of reference materials checked in and out. Such a room may be approximately 12 by 20 feet or 15 by 20 feet.

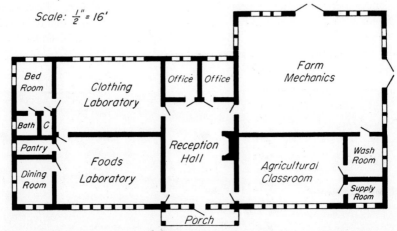

FIG. 41. Floor plan of a combination vocational agriculture and vocational home economics building for a rural consolidated school.

The Teacher's Office. Each teacher needs an office of approximately 10 by 12 feet where he can hold conferences, prepare his teaching plans, review materials, study, and make reports. The office should have a desk

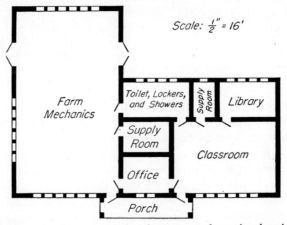

FIG. 42. Floor plan for a one-teacher department of vocational agriculture.

and office chair, several chairs for visitors, a typewriter desk, a bookcase, and one or more four-drawer filing cases. This office is often so located as to permit a clear view of the classes in both the classroom and shop.

Washrooms. The washroom should have space enough for showers, toilet facilities, and individual lockers. After working in the farm-mechanics shop for an hour or two, especially at forge, concrete, and machine work, students often need a shower before dressing. Boys usually keep unionalls to wear during shop periods. They seldom need heavy coats or sweaters while they are working in the shop. For safety purposes, snug-fitting clothes should be worn. Individual lockers for keeping articles of clothing are desirable. A recommended size for the washroom is approximately 10 by 20 feet.

Storage and Supply Rooms. The agricultural teacher needs a supply or storage room for visual-aid equipment and for other apparatus used in teaching. It is possible that all such equipment may be kept in large cabinets located on one side of the classroom.

The teacher may use a part of the supply room provided for the farm-mechanics shop. Storage space must be provided for lumber, nails, screws, paints, glue, and welding rod either in the shop or in a supply room. If the supply room is easily accessible, many special tools can be kept there rather than in the shop.

A recommended size for the supply room serving the agricultural classroom is approximately 8 by 10 feet. The supply room for the farm shop should be approximately 10 by 20 feet; length is needed for storing lumber and iron or steel rod.

Provisions for Ventilation. Windows spaced properly will usually provide a sufficient amount of fresh air in the classroom. It is possible in warm climates to place glazed half windows on the opposite side from the regular windows. These small windows are similar in operation to a transsom placed above a door.

Exhaust fans may be required for ventilating the farm shop or the school cannery. The chief objection to their use, in addition to the cost, is the noise they make. In the farm shop, cross ventilation can be obtained from windows on two or more sides of the building.

Provisions for Lighting. In the classroom and library, the windows should be placed on one side of the room. The bottom of the windows should be placed on a level with the students' eyes when they are seated. The window area of a classroom is usually equal to 20 percent of the floor area. In the farm shop, windows may be placed on two or three sides.

Appropriate artificial lighting is necessary in order to use the buildings at night and is sometimes desirable on dark, rainy days.

Provisions for Heating. The most satisfactory method of heating is by hot water or steam. If possible, the main heating plant of the school should be used for this purpose. Since the agricultural building is often used at night when adequate heat is not necessary in the main building, a cutoff valve is desirable.

Often it is necessary to have a separate heating plant. Such a plant may be a small boiler with radiators heated by coal or by means of an automatic oil burner. Other common methods of heating individual classrooms and offices are the use of jacketed hot-air furnaces or jacketed stoves. If jacketed stoves are to be used and heated with coal or wood, well-built flues must be provided for each stove. In many areas of the United States, little heat is needed for the farm shop except during two or three months of the year.

Fig. 43. A typical Vermont one-teacher department located at Enosburg Falls. This building contains a classroom, shop, workroom, and heating plant. (*Courtesy of C. D. Watson, Vermont.*)

Types of Floors. Regular wood flooring should be used in the agricultural building except in the washroom and in the farm shop. Floor materials for the farm shop may be of wood, concrete, inlaid linoleum, asphalt, or sand clay. Hand tools are usually damaged if dropped on a concrete floor, and wood flooring is undesirable in the forge and electric-welding areas. Many schools are using wood floors in the area for woodwork and concrete floors in the other areas.

Some General Guides in Building. It will be well to consider the following guides in planning buildings for vocational agriculture and farm-shop work:

1. Follow the same general style of architecture and the same materials in so far as possible as found in the main school building.

2. Use a permanent self-supporting type of roof so that no pillars are needed.

3. In the electric wiring provide for a number of service outlets in each room in addition to the regular light outlets. In the shop provide wiring suitable for power lines.

4. Plan for windows about three feet wide. In the classroom they need to be placed on a level with the students' eyes when seated and should extend as near to the ceiling as possible. In the farm shop the windows need to be placed so as to be above the workbenches.

5. Adequate blackboard and bulletin-board space needs to be provided both in the classroom and in the farm shop.

6. Provisions must be made for water in the classroom as well as in the washroom and the farm shop.

Fig. 44. This California building, located at Lodi, was designed for four full-time teachers of vocational agriculture. (*Courtesy of G. P. Couper, California.*)

7. Some provision should be made for heating water when necessary in the classroom.

8. The farm shop should be provided with two sets of 10-foot double doors placed so that a truck, tractor, or wide machine may be driven in one door and out the other.

9. Adequate flues are necessary for the forge and for heating units.

10. Exhaust fans are desirable in the farm shop and in the cannery.

11. Locks and other hardware should be of the best grade and of heavy materials.

The School Cannery. The minimum essentials for a school-cannery unit include space for the following equipment:

1. Preparation table, 4 by 9 feet
2. Double sink for washing products
3. Double blanching sink

4. Steam-jacketed kettle
5. Packing table, 4 by 8 feet
6. Exhaust box
7. Sealing table

FIG. 45. Typical Alabama school-community canning plant. (*Courtesy of T. L. Faulkner, Alabama.*)

FIG. 46. Students assisting with the installation of a school-community canning kitchen. (*Courtesy of R. W. Roberts, Arkansas.*)

8. Retort
9. Chain hoist
10. Cooling vat
11. Boiler
12. Storage space for materials

It is seldom advisable to construct less than a two-unit cannery. In such a case, the first 10 items listed above will have to be multiplied accordingly.

The boiler should be large enough to furnish the steam and hot water necessary for the maximum output of the cannery.

As already indicated, the size of the cannery depends upon the number of units. For a three-unit plant, a building would need to be approximately 30 by 60 feet. The boiler room and the storage room would occupy about eight or ten feet across one end.

It is suggested that any school interested in constructing a cannery contact the state supervisor of agricultural education and request plans and suggestions.

SELECTED REFERENCES

Buildings and Equipment for Teaching Vocational Agriculture, *Bulletin*, State Department of Vocational Education, Phoenix, Ariz.

Buildings and Equipment for Vocational Agricultural Instruction, *Bulletin* 36, Kansas Engineering Experiment Station, Manhattan, Kan.

Community Canning Centers, U.S. Department of Agriculture, *Miscellaneous Publication* 544, rev. 1946.

COOK, G. C., and L. J. PHIPPS, "A Handbook on Teaching Vocational Agriculture," The Interstate, Danville, Ill., 1952.

Establishing, Operating, and Using School Community Canning Plants, *Bulletin* 11, University of Georgia, Athens, Ga., 1943.

HAMLIN, H. M., "Agricultural Education in Community Schools," The Interstate, Danville, Ill., 1949.

HARTZOG, D., Planned Housing for Vocational Agriculture, Washington State Board for Vocational Education, Olympia, Wash.

Local and State Vocational Building Plans

The Program of Vocational Agriculture in Kentucky, *Bulletin* 8, State Department of Education, Frankfort, Ky.

Training for Farming, *Bulletin* 272, Michigan State Board for Vocational Education, Lansing, Mich.

Vocational Education in Agriculture, *Bulletin* 138, State Department of Education, Indianapolis, Ind.

Vocational Education in Agriculture for Louisiana, *Bulletin* 587, State Department of Education, Baton Rouge, La.

5. Planning Equipment and Supplies

THE TEACHER of vocational agriculture is often asked to have his students construct a part of the built-in equipment for the classroom and farm-mechanics shop, and he is responsible for preparing a list of the equipment and supplies that will be needed. Although farm mechanics is taught in a separate building or room from that of agricultural instruction, the equipment and supplies for a school farm shop will also be considered in this chapter.

FIG. 47. Individual student tables in a vocational agriculture classroom. (*Courtesy of J. K. Coggin, North Carolina.*)

Tables for the Classroom. Agricultural instruction is carried on easily and satisfactorily with the aid of tables for students in the classroom. Tables are suitable for demonstrations, discussions, laboratory work, supervised study, and other forms of group instruction. They may be purchased from a school furniture company or they may be built locally. A common size recommended is 24 to 28 inches wide, 60 to 72 inches long, and 28 to 32 inches high. Longer tables are also used. The average height of a table is 30 inches, but any class may have a few students short in stature who need 28-inch tables and a few at least six feet tall who need 32-inch tables. Satisfactory tables can be constructed of oak, cypress, gum, maple, or pine. The legs are commonly made from either 2- by 2-inch or 3- by 3-inch stock.

If it is desired, a table top may be made acidproof by following this procedure:

SOLUTION 1

Boil 50 grams of copper sulfate and 50 grams of potassium chlorate in 400 grams of water.

SOLUTION 2

Dissolve 60-grams of aniline oil in 80 grams of hydrochloric acid. Dilute the solution with enough water to make a total of 500 grams.

Apply Solution 1 while it is hot, using a regular paint brush. After the table top is dry, apply a coat of Solution 2. Make three or four applications

FIG. 48. This well-arranged and well-equipped teacher's office is in the Department of Vocational Agriculture of Butler, Missouri. (*Courtesy of G. F. Ekstrom, Missouri.*)

of each solution, allowing for time to dry between coats. After the last coat has dried, wash the table top thoroughly with warm, soapy water. When the table top is dry, rub it hard with a cloth that has been saturated with linseed oil or petroleum jelly. The top of the table may be made of plywood, Celotex, hard-tempered Canec, or Masonite placed on top of matched pine lumber and then finished appropriately at the edges. Other parts of the table may be stained to match the room furniture and then given an application of clear varnish or shellac.

One of the most satisfactory plans for arranging tables in the classroom is to place them in rows, usually two, with the students seated on one side and facing the teacher. Two students are seated at each table. In some schools a small individual table is provided for each student. This plan of seating allows the light to come over the left shoulder of each student.

A second method of table arrangement which is sometimes used is to place the tables in the form of a T. The disadvantage of this plan is that some pupils have to face the light. This arrangement is quite convenient for the teacher in assisting pupils during supervised study, however.

A third method is to arrange tables in the form of a U with the open end toward the teacher. This method has the same disadvantage as the second method in that some pupils may have to face the light. It is a widely used plan of seating nevertheless because of the ease in instruction and in changing quickly from one type of teaching to another.

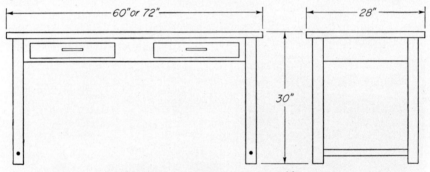

Fig. 49. Laboratory classroom table.

Where the T or U plan of arranging tables is used, long tables are preferred, the length being determined largely by the actual room shape and dimensions and the total number of students to be accommodated. Both of these table arrangements are particularly desirable where the available natural light is not satisfactory and adequate fluorescent light is used.

A demonstration table or desk is needed for the teacher. The desk should be 34 inches high since the teacher is usually standing while giving instruction; it should be 30 to 36 inches wide and approximately 6 feet long. Running water and gas or electric connections should be available at the demonstration desk.

Chairs for the Classroom. Comfortable chairs are needed for the students' use at the study tables. Unfinished chairs may be purchased and finished to match the tables. Experience has proved that it is economical to purchase well-constructed heavy chairs. Lightweight wood chairs are soon broken by active youths, and they slide along the floor too easily. Heavy oak chairs are recommended. A few schools are now using aluminum chairs. They are light and quite satisfactory but higher in price. Rubber tips or cushions placed on the bottom of the legs reduces noise and slipping.

Cabinets. Plenty of cabinet space is essential, especially if the classroom has no adjoining supply room. Cabinets are usually located on the opposite side of the classroom from the windows. The size of the cabinets depends upon the use to be made of them. In cabinets 7 feet high, the bottom section is usually 3 feet high and the second section 4 feet high. The bottom section may be 18 to 24 inches wide and the top sections 12 inches wide. The top section can be equipped with shelves as desired. Glass doors are appropriate if books, bulletins, seed samples, fertilizer samples, and the like are to be kept there. The bottom section often has drawers, shelves, and doors to fit the materials to be stored. Cabinets should be constructed of the

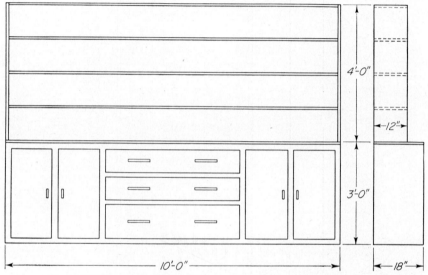

Fig. 50. Cabinet and bulletin shelves or bookshelves for the classroom.

same materials as the wood trim of the classroom and finished in the same manner.

Exhibit Cases. The agricultural department can make good use of one or more exhibit cases. Such cases are commonly made on top of a table of convenient size, the top, ends, and front sides being made of glass. In order to slide open, the back can be made of plywood cut in two sections. Locks are desirable.

A recommended exhibit case is made on a table 36 inches high, 24 inches wide, and 36 inches long. Frame wood for the sections of glass is made of 1- by 1-inch material. The posts for the frame are set 1 inch from each corner, making the table area under glass 22 by 34 inches. The posts are from 15 to 18 inches high. In order to get the best lighting, each case should have a fluorescent light attached on the inside at the top.

Exhibit cases have real educational value if they are properly planned, constructed, and used.   Exhibits of diseased plant specimens; animal parasites; model farm layouts; samples of fertilizers, seeds, feeds, contest material, spray and dust material; and exhibits made from products grown by the students may be displayed in such cases.

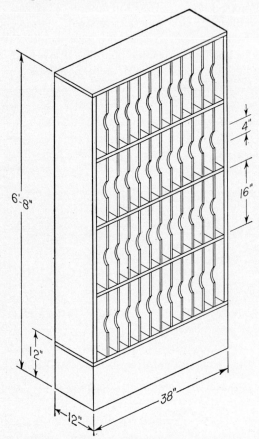

FIG. 51. Cabinet for classroom notebooks.

Blackboards. A blackboard is used more by the teacher of vocational agriculture than by the student.   As a rule, it is best to place the blackboard across one end of the classroom just behind the teacher's desk or table.   A slate blackboard is more durable than any other type, but composition material well coated with liquid slating is also quite satisfactory.   If cabinets are not placed on the side of the classroom opposite the windows, additional blackboards may be put there if desired.

Bulletin Boards. The best location for a bulletin board is near the entrance in the front of the classroom. Corkboard makes very desirable material for the surface of a bulletin board, although soft white pine covered with burlap is also quite satisfactory. The burlap board looks better if the burlap is dyed green or dark brown and tightly stretched. Bulletin boards are usually built to fit specific spaces; however, one which is 3 by 5 feet should be sufficient in size for most departments.

Use the bulletin board to display important notices, pictures, charts, graphs, newspaper clippings, and other interesting and informative material.

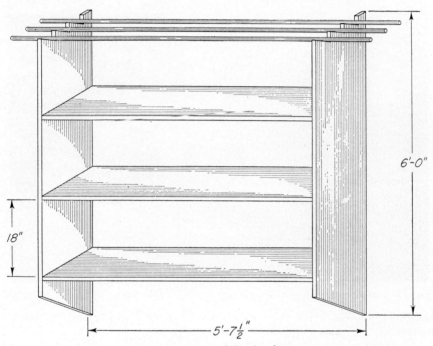

FIG. 52. Magazine rack for the classroom.

Material on bulletin boards needs to be changed often to maintain student interest.

Magazine Racks. A magazine rack large enough to display various current agricultural magazines and maintained in a neat and orderly condition is needed for each classroom or for the library. There are several types of magazine racks available from which to make a selection. One type commonly used in libraries for newspapers has the magazines suspended over small rods. A second type is a bookcase with elevated shelves. Magazines are prevented from sliding from the shelves by a strip of molding. Other simple types of racks hold the magazines by means of springs or by punching two holes in the top of the magazines and suspending them on long nails.

Filing Cabinets.   Each teacher is expected to keep copies of official correspondence, reports, student records, teaching plans, courses of study, and other similar working and record materials.   One or more four-drawer filing cabinets are needed for this purpose.   Follow a definite system of filing in order to be able to find any desired item readily.   It is the custom in many states to recommend a uniform filing system for all departments. Such a system has to be modified from year to year to meet new conditions

Fig. 53. Testing seeds in a special electric germinator.   (*Courtesy of G. P. Deyoe, Illinois.*)

and different situations.   (See Appendix XI, page 377, for a sample filing system.)

It is suggested that if the teacher has two filing cabinets he should divide the space in one as follows: correspondence and F.F.A. or N.F.A. material in the top drawer, reports in the second drawer, veteran-training-program material in the third drawer, and student records in the fourth drawer. The second filing cabinet might have teaching materials in the first drawer, special reference materials in the second drawer, catalogues and general reference materials in the third drawer, and transfer files of correspondence and old reports in the fourth drawer.

Equipment for Special Subject Areas.   Soil and climatic changes make it desirable for farmers to often operate specialized farms.   Since the types of farming in a given locality largely determine the courses of study offered, no general list of apparatus is suitable for all teachers.   Agricultural teachers have to become familiar with the agricultural enterprises that are important in the community before the selection of equipment and apparatus can be made intelligently. Specific selections for teaching vegetable growing, fruit

Fig. 54. Practical teaching calls for practical tools in the hands of the learners. (*Courtesy of C. D. Watson, Vermont.*)

growing, dairy husbandry, poultry husbandry, etc., will depend upon such factors as

1. The real importance of the enterprise in the local area.
2. The number of students interested.
3. The background and training of the instructor.
4. The amount of money available for purchasing equipment.

(See Appendix III, page 358, for a suggested list of equipment for the classroom and laboratory.)

General Supplies for the Classroom and Laboratory. The teacher of vocational agriculture uses a variety of supplies. Many items must be purchased on order, whereas others may be secured or collected locally. If possible, the teacher should have an annual supply fund to purchase various items needed to make his teaching practical. (See Appendix IV, page 360, for a suggested list of supplies for the classroom and laboratory.)

Equipment for Teaching Farm Mechanics. The agricultural teacher faces the responsibility of directing the learning activities of students in the field of farm mechanics. The terms "farm mechanics" and "farm shop" are often used to mean the same thing; however, the members of the American Society of Agricultural Engineers feel that the farm shop is only a division of farm mechanics.

Fig. 55. A well-lighted school farm shop where equipment can be efficiently used. (*Courtesy of J. K. Coggin, North Carolina.*)

According to a report of the American Society of Agricultural Engineers and representatives in agricultural education on June 22, 1944, the main areas of agricultural engineering in which teachers of vocational agriculture need specific skills are

1. Farm-shop work
2. Farm power and machinery
3. Farm buildings and conveniences
4. Soil and water management
5. Rural electrification

The Southern Conference of Agricultural Engineers and Vocational Agricultural Educators, meeting at Athens, Georgia, June 13 to 15, 1945, recommended that an additional division on community service facilities, especially on food processing, be added.

Generally speaking, the teacher will need to select equipment for teaching farm mechanics in accordance with the type of mechanical work done on farms and ranches in the locality or that which should be done.   The following enterprises are important:

1. Making farm sketches and drawings
2. Fitting handles in tools
3. Sharpening farm tools
4. Painting and glazing
5. Cutting, sanding, jointing, nailing, gluing, puttying, and finishing wood
6. Constructing small wood appliances

Fig. 56. Welding equipment for instructional purposes is becoming more important in order to keep pace with the increased use of farm power and machinery. (*Courtesy of G. P. Couper, California.*)

7. Constructing simple farm buildings
8. Making concrete constructions
9. Soldering metals
10. Bending, cutting, and shaping sheet metal
11. Making rope knots, splices, and hitches
12. Cutting, bending, shaping, and tempering metals
13. Welding metals with oxyacetylene
14. Welding metals with an electric arc
15. Welding metals with the forge
16. Drilling holes in metals
17. Cutting, threading, and fitting pipes for farm plumbing
18. Repairing leather
19. Repairing and servicing farm machinery
20. Repairing and servicing internal combustion engines

21. Lacing belts for machinery
22. Doing construction and repair jobs needed for rural electrification
23. Constructing and repairing farm roads
24. Constructing and repairing farm fences
25. Repairing brick and plaster work
26. Constructing terraces and drainage ditches
27. Constructing irrigation laterals and checks for farm land
28. Operating and adjusting the machinery for a food-processing plant
29. Installing a heating system in the farm home
30. Installing a system for sewage disposal

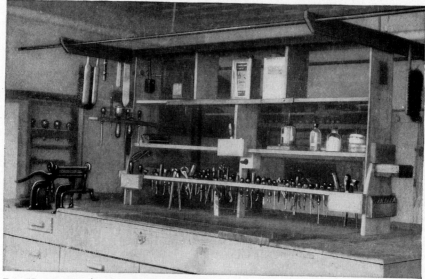

Fig. 57. Leather-working tools and bench located in one section of a school farm shop. (*New Mexico State Department of Education.*)

The final selection of specific farm-mechanics equipment will depend upon the community, customs, shop space, and available funds. A teacher in a new department is seldom able to purchase at once all the tools needed for instruction work. In the beginning, he has to select those that he believes are absolutely essential, adding others from time to time as funds become available. (See Appendix V, page 362, for a suggested list of tools for a farm-mechanics shop.)

Supplies for Teaching Farm Mechanics. The teacher of vocational agriculture will need a variety of supplies for use in teaching farm-mechanics work. In some cases, the student may be expected to purchase a few of his own supplies. This is especially true of construction and repair jobs on equipment brought from the home farm. Teachers find, however, that it is desirable to have ample supplies on hand even when students pay for the materials they use on articles made for the home farm. Funds should be made available so that supplies can be purchased during the summer prior

Fig. 58. Benches and cabinets arranged against the school-shop wall. (*California State Bureau of Agricultural Education.*)

to the beginning of the school year. Even when this is done, there will be a need for extra supplies to be added at intervals during the year. *Every farm shop needs a first-aid kit*, but the students must be instructed in the use of

Fig. 59. Well-constructed and well-arranged small tool cabinet.

the kit. (See Appendix V, pages 362 to 365) for a suggested list of supplies for a farm-mechanics shop.)

Storing Farm-mechanics Tools and Supplies. It is highly desirable for a teacher to follow some definite plan for storing tools and supplies that are to be used in teaching farm-mechanics jobs.   In general, two or three recommended plans are followed:

1. A separate tool and supply room.
2. Tool and supply cabinets located around the walls of the shop on a unit basis.
3. Tool and supply cabinets placed on rollers and located in the center of the shop and movable to any area.

The silhouette method of placing tools in cabinets is recommended because a missing tool can be easily detected.   There are other systems that have proved to be entirely satisfactory, also.   All tools when not in use should be kept in a definite place.   It is very essential that tools be wiped with an oily rag before they are placed in storage for any length of time.

Cabinets of a post-office type, either rotary or stationary, are desirable for storing small supplies, such as nails, screws, and bolts.

SELECTED REFERENCES

Buildings and Equipment for Teaching Vocational Agriculture, *Bulletin*, State Department of Vocational Education, Phoenix, Ariz.

Buildings and Equipment for Vocational Agricultural Instruction, *Bulletin* 36, Kansas Engineering Experiment Station, Manhattan, Kan.

COOK, G. C., and L. J. PHIPPS, "A Handbook on Teaching Vocational Agriculture," The Interstate, Danville, Ill., 1952.

Equipment for a Department of Vocational Agriculture, *Bulletin* 252, State Department of Education, Harrisburg, Pa.

Farm Mechanics in the Program in Vocational Agriculture, *Bulletin* 89, Illinois State Board for Vocational Education, Springfield, Ill.

COGGIN, J. K., Farm Shop Activities and Equipment, *Bulletin* 4, North Carolina State College, Raleigh, N.C.

The Program of Vocational Agriculture in Kentucky, *Bulletin* 8, State Department of Education, Frankfort, Ky.

Suggested Lists of Tools and Equipment for a High School Vocational Agriculture Farm Mechanics Shop, U.S. Office of Education, Division of Vocational Education.

Supplies and Equipment for Departments of Vocational Agriculture, *Bulletin* 29, North Carolina State College, Raleigh, N.C.

Training for Farming, *Bulletin* 272, Michigan State Board for Vocational Education, Lansing, Mich.

Vocational Education in Agriculture, *Bulletin* 138, State Department of Education, Indianapolis, Ind.

Vocational Education in Agriculture for Louisiana, *Bulletin* 587, State Department of Education, Baton Rouge, La.

6. Planning the Agricultural Library

TEACHERS of vocational agriculture have found that they can make good use of textbooks, reference books, bulletins, magazines, and newspapers. Many of the needed reference materials are free to teachers. Time and system are essential to keep in constant touch with the sources of current materials and to secure them as they become available. The teacher

FIG. 60. Interior of a classroom showing books with bulletins in cases in the background. (*Courtesy of D. C. Aebischer, Wisconsin.*)

must also spend time in filing appropriate and useful reference materials in the classroom in such a way that they may be easily found by the students and the teacher.

Agricultural Textbooks. Many schools in the United States furnish textbooks free to students. Most states prepare an approved list of textbooks that are for use in connection with various high school subjects.

The specific agricultural needs in different localities of a state may vary considerably, making the selection of several different books advisable. To meet this variation of needs, many states develop and adopt a multiple listing of textbooks. The teacher then has the responsibility of selecting appropriate books for each student's use. A teacher who has 60 students might select 10 copies each of 6 appropriate textbooks or devise any other suitable combination.

The teacher can usually get a list of state-adopted or state-recommended textbooks for vocational agriculture from the state supervisor of agricultural education or from the institution in the state responsible for the training of teachers of vocational agriculture.

In using textbooks, the teacher will need to supplement such information with important and applicable data from current bulletins and other sources. Certain textbooks are written in rather general terms to cover a wide area; therefore, they are sometimes not specific enough in recommendations on such matters as, for example, time to plant, fertilizers to use, spray programs to follow, and the like. Other books are more specific and regionalized.

Agricultural Workbooks. Student workbooks are being used by a relatively few teachers of vocational agriculture these days. Workbooks may be had for such enterprises as field crops, soils, vegetable crops, fruits, poultry, dairy cattle, swine, beef cattle, sheep, bees, farm tractors, and farm machinery. The chief weakness in their use in vocational agriculture is that the material is too general. Then, too, workbooks tend to contribute to straight informational teaching and "busy work" for students rather than to practical instruction which has as its objective the development of "doing ability" on the part of the learner.

Reference Books. The teacher of vocational agriculture is constantly in need of reference books in every important division of agriculture. Generally speaking, he needs multiple copies of reference books on field crops, vegetable crops, fruits, soils, fertilizers, insects, diseases of crops and animals, poultry, dairy cattle, beef cattle, sheep, swine, turkeys, bees, ornamental plants, soil and water conservation, work animals, farm mechanics, farm machines, farm management, marketing, farm finance, plant and animal breeding, and many other similar topics. Several students often need the same information at the same time.

The teacher should keep in close contact with the various publishing companies and add new reference books to the library annually. Any prepared list of reference books soon goes out of date unless revised frequently.

The U.S. Department of Agriculture publishes at intervals valuable reference materials in book form. "The Yearbook," published annually, is a very valuable reference to use. It may be secured free from a Congressman or a Senator until the allotment is exhausted. (See Appendix VII, page 368, for a list of companies publishing agricultural books.)

Any teacher and his students will have need for a number of good references on farm mechanics, farm tractors, farm machines, and the farm shop. Such reference material may be kept either at a suitable location in the shop or in the classroom. Such books made available for ready use are prepared from compiled listings and must be added to from year to year as appropriate new literature in this classification makes its appearance. (See Appendix VIII, page 369, for a list of agricultural books.)

FIG. 61. Magazine rack designed and made by members of Alpha Tau Alpha at the University of Missouri. (*Courtesy of G. F. Ekstrom, Missouri.*)

F.F.A. Books. It will be found desirable to establish a special library or section of an agricultural library for members of the local chapter of the F.F.A. or N.F.A. Each member needs to develop the habit of reading. To do so, books must be selected that will appeal to the interests and desires of rural boys. These books may well cover fiction, biography, travel, customs, science, invention, etc. (See Appendix VIII, page 369, for a suggested list of books for the F.F.A. library.)

Agricultural Magazines and Newspapers. Carefully selected magazines and newspapers constitute a very essential part of the reference library for any department of vocational agriculture. The magazines should be selected to correlate with the types of farming represented in the area. Other things being equal, those published in a given state or region are usually more useful than those which are published in distant states or which are extremely wide in scope.

Many agricultural magazines will send complimentary copies to teachers of agriculture and many of these magazines will make special rates for group subscription. (See Appendix VI, page 366, for a suggested list of agricultural magazines.)

FIG. 62. Method of filing bulletins in drawers rather than in bulletin cases. (*Courtesy of G. F. Ekstrom, Missouri.*)

Agricultural Bulletins. Agricultural bulletins may be secured from each of the following main sources:

1. State agricultural experiment stations
2. State agricultural extension services
3. State departments of agriculture or commerce and industry
4. U.S. Department of Agriculture
5. Commercial and industrial concerns

Each state agricultural experiment station is required by law to publish the results of completed experiments and research studies. A list of available bulletins may be obtained upon request. From the list the teacher may order copies of those he believes to be most useful in terms of the agricultural situation in his locality.

The state agricultural extension service issues bulletins of various kinds at intervals. The data used for the bulletins are usually secured from the experiment station, and the style is kept simple enough for the average layman to understand. A list of available bulletins may be obtained upon request.

In most states there is some agency—state department of agriculture, state board of agriculture, or state department of commerce and industry—that advertises the agriculture of the state through various types of publications. In many instances, bulletins have been written for the specific purpose of assisting farmers. A list of available bulletins may be obtained upon request if the state publishes this type of literature.

The U.S. Department of Agriculture issues a number of different types of bulletins. The following classified list is partially complete:

1. Farmers' bulletins
2. Technical bulletins (each bureau)
3. Miscellaneous bulletins
4. Leaflets
5. Bulletins from the Production and Marketing Administration
6. Bulletins from the Farmers Home Administration
7. Bulletins from the Soil Conservation Service
8. Bulletins from the Farm Credit Administration
9. Bulletins from the Rural Electrification Administration

A list of available bulletins from the U.S. Department of Agriculture may be secured by writing the Bureau of Publications, U.S. Department of Agriculture, Washington, D.C.; many of the bulletins may be obtained free through Senators or Representatives in Congress. All available bulletins can be purchased at a nominal cost from the Superintendent of Documents, U.S. Government Printing Office, Washington 25, D.C.

Hundreds of commercial companies publish very desirable bulletins. Although these bulletins usually have some advertisement features, they often contain material not available from other sources. A teacher should be able to use the bulletins without local criticism if he makes it clear to students that he has no interest in any specific company. Commercial companies often form trade associations for the purpose of advertising a specific product. Bulletins thus issued advertise the use of the product and not any specific brand name produced by one concern.

Filing Books.   In a large library, books are filed according to the Dewey decimal system.   In agricultural departments the number of books available is often limited and some more simple system is quite adequate.

Agricultural books may be filed alphabetically by authors according to subjects.   Each section of the filing cases may be labeled according to the subject divisions.   For example, these divisions may be farm crops, soils, vegetables, fruits, animal husbandry, poultry, agricultural economics, and agricultural engineering.   In each section the books are filed alphabetically

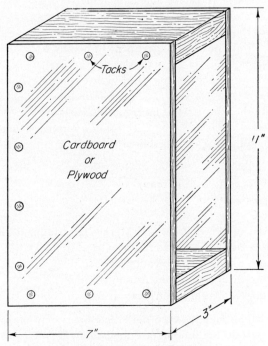

FIG. 63. Homemade bulletin case.

by authors.   It is desirable to label each book—using white ink—according to the division and according to the first letter of the author's name.

Students who desire to use reference books at home should be furnished with simple library blanks providing space for the date of withdrawal, the title of the book, and the signature of the pupil.

Filing Bulletins According to Subjects.   Bulletins may be filed according to agricultural enterprises or subjects.   All available bulletins on a given subject are placed in a bulletin case and the case labeled to indicate its contents.   The teacher may follow a listing of enterprises and subjects similar to the partial list that follows:

Animal breeding
Asparagus
Beans
Beef cattle
Bees
Beets
Broccoli
Cabbage
Cassava
Cauliflower
Chufas
Citrus fruit
Commercial fertilizers
Conservation
Corn
Cotton
Cover crops
Cowpeas
Cucumbers
Dairy cattle
Diseases of animals
Diseases of plants
Drainage
Farm buildings
Farm fencing
Farm machinery
Farm management

Farm roads
Farm shop
Feeding livestock
Forestry
Goats
Grapes
Hay
Home gardens
Home orchards
Horses
Insects
Irish potatoes
Irrigation
Lettuce
Manures
Marketing
Miscellaneous
Mules
Nuts
Oats
Ornamental plants
Pastures
Peaches
Peanuts
Pears
Pepper
Persimmons

Plums
Poultry
Pumpkin
Radishes
Rice
Rye
Sheep
Soils
Sorghum
Spinach
Squash
Strawberries
Subtropical fruits
Sugar cane
Sweet potatoes
Swine
Tobacco
Tomatoes
Tractors (gas engines)
Truck crops (miscellaneous)
Turnips
Velvet beans
Vetch
Watermelons
Weeds
Wildlife

Any list of selected topics or enterprises will have to be expanded from time to time to include the additional bulletins that are obtained. When there are more bulletins for some of the main enterprises than can be filed in one case, some method of further dividing the system must be devised. The enterprise of poultry, for example, might then be divided as follows:

Breeding
Breeds
Brooding
Caponizing
Culling

Disease
Dressing
Equipment
Fattening
Feeding chicks

Feeding hens
Grading eggs
Houses
Insect pests
Incubation

Judging
Marketing
Miscellaneous
Records
Trap-nesting

In using such a plan, each bulletin case would be labeled "Poultry," with the appropriate division of the enterprise placed on the line below. By following this system, no card index is necessary. The cases are usually placed alphabetically on the shelf and the student must look for the subject in which he is interested.

A modification of this plan of filing is to give numbers to each subject enterprise. The number assigned to the enterprise is placed on the bulletin case and on top of each bulletin on the subject. For example, if the number 10 is assigned to corn, all bulletins on corn would be numbered 10 and placed in the case. When the first case is filled, additional cases may be added by numbering them 10*a*, 10*b*, and 10*c*. The key of numbers for the system must be posted in some conspicuous place where students can use it readily.

It is also possible to use a card-index system. Each card, if an index system is followed, should give the number of copies of the bulletins that are available. This information is valuable to the teacher if he plans to use group-supervised study.

Filing Bulletins According to the Dewey Decimal System. For a large library the Dewey decimal system, or some modification of it, is desirable. According to this system, the numbers 630 to 639.9 are assigned to the field of agriculture. Each time the system is expanded it must be done by tens. For example, the field of agriculture may be divided as follows:

630.0–630.9	General Agriculture
631.0–631.9	Soils
632.0–632.9	Field Crops
633.0–633.9	Horticulture
634.0–634.9	Diseases, Insects, and Pests
635.0–635.9	Animal Husbandry
636.0–636.9	Dairy Husbandry
637.0–637.9	Agricultural Engineering
638.0–638.9	Agricultural Economics
639.0–639.9	Miscellaneous

Each of the 10 divisions may be divided into 10 each as indicated:

630.0–630.9	General Agriculture
630.0	Agricultural Education
630.1	Rural Sociology
630.2	Reports, Surveys, etc.
630.3	Fairs, Exhibits, Publicity
630.4	Experiment Station Reports
630.5	Cooperative Community Programs
630.6	Short Courses
630.7	Agricultural Extension Work
630.8	Related Sciences
630.9	Miscellaneous

631.0–631.9	Soils
631.0	Soil Surveys
631.1	Crop Rotations
631.2	Manures and Fertilizers
631.3	Tillage
631.4	Soil Bacteriology
631.5	Soil Physics
631.6	Soil Moisture
631.7	Soil Conservation
631.8	Soil Testing
631.9	Miscellaneous
632.0–632.9	Field Crops
632.0	Cereals
632.1	Forage Crops
632.2	Legumes
632.3	Root Crops
632.4	Potatoes
632.5	Fiber Crops
632.6	Sugar Crops
632.7	Silage Crops
632.8	Tobacco
632.9	Miscellaneous
633.0–633.9	Horticulture
633.0	Vegetable Crops
633.1	Floriculture
633.2	Orchard Fruits
633.3	Small Fruits
633.4	Forestry
633.5	Landscape Gardening
633.6	Subtropical Fruits
633.7	Home Gardening
633.8	Propagation, Pruning
633.9	Miscellaneous
634.0–634.9	Diseases, Insects, and Pests
634.0	Fungi
634.1	Bacteria
634.2	Entomology
634.3	Weeds and Parasites
634.4	Animal Pests
634.5	Damage by Hail, Floods, etc.
634.6	Veterinary Science
634.7	Control of Insects

634.8	Control of Diseases
634.9	Miscellaneous
635.0–635.9	Animal Husbandry
635.0	Horses and Mules
635.1	Beef Cattle
635.2	Sheep and Goats
635.3	Swine
635.4	Poultry
635.5	Pets, Birds, etc.
635.6	Butchering
635.7	Preservation of Meats
635.8	Feeds and Feeding
635.9	Miscellaneous
636.0–636.9	Dairy Husbandry
636.0	Milk
636.1	Cream
636.2	Butter
636.3	Cheese
636.4	Ice Cream
636.5	Breeds of Cattle
636.6	Dairy Barns and Equipment
636.7	Feeding
636.8	Testing
636.9	Miscellaneous
637.0–637.9	Agricultural Engineering
637.0	Farm Shop
637.1	Drainage
637.2	Irrigation
637.3	Farm Buildings
637.4	Farm Motors
637.5	Farm Machinery
637.6	Roads, Bridges, Fences
637.7	Concrete, Sewage, Sanitation
637.8	Clearing Land
637.9	Miscellaneous
638.0–638.9	Agricultural Economics
638.0	Farm Management
638.1	Marketing
638.2	Cooperative Associations
638.3	Taxation, Rents
638.4	Farm Finance, Insurance
638.5	Farm Labor

638.6	Communication
638.7	Transportation
638.8	Crop Outlook
638.9	Miscellaneous
639.0–639.9	Miscellaneous
639.0	Weather Reports
639.1	Hides and Tanning
639.2	Fishing, Hunting
639.3	Bees and Honey
639.4	Seed Catalogues
639.5	Supply Catalogues
639.6	Equipment Catalogues
639.7	Nursery Catalogues
639.8	Publications
639.9	Miscellaneous

Each of the above divisions may be further expanded. For example, poultry may be divided in this manner:

635.40	Breeds
635.41	Brooding
635.42	Culling
635.43	Diseases and Pests
635.44	Feeding
635.45	Houses and Equipment
635.46	Killing and Dressing
635.47	Incubation
635.48	Marketing
635.49	Miscellaneous

The first step in filing bulletins according to the Dewey decimal system is to place the classification number in the upper left-hand corner of the bulletin. Bulletins are then placed in bulletin cases of the corresponding numbers. When the library is for agriculture only, it is suggested that the "63" be dropped and thus the numbers used would be from 0.0 to 9.99.

The second step is to prepare a filing card for each bulletin. In some cases, two or three cards are needed for the same bulletin; this is commonly called "cross-indexing." Place the number in the upper left-hand corner of the card. It is also desirable to put the source of the bulletin under the number and the first letter in the title. For filing *Farmers' Bulletin* 1758, Cover Crops for Soil Conservation, the file number would be written thus:

631.7	1.7
F.B. or simply	F.B.
C	C

The file number would indicate that the bulletin is a *Farmers' Bulletin* and that the first word of the title begins with a "C". The completed filing card would be as shown below.

FILING CARD: FRONT SIDE

631.7 or 1.7   Cover Crops for Soil Conservation

F.B.   U.S.D.A., 1936

C.   14 pages

                        Farmers' Bulletin 1758

FILING CARD: BACK SIDE

Advantages and disadvantages of cover
crops are discussed. A good outline on
the kinds--legumes and nonlegumes--of
cover crops. Information on the time to
have cover crops turned under.

Bulletin Filing Cases. Bulletin filing cases may be purchased from a number of commercial companies. A teacher may also have his students make the bulletin cases as a shop project. The average size of a bulletin is

6 by 9 inches.   In order to have sufficient space for taking the bulletins out of the case, the sides are usually 7 by 11 inches.   The sides for the cases may be of cardboard, metal, plywood, or wood.   The back and the ends are made of soft wood, such as cypress, white pine, or cedar.   The strips for the back and ends are made 2, 2½, or 3 inches in width, depending upon the desired width of the cases.   The thickness of the strips is usually ¼ inch.   The case is nailed together with small wire nails.   The back of the case may be stained or painted black and labeled as desired with white ink.   If gum labels are

FIG. 64. A common method of filing bulletins in cases on shelves is shown in the background of this classroom.   (*Courtesy of L. B. Lindsey, Florida.*)

used on the bulletin cases, they should be covered with shellac to prevent soiling and insect damage.

Binding Agricultural Bulletins and Manuscripts.   The teacher will often want to bind a set of bulletins or papers for a manuscript.   A student interested in a major enterprise may want to collect a set of bulletins on a given subject and have them bound for his own use.   An index page may be prepared and bound in front of the bulletin following the flyleaf.

Bulletins may be bound permanently by any bookbinding company, but the charge for the binding is often more than farm boys like to pay.   For a temporary binding, bulletin covers are available from a number of printing companies.   The bulletins are punched and fastened in the cover.   Unless the holes are punched at the extreme edge of the bulletin, trouble may be experienced in opening the bound volume wide enough to read it easily.

The practice of binding the bulletins by this method will allow new ones to be added as they are obtained.

To reduce costs, the teacher and his students can undertake the binding of bulletins or magazines as a farm-shop project. To bind bulletins, the following equipment and supplies will be needed. These may be purchased locally or from a library supply house.

1 drill and sewing clamp	1 pint of book lacquer
1 hand or breast drill	10 yards of bookbinding cloth
6 $\frac{3}{32}$-inch drill bits	1 quart of library paste
1 package of bookbinder's needles	3 yards of unbleached homespun
3 skeins of bookbinder's thread	1 box of oiled paper (grocery store)
1 pair of long shears	1 bottle of white ink
1 paste brush	1 roll of bookbinder's cord
1 lacquer brush	

The following steps outline the procedure to follow in binding:

1. Select 10 or 12 bulletins on *one* subject and place them evenly in the clamp. If an index is desired, prepare one on a sheet the size of the bulletins and place it in front of them. Drill holes through the bulletins. Hold the drill straight and with a very small amount of pressure.

2. Open the clamp, push the bulletins up about ¼ inch, and clamp again. Cut a strip of the unbleached homespun wide enough to go across the back and leave about one inch extra for each side. Place the cloth over the back and sew through the bulletins, using a "Singer stitch." Follow the holes from one end to the other and back again. Remove from the clamp.

3. Secure two pieces of cardboard just a little larger than the bulletins. The cardboard may be purchased or the sides of boxes will do. Cut a strip of the bookbinding cloth wide enough to go across the sewed back of the bulletins and about one inch extra on each side. Have the strip about one inch longer than the bulletins. Make a medium-heavy paste. Paste the book cloth on the outside of the back of the cardboard, leaving the width between the two pieces of cardboard just a fraction of an inch wider than the bound bulletins. Cut two pieces of the bookbinders cord the same length as the width of the cloth and place at each end. Turn inward the ½-inch margin of cloth at each end and glue. Let the back dry.

4. Trim the bound bulletins, using a paper cutter, if they are not level.

5. Place the sewed bulletins in the prepared cardboard back. Glue the 1-inch unbleached cloth to the inside of each side of the cardboard cover. Use heavy paste. Place a piece of the oiled paper on the inside of each

side of the bulletin to prevent the bulletin from sticking to the cover but allow the cloth to do so.

6. Groove the bulletin covers, at the back of the cardboard, down each side. Use a ruler, bone folder, or fingernail.

7. Place the bound volume in a dry location and put a heavy weight on it.

8. Remove the volume after it has thoroughly dried and take out the oiled paper. Cut two pieces of white paper, the same size as the bulletin covers, and glue them to the inside of the cardboard back and across the sewed stitches, leaving the other portion for the "flyleaf." Do the same for the back side. Place in a press to dry.

9. Label the back as desired, using white ink.

10. Cover the outside of the bound volume with a coat of lacquer.

SELECTED REFERENCES

Cook, G. C., and L. J. Phipps, "A Handbook on Teaching Vocational Agriculture," The Interstate, Danville, Ill., 1952.

Hammonds, C., "Teaching Agriculture," McGraw-Hill Book Company, Inc., New York, 1950.

Schmidt, G. A., "New Methods in Teaching Vocational Agriculture," Appleton-Century-Crofts, Inc., New York, 1924.

7. Planning the Outdoor Laboratory or School Farm

TEACHING vocational agriculture can only be done successfully when approached from the practical point of view. This calls for firsthand experience on the part of the learner and can be obtained only by actually working on and with the soil. The land laboratory or school farm offers an opportunity to provide or supplement such experience.

FIG. 65. Students harvesting tomatoes on an F.F.A. chapter project. (*Courtesy of Otis Bell, Florida.*)

The Land Laboratory. As usually defined, a land laboratory and a school farm differ essentially in size and scope. A land laboratory may occupy only a small land area, whereas a school farm is thought of as being the size of an average farm in the community. Naturally, the labor, machinery, and equipment necessary for the operation of a school farm is much greater than for a land laboratory. The size of a land laboratory may vary from the space needed for a greenhouse or a slat house for growing vegetables, fruits, or ornamental plants to several acres of land used to produce field crops and perhaps raise some livestock.

84

Uses of a Land Laboratory.   The land laboratory may be used for any one or a combination of the following purposes:

1. Carrying through a cooperative F.F.A. or N.F.A. project
2. Growing stock to propagate fruit and ornamental trees
3. Teaching specific farm skills and technical facts
4. Conducting fertilizer demonstrations
5. Conducting soil-improvement demonstrations
6. Conducting livestock demonstrations
7. Growing an observation or testing plot
8. Growing flowers and ornamental plants for school use
9. Breeding stock in pens

Fig. 66. A vegetable garden worked by students of vocational agriculture.

Plan for the Land Laboratory.   It is best for the teacher to prepare a definite plan for the land laboratory.   Such a plan should include what he expects to grow, when each planting is to be made, how labor and equipment will be secured, what is to be done with the products, and how the operations are to be financed.

What is grown in the land laboratory or housed there will depend upon such factors as the following:

1. The objective of the department
2. The equipment available
3. The soil conditions
4. The adaptations of the climate

5. The cost of growing the crop or animal

6. The use to be made of the products

7. The need for a central place to keep breeding stock

Equipment for the Land Laboratory. It is possible for the school to either own or rent the necessary equipment. Less difficulty will be encountered if all tools and equipment are owned by the school. It is essential to have a complete line of equipment available when it is needed.

The nature of the equipment will depend upon the program and the teacher. Where the teacher is using a greenhouse or a slat house for growing

FIG. 67. Planting a forestry seedbed at the school land laboratory.

flowers and ornamental plants, the equipment will be quite different from the equipment used by the teacher who is conducting a demonstration on some phase of potato production.

Teachers are often able to secure a garden tractor for use in preparing the soil and for cultivating crops. The garden tractor is satisfactory for small areas. Many types of hand tools will be required. The following miscellaneous list contains at least a few of the ones commonly needed:

Hoes	Push garden plows	Steel square
Rakes	Metal tape for measuring	Spray outfit
Diggers	Plant dibble	Dusting gun
Wheelbarrow	Handsaw	Farm level
Water hose	Hammer	Flowerpots

It is suggested that the equipment be kept in a tool house at the land laboratory or at the school.   A tool house should be large enough to keep supplies of fertilizers, spray or dust materials, seeds, and feeds.

Labor for the Land Laboratory.   Students may be expected to do a reasonable amount of work on the land laboratory.   As long as students feel that they are learning new facts and skills, they are satisfied to work without pay.   Of course, there should be no question about pay on a chapter cooperative project where the group will receive the profit.

In some communities the teacher may want to employ students for extra labor and for which pay will be given.   This labor may be needed after

Fig. 68. A slat house used for plant propagation in the land laboratory.

school hours each day and on week ends.   The pay should be at the regular local rates for labor and according to the qualifications the students may have.

A land laboratory where animals are kept will require labor during the summer months.   In such instance, a student may be employed or one person may be secured to work daily throughout the year.   If power labor is needed and it cannot be supplied by the school, it may have to be secured from a local farmer.

Financing the Land Laboratory.   If the main objective of the department is to use the land laboratory for a teaching device, the costs should be met out of regular public-school funds.   A specific amount of money for the land laboratory should be put in the annual budget for equipment, operating supplies, and labor.   Any money received from products sold may well be credited to a land-laboratory fund.

Where the students are to receive all the profits from a chapter project for their treasury, the students should be willing to pay the cost of producing the crop or animal if the school furnishes the land and equipment.

There should be a definite plan adopted and approved by the local school for financing the land laboratory. The same is true of the type of accounts to keep on purchases and sales. The teacher must take steps to protect himself from any possible questions regarding the handling of funds in a careless manner.

Fig. 69. Students dressing poultry at Norfolk County Agricultural School in Massachusetts. (*Courtesy of J. A. Taft, Massachusetts.*)

The School Farm. The school farm presents many more problems to the teacher than does a land laboratory or observation plot, but it gives him a number of advantages, some of which are

1. It provides a place to demonstrate long-time projects as well as annual projects.
2. Students are able to participate in many situations on a farm-wide basis and supplement their farming experiences.
3. Students who have no facilities for obtaining supervised farming experiences at home can be provided land for crop projects and space for livestock projects or given work experience to meet the requirements.
4. The teacher has to keep his instruction on a more practical basis if he executes his work according to his class instruction.
5. It provides an ideal situation to make more effective use of the advisory council.
6. The school farm can furnish purebred animals, ornamental plants, and various types of seeds to the farmers of the community.

FIG. 70. Planting sweet potatoes in the land laboratory in order to have plants available for the community. (*Georgia State Department of Education.*)

FIG. 71. This F.F.A. chapter maintains a forest project. (*Georgia State Department of Education.*)

Some of the chief disadvantages and problems confronting a teacher who has a school farm to operate are

1. It often gives the teacher more work than he can do efficiently.
2. People of the community are ready to criticize the management of a school farm if it does not show a profit. They forget that the chief func-

tion of the farm is for educational purposes and that school departments are not operated for profit. The teacher is in a "showcase."

3. The labor problem is often acute. Students should work only for the educational value. Any additional labor needed should be paid for by the hour or day.
4. Where student labor is used during the school term, the teacher may have difficulty in securing additional labor during the summer months. To avoid criticism, the school farm must be kept especially neat and attractive at all times.
5. Financing a school farm may be a major problem. It is essential to equip the farm adequately and it is often necessary to hire a manager.
6. Crops or animals owned by the school are sometimes the object of dishonest people.
7. Many problems arise when the teacher leaves the school and a new man takes his place unless an active advisory council is fully acquainted with the operation of the farm.
8. Teachers sometimes spend too much time in practical work on the farm and too little time on the instructional phases. To protect the teacher from such a situation as well as assure close supervision of the farming activities, a part-time or full-time manager should live on or near the farm.

Size of the School Farm. The school farm is maintained for educational purposes. On the other hand, it should be of the proper size to be economically operated and should require the use of the same size equipment as is used locally by successful farmers. Since the size of a farm usually depends upon the type of farming, the same thing should hold true for a school farm. For certain specific crops or for poultry, a school farm need not be larger than 10 to 15 acres, whereas for field crops and for beef-cattle operations a much larger acreage is necessary.

The teacher should guard against the operation of a large farm that will take too much of his time to manage unless the school provides a farm manager. He must remember that individual and group instruction, community service, and the supervision of individual farming programs are also a part of his total responsibilities.

Buildings and Equipment for the School Farm. In order to operate a school farm properly, the teacher will need the same equipment that a successful farmer would use. He certainly will want all the new or improved types of farm machinery and equipment. It is his responsibility to see that the farm machinery and other tools are properly stored, repaired, serviced, and operated.

The buildings needed will depend upon the type of farm. If dairy cattle and poultry are to be kept, suitable buildings will be required; if flowers are to be grown, a greenhouse or a slat house may be desirable. Most school farms will need undercover storage space for seeds, feeds, insecticides,

Fig. 72. Student checking on the egg production of chickens kept on the F.F.A. chapter farm. (*Courtesy of Otis Bell, Florida.*)

Fig. 73. A school dairy where Grade A milk is produced.

fertilizers, farm machinery, and many miscellaneous items. In planning buildings, the original cost is a major consideration.

Uses of the School Farm. A teacher of vocational agriculture may use the school farm for the same purposes that another teacher will use his land laboratory or observation plot. In general, the school farm is useful for the following purposes:

1. To provide teaching-learning situations for students enrolled in classes.
2. To demonstrate desirable farm practices to farmers and students.
3. To grow purebred animals or plants to be distributed in the community for the improvement of farm income.

FIG. 74. Chapter-owned Brahmans at a "christening." Note the vegetable corsage. (*Future Farmers of America chapter, Sarasota, Florida.*)

4. To test certain practices recommended by the agricultural experiment station. Such activities need to be planned with representatives of the experiment station.
5. To produce vegetables, fruits, and milk for the school lunchroom.
6. To keep breeding stock for use of the students in upgrading their livestock.
7. To provide the space and equipment needed to supplement the farming programs of students.

Financing the School Farm. The school farm should be financed similar to any other supplies and equipment of the school. In a few places, counties have a special tax for the support of school farms, making the funds additional to those provided for actual instructional purposes. Under all circumstances, the teacher should have a definite amount of money allotted for the school farm in his budget. Because the farm is operated for educational purposes, it seldom ever pays for operating expenses.

A special system of accounting should be adopted for the school farm. All items purchased for the school farm should be charged to the special account, and all products from the farm sold should be credited to the same account. All accounts should be audited annually.

FIG. 75. Farm machinery owned by the Atascadero, California, F.F.A. chapter. (*Courtesy of G. P. Couper, California.*)

In a few instances, F.F.A. chapters operate the school farm for the purpose of making a profit. This plan has less educational values than where the chapter is not so deeply interested in profits. Members, of course, will secure valuable practical training in the principles of cooperation.

8. Making and Using Surveys

SINCE agricultural teachers are expected to base their instruction on the needs of students in terms of the local farming situation, there are many uses for local agricultural data. No survey blank can be designed to suit all teaching purposes. Teachers usually find a need for the following types of surveys:

1. The farm-inventory survey
2. The farm-enterprise survey
3. The progress and achievement survey of a farm family
4. The contributions of the farm to living
5. The farm-management survey
6. The farm-mechanics survey

The Farm-inventory Survey. A new teacher who begins work in a community must become familiar with the details of the local farming. Considerable information of value about local farms, livestock, and crops can be obtained from the office of the county assessor. An experienced teacher must know the changes taking place in his area. A teacher needs to know what crops and animals are being produced, who is producing purebred animals, what farm equipment is commonly used, which crops are planted for the market, and what types of farming are being followed. Such information is needed to enable the teacher to prepare the course of study to use in various types of instruction. It is also valuable in planning field trips.

The teacher may use a summary of 50 to 100 inventory surveys to determine the size of the average farm in the community, the average number and kind of animals on each farm, and similar information. Charts and graphs can be made from a summary of these facts.

To teach students how to use the farm-inventory survey, a teacher should visit several farms and secure the needed information. By following this procedure, each student can make an inventory farm survey of his home farm or of several farms near his home.

FARM-INVENTORY SURVEY

Name of farmer_____Address_____

Distance and direction from the school_____

Acres owned by the operator_____Acres cash rented_____

Acres share rented_____Acres in improved pasture_____

Acres in woods pasture_____Tillable land lying out_____

Total acres in farm_____

Give the information for the year beginning:_____19__and ending_____19__

Crops	Acres	Total yield	Amount sold	Animals	Breed	Number on farm	Number sold
Field				Dairy cows			
				Dairy calves			
				Dairy heifers			
				Dairy bulls			
				Beef cows			
				Beef bulls			
				Beef calves			
				Horses			
				Mules			
				Sheep			
				Goats			
				Bees			
Soil improvement				Brood sows			
				Boars			
				Meat Hogs			
				Pigs			
Fruit and nut				Poultry			
				Laying hens			

FARM-INVENTORY SURVEY (*Continued*)

Crops	Acres	Total yield	Amount sold	Animals	Breed	Number on farm	Number sold
				Roosters			
				Pullets			
				Cockerels			
				Young chicks			
Vegetable				Ducks			
				Geese			
				Capons			
				Turkeys			
				Guineas			
				Pigeons			
				Rabbits			

FARM EQUIPMENT
(Place number at left of item.)

	Item		Item
	Anvil		Forge
	Automobile		Grain drill
	Brace and bits (sets)		Grass seeder
	Brooder		Grindstone
	Buggy or carriage		Harness, single
	Buildings, portable		Harness-stitching machine
	Cart, milk		Harness, work (sets)
	Chisels, cold (sets)		Harrow, disk
	Chisels, wood (sets)		Harrow, spike
	Corn planter		Harrow, spring-tooth
	Corn sheller		Hay baler
	Cotton planter		Hoes
	Cultivators, power		Incubator
	Cultivators, riding		Level, farm
	Cultivators, walking		Levelers, land
	Ditching machine		Loader, manure
	Drill, post		Manure spreader
	Duster, hand or power		Marker, row
	Emery wheel grinder		Milk tester
	Engine, stationary		Milking machine
	Ensilage cutter		Mowing machine
	Feed mill		Planes, wood
	Feeders, self, for livestock		Plant setter
	Fertilizer distributor		Plow, gang

FARM EQUIPMENT (*Continued*)

Plow, sulky		Sirup kettle	
Plow, tractor		Sirup mill	
Plow, walking		Soldering outfit	
Plow stock		Sprayer, power	
Potato cutter		Stalk cutter	
Potato digger		Sweeps, cultivator	
Potato planter		Taps and dies	
Potato shovel plow		Tractor	
Pump, irrigation		Truck	
Rake, hay		Wagon	
Roller		Waterers, livestock	
Saws, hand		Weeder	
Scales, farm		Welding set, electric arc	
Scales, milk		Welding set, oxyacetylene	
Scraper, slip or fresno		Windmill	
Separator, cream			

NOTE: Insert other items common to the community.

LIVESTOCK PRODUCTS

Product	Sold		Used at home
	Wholesale	Retail	
Baby chicks			
Breeding services			
Cream			
Eggs for food			
Eggs for hatching			
Hides			
Honey			
Meat, beef			
Meat, pork			
Milk			
Poultry, meat			
Turkeys, meat			
Wool			

MATERIALS PURCHASED

Item	Kind	Amount
Fertilizers		
Feed for animals		
Seeds		
Spray materials		
Medicines and minerals for livestock		
Containers for vegetables		
Containers for fruits		

Amount of hired help used on the farm_____

Amount of timber sold_____

Farm buildings constructed_____

_____

Kinds of soils most common on the farm_____

_____

Repair and construction jobs performed on the farm_____

_____

_____

_____

_____

_____

_____

The Farm-enterprise Survey. For instructional purposes, there is a need for a detailed study of certain enterprises. The survey should give the

Fig. 76. Making a farm-enterprise survey on an Ohio farm. (*Courtesy of R. J. Woodin, Ohio.*)

student a clear picture of the enterprise from the beginning to the marketing period. A summary of the surveys should aid any student who has the same enterprise in his supervised farming program.

One example of this type of survey is offered for illustrative purposes.

These outlines could be expanded to include many other items, or the teacher may survey only one or two farm practices for a given enterprise.

SWINE-ENTERPRISE SURVEY

1. Name of farmer_____Date_____
   P.O. address_____County_____
   Acres in feed crops for hogs_____
   Acres in pasture for hogs_____
   Number of hogs on farm: Sows_____Boars_____Meat hogs_____Pigs_____
   Breed or breeds produced_____
2. Number of hogs raised last year for sale or for home use_____
   Average number of pigs farrowed per sow_____
   Average number of pigs raised per sow_____
   Number of breeding stock purchased_____
   Number of feeder pigs purchased_____
3. Care of the sow:
   Age of sow when first bred_____Farrowing dates_____
   Fleshing condition of sow at farrowing time_____
   Feed during pregnancy: Pasture_____Concentrates_____Minerals_____
   Care during farrowing time: Removed from other hogs_____
     On clean pasture_____
     Clean water supply_____Type of house used_____
   How fed just after farrowing_____
   _____
4. The growing pigs:
   Baby teeth removed?_____
   Feed before weaning: Pasture_____Minerals_____
     Concentrates_____
   Age at weaning_____Weight at weaning_____
   Age at castration of males_____
   Source of water supply_____
   Vaccinated for cholera_____
   Registered_____
   External pests controlled_____
   Wormed_____
5. Finishing hogs for market:
   Fed in dry lot?_____Feed used in dry lot_____
   Hand-fed_____Self-fed_____
   Green grazing crops_____
   Supplements: Minerals_____Proteins_____
   Average weight when put on feed_____Age_____
   Average weight when sold_____Age_____
   Time hogs were kept on feed_____
   Number of hogs each feed crop on this farm could finish for market_____
6. Marketing hogs:
   Age when marketed_____
   Weight and grade_____
   Price received per pound_____
   When marketed_____
   Where marketed_____
   Method of marketing_____
   Number of hogs used for home use_____

How was meat cured for home use?_____

_____

Breeding stock sold: Sows_____Pigs_____

                     Boars_____Gilts_____

7. Care of the boar:

Age at first breeding_____

Number of sows per boar_____

Does boar run with sows?_____

Run on pasture?_____

Kind of feed used_____

Number of years kept for breeding purposes_____

Is inbreeding practiced?_____

Safety practices followed_____

The Progress and Achievement Survey of a Farm Family. The progress and achievement survey of a farm family was prepared by agricultural

FIG. 77. Family food needs are better met with the help of the school-community cannery. (*Courtesy of T. L. Faulkner, Alabama.*)

and home economics leaders of the South. Several leaders of the agricultural press have also been interested in such a survey. The primary purpose of this survey is to improve farm-family living. The farm family is to rate itself annually and try to make improvements for the next year.

The results of the survey should often indicate to the boy the need for farm-mechanics jobs, improvement projects, and supplementary farm-practice jobs.

Results of the survey should indicate to the teacher the need for special

FIVE-YEAR PROGRESS AND ACHIEVEMENT SURVEY

Directions:

1. After each question you can now answer "yes," put a circle around the figures to the right shown in the first-year points-and-year column.
2. If you cannot now answer "yes" to any question, leave unmarked that question and the figures to the right of it.
3. Leave all second-, third-, fourth-, and fifth-year columns unmarked until these years arrive.

Questions	Points and year				
	1st	2d	3d	4th	5th
Health (195 points):					
1. Does each member of the family have an annual physical checkup by a doctor or health officer?	30	30	30	30	30
2. Does each member of the family over three years old have an annual checkup by a dentist?	20	20	20	20	20
3. Is the water supply protected from surface drainage?	15	15	15	15	15
4. Is the water supply protected against the seepage of underground drainage from barns, corrals, and outhouses?	15	15	15	15	15
5. Are the cows that furnish our milk tested for:					
a. Tuberculosis?	10	10	10	10	10
b. Brucellosis?	10	10	10	10	10
6. Is our milk kept sanitary by:					
a. Clean places for milking?	7	7	7	7	7
b. Clean milkers using covered buckets?	7	7	7	7	7
c. Scalded milk buckets?	6	6	6	6	6
7. Are all members of the family immunized against:					
a. Typhoid?	15	15	15	15	15
b. Diphtheria?	10	10	10	10	10
c. Smallpox?	5	5	5	5	5
8. Have we a septic tank or sanitary, flyproof outhouse?	25	25	25	25	25
9. Are all doors and windows in our house tightly screened?	10	10	10	10	10
10. Do yards around our house and barn drain well?	10	10	10	10	10
Income and expenses (145 points):					
1. Do we have a carefully thought-out plan for earning and spending the family income?	15	15	15	15	15
2. Do we keep a record of our major income and expenses?	15	15	15	15	15
3. Do we get at least one-third of our cash income from livestock, dairy, and poultry?	30	30	30	30	30
4. Do we pay cash in buying supplies from merchants, borrowing if necessary from credit agencies to avoid "time prices"?	20	20	20	20	20
5. Do we carefully grade our farm products for both quality and appearance before selling?	25	25	25	25	25
6. Are we getting full value from our timber crop by:					
a. Culling inferior trees for fuel or for pulpwood?	5	5	5	5	5

FIVE-YEAR PROGRESS AND ACHIEVEMENT SURVEY (*Continued*)

Questions	Points and year				
	1st	2d	3d	4th	5th
b. Marketing trees to be sold for timber?...............	5	5	5	5	5
c. Learning market values before selling?.............	5	5	5	5	5
7. Is the land we farm either our own or farmed with a written lease with the privilege of renewing?...........	25	25	25	25	25
Home-grown food and feed (190 points):					
1. Do we regularly produce for home use:					
a. Enough vegetables?.............................	7	7	7	7	7
b. Enough milk and butter?........................	7	7	7	7	7
c. Enough meat?...................................	7	7	7	7	7
d. Some fruit?.....................................	7	7	7	7	7
e. Enough poultry and eggs?......................	7	7	7	7	7
2. Do we regularly have a year-round garden and grow at least ten vegetables in it?...........................	15	15	15	15	15
3. Do we have a home poultry flock of at least fifty hens?....	35	35	35	35	35
4. Do we regularly produce:					
a. Enough potatoes for home use?....................	15	15	15	15	15
b. Enough corn for all meal we use?.................	15	15	15	15	15
5. Do we include in our meals every day:					
a. Some leafy vegetables?..........................	7	7	7	7	7
b. Some raw vegetables?...........................	7	7	7	7	7
c. Some fruit, fresh or canned?.....................	7	7	7	7	7
d. Some eggs or lean meat?.........................	7	7	7	7	7
e. One cup to one qt. of milk per person?.............	7	7	7	7	7
6. Do we regularly produce and provide for all livestock:					
a. Enough pasture?...............................	10	10	10	10	10
b. Enough grain feed?............................	10	10	10	10	10
c. Enough hay?..................................	10	10	10	10	10
d. Enough other feeds and supplements?................	10	10	10	10	10
Conservation (120 points):					
1. Do we plow under some soil-improving crop on at least one-fourth of our cultivated land each year?.............	25	25	25	25	25
2. Do we protect and increase the fertility of our land by:					
a. Terracing and contour farming?...................	5	5	5	5	5
b. Strip cropping?................................	5	5	5	5	5
c. Draining wet land?.............................	5	5	5	5	5
d. Saving and applying barnyard manure?.............	5	5	5	5	5
3. Do we improve our permanent pastures by mowing weeds, fertilizing, and preventing soil washing?...............	15	15	15	15	15
4. Are our woods protected by "fire lanes" or "firebreaks" either plowed or raked clean each fall or winter?.........	20	20	20	20	20
5. Are the buildings on our farm insured against fire?.......	15	15	15	15	15
6. Do we can, dry, and preserve surplus fruits, berries, and vegetables in season so as to have them available for use the rest of the year?....................................	25	25	25	25	25

FIVE-YEAR PROGRESS AND ACHIEVEMENT SURVEY (*Continued*)

Questions	Points and year				
	1st	2d	3d	4th	5th
Equipment, conveniences, and general improvements (175 points):					
1. Is our water supply made available in the house by:					
a. A running-water system?	10	10	10	10	10
b. A pump?	4	4	4	4	4
c. A kitchen sink with drain?	5	5	5	5	5
2. Have we enough power for profitable farming, such as:					
a. Two or more horses?	10	10	10	10	10
b. One or more tractors?	7	7	7	7	7
3. Does our source of lighting come from electricity or gas?	8	8	8	8	8
4. Have we adequate storage for:					
a. Food?	4	4	4	4	4
b. Kitchen utensils?	3	3	3	3	3
c. Clothes?	4	4	4	4	4
d. Farm tools and machinery?	5	5	5	5	5
e. Farm crops?	5	5	5	5	5
5. Have we refrigeration in our home?	10	10	10	10	10
6. Have we modern conveniences for laundry work, such as washing machines and electric irons?	5	5	5	5	5
7. Have we a telephone?	8	8	8	8	8
8. Have we a radio or television?	8	8	8	8	8
9. Are our farm buildings adequately painted?	20	20	20	20	20
10. Are our grounds properly landscaped?	15	15	15	15	15
11. Is the yard around the house kept free from trash?	5	5	5	5	5
12. Do we cooperate with other farmers by:					
a. Selling crops?	5	5	5	5	5
b. Selling livestock and livestock products?	5	5	5	5	5
c. Selling poultry and eggs?	2	2	2	2	2
13. Are our main crops planted from seeds of purebred varieties?	15	15	15	15	15
14. Do we use purebred sires for all our livestock?	12	12	12	12	12
Personal development (175 points):					
1. Do all our children between the ages of six and sixteen attend school?	35	35	35	35	35
2. Does the family or some member of it read regularly:					
a. Daily newspapers?	5	5	5	5	5
b. Farm magazines?	5	5	5	5	5
c. Other magazines?	5	5	5	5	5
d. Library books?	10	10	10	10	10
3. Do we attend church and Sunday school regularly?	30	30	30	30	30
4. Do our adult members of the family vote in all elections?	20	20	20	20	20
5. Do we frequently enjoy in the home:					
a. Music?	5	5	5	5	5

FIVE-YEAR PROGRESS AND ACHIEVEMENT SURVEY (*Continued*)

Questions	Points and year				
	1st	2d	3d	4th	5th
b. Games?..	5	5	5	5	5
c. Radio or television programs?......................	5	5	5	5	5
6. Does each member of the family practice some form of outdoor recreation?...............................	20	20	20	20	20
7. Does our family join with neighbors in:					
a. Recreational activities?...........................	5	5	5	5	5
b. Educational activities?............................	5	5	5	5	5
c. Farm-organization memberships?...................	10	10	10	10	10
d. Exhibits at community or county fairs?..............	10	10	10	10	10
Add your total score for the year........................					

stress to be given to certain phases of his course of study. He may need the information to prepare his five-year community agricultural-improvement program.

The results of a number of surveys made in a community may indicate joint problems for the cooperative effort of the teacher of vocational agriculture and the teacher of home economics.

The Contributions of the Farm to Living. Farm people seldom realize just how much the products they produce contribute to the total cost of living. Not having to pay cash for rent, firewood, and food, they fail to realize their true value. A study of the information that can be obtained on a survey blank like the following one will give a picture of this important phase of farm life.

SURVEY OF THE CONTRIBUTIONS OF THE FARM TO HOME LIVING

Year_____

Name of farmer_____Number in family_____
P.O. address_____Farming status_____
Total acres in farm_____Acres in crops_____
Acres in woodlands_____Acres in pasture_____
Tillage acres_____Untillable acres_____
Amount of wood used at home_____
Average weekly cash spent for groceries_____
Percentage of total food consumed that is grown on the farm_____
Amount of food canned (qt)_____
Amount of food dehydrated (lb)_____
Amount of food quick-frozen (lb)_____
Value of farm products traded for food bought at the store_____

FARM CONTRIBUTIONS TO LIVING

Product	Unit	Amount used fresh	Amount canned	Amount quick frozen	Amount dehy- drated	Value
Peas						
Beans						
Irish potatoes						
Sweet potatoes						
Tomatoes						
Cabbage						
Squash						
Miscellaneous vegetables						
Grits						
Meal						
Sirup						
Honey						
Milk						
Butter						
Cream						
Buttermilk						
Beef						
Pork						
Cured meats						
Poultry						
Lamb						
Eggs						

FARM CONTRIBUTIONS TO LIVING (*Continued*)

Product	Unit	Amount used fresh	Amount canned	Amount quick frozen	Amount dehydrated	Value
Lard						
Grapes						
Pears						
Apples						
Peaches						
Berries						
Citrus fruit						
Other fruits						
Nuts						

The Farm-management Survey. The results obtained from farm-management surveys should be used for advanced high school classes and for young-farmer and adult-farmer classes. Their greatest use should be in classes where the students actually operate their own farms.

Results from the farm-management surveys are valuable for use in making charts and graphs for teaching. The results should show weaknesses in the organization of any given farm.

Take the farm-management surveys at the close of the crop season. The facts obtained should be for a period of 12 months. Farm-management survey blanks may be obtained from the department of agricultural economics, college of agriculture, in practically every state. It is best to use the blank designed for your particular state.

The Farm-mechanics Survey. The farm-mechanics jobs on every farm are of great importance to the operator. The teacher often desires to know what tools and equipment are available on the farms of the community and what construction, service, and repair jobs are usually performed. Students should have this information in order to plan their home shop jobs and the work to be performed in the school farm-mechanics shop.

FIG. 78. An adult evening-class group ready to make a farm-management survey. (*Courtesy of T. L. Faulkner, Alabama.*)

FIG. 79. Checking the condition of farm machines in connection with a farm-management survey. (*U.S. Office of Education.*)

INVENTORY OF SHOP TOOLS AND FARM EQUIPMENT ON THE HOME FARM

Name of farmer_____Date_____

Item	Number	Condition
Claw hammer		
Sledge hammer		
Hatchet		
Ax		
Adz		
Hack saw		
Crosscut saw		
Ripsaw		
Wood saw		
Steel square		
Miter square		
Planes		
Soldering outfit		
Forge		
Post drill		
Saw set		
Screw driver		
Wood chisel		
Cold chisel		
Steel vise		
Wood vise		
Miter box		
Anvil		
Hardy		
Bench saw		
Hoes		
Rakes		
Spades		
Shovels		

INVENTORY OF SHOP TOOLS AND FARM EQUIPMENT ON THE HOME FARM (*Continued*)

Item	Number	Condition
Wheelbarrow		
Farm level		
Drawing knife		
Brace and bits		
Pipe dies		
Adjustable wrench		
Measuring tape		
Trowels		
Tractor		
Planting machines		
Transplanting machines		
Disk harrows		
Spike-tooth harrows		
Cultivators		
Mowing machines		
Hay balers		
Manure spreaders		
Truck		
Stationary engines		
Feed mills		
Ensilage cutters		
Peanut pickers		
Spray outfits		

FARM-MECHANICS SURVEY

Jobs Needed to Be Done

Name of student_____Date_____

Suggested jobs	Check jobs needed		Check jobs to include in the individual farm-mechanics program
	On the home farm	In the supervised farming program	
Home and grounds			
1. Constructing or repairing doorsteps			
2. Screening windows			
3. Replacing broken windowpanes			
4. Repairing the roof			
5. Repairing the fireplace or chimney			
6. Painting the home			
7. Refinishing furniture			
8. Constructing or repairing flyproof outhouses			
9. Constructing or repairing the yard fence and gate			
10. Constructing shelves or cabinets for the kitchen			
11. Constructing flower boxes			
12. Constructing tables for the home			
13. Constructing a wood box			
14. Constructing bookshelves			
15. Constructing an ironing board			
16. Installing a kitchen sink			
17. Constructing lawn chairs, seats, or benches			
18.			
19.			
20.			
21.			
Livestock			
1. Constructing or repairing barns			
2. Constructing feed troughs and self-feeders			
3. Constructing a farrowing pen			
4. Constructing a milking stool			
5. Constructing a water trough			
6. Constructing breeding pens			
7. Constructing poultry houses			
8. Constructing a pig brooder			
9. Constructing a poultry brooder			
10. Constructing a loading chute			

FARM-MECHANICS SURVEY (*Continued*)

Name of student_____Date_____

Suggested jobs	Check jobs needed		Check jobs to include in the individual farm-mechanics program
	On the home farm	In the supervised farming program	
11. Constructing a mineral box			
12.			
13.			
14.			
Tools and machinery			
1. Sharpening cutting tools			
2. Painting tools and machinery			
3. Replacing handles			
4. Setting scrapers			
5. Making cold chisels			
6. Constructing a machinery shed			
7. Constructing a home shop			
8. Repairing plows			
9. Sharpening knives and shovels			
10. Making a cane stripper			
11. Constructing a terracing wing for a turnplow			
12. Constructing a tool cabinet			
13. Overhauling a gasoline engine			
14. Adjusting farm machinery			
15. Repairing planting machines			
16. Repairing harrows			
17. Repairing harvesting machines			
18.			
19.			
20.			
General farm jobs			
1. Constructing a sweet-potato curing or storage house			
2. Preparing budding tape			
3. Repairing fences			
4. Making a ratproof barn			
5. Repairing a grape arbor			
6. Building a hotbed or cold frame			
7. Repairing harnesses			
8. Constructing a cattle gap			
9. Repairing a cane mill and furnace			
10. Repairing a wagon or truck body			
11. Building a trailer			

FARM-MECHANICS SURVEY (*Continued*)

Name of student_____Date_____

Suggested jobs	Check jobs needed		Check jobs to include in the individual farm-mechanics program
	On the home farm	In the supervised farming program	
12. Making a trailer hitch			
13. Making a set of firedogs			
14. Making a machinery trailer			
15. Making a land leveler			
16. Making a ditcher			
17.			
18.			
19.			
20.			
21.			
School			
1. Making bookshelves			
2. Making display cases			
3. Making bulletin boxes			
4. Making tables			
5. Making cabinets			
6. Framing pictures			
7. Making magazine racks			
8. Installing laboratory equipment			
9. Installing playground equipment			
10. Making tool cabinets			
11.			
12.			
13.			
14.			
15.			
16.			

9. Organizing the Course of Study

IN VOCATIONAL AGRICULTURE it is properly assumed that problems in the supervised farming programs of students form the core of the day-school course of study. These problems will not be foreign to the type or types of agriculture represented in the area. The agriculture of any state varies from one section to another. Since no general course can be satisfactorily prepared for the entire state, the local course of study should follow local agriculture. Hence each teacher has to design a course of study for his particular community and the student needs for instruction.

If the aims of vocational agriculture are to be attained, the course of study must be designed to launch students into the type of farming of their choice and the type adapted to the climatic and soil conditions of the area in which the farming operations will be carried on. In order to be able to prepare the course of study well, a teacher must, therefore, be acquainted with local farming facts, conditions, and situations.

No one method of obtaining local agricultural information concerning the crops and animals being produced and the farming equipment used can be recommended. The teacher will do well to use a combination of methods. He may secure a great deal of usable information by following these procedures:

1. Contacting various agencies and representatives
    a. The county agricultural agent
    b. The supervisor of the Farmers Home Administration
    c. Soil-conservation agents
    d. Local farm organizations
    e. Local markets
    f. Local chamber of commerce
    g. Federal and local credit organizations
    h. County assessor
2. Obtaining copies of studies and reports
    a. Federal census (farm)
    b. State census (farm)

    c. Land use

    d. Farm management

3. Making surveys and contacting farmers in the community

    a. Inventory surveys

    b. Home-improvement surveys

    c. Enterprise surveys

    d. Farm-mechanics surveys

    e. Visits to leading farmers

After using all the above methods for securing local farming data, it is desirable to use an advisory council, composed of farmers and businessmen,

FIG. 80. Teaching improved corn production is important in many localities. (*Courtesy of J. K. Coggin, North Carolina.*)

to review the facts as summarized. (See Chapter 3, Analyzing Duties and Responsibilities of Teachers, pages 24–45.) From the local facts obtained, a teacher should be able to determine the following:

1. The types of farming in the community
2. The relative importance of the various agricultural enterprises in making a contribution to the income
3. The most important and urgent farm problems
4. The factors associated with successful farming
5. General farming conditions, such as drainage, soil fertility, markets, and home conveniences
6. Long-time trends in land use, water use, changes in types of farming, and rural living

Problems for the First Year. If the course of study is to be functional in the sense of helping a student solve the problems that arise in connection with his supervised farming program, it must be so designed. The plan is often called the "cross-sectional method." Where the teacher uses subject-matter materials to develop broad programs of supervised farming, leading each student toward establishment in farming and solving local problems from day to day, he is organizing his course of study for effective teaching.

The major emphasis in the first year is to assist the student in launching his long-time supervised farming program, leading toward establishment in farming at the earliest-possible date. In the first year, therefore, the teacher must provide units of instruction that will acquaint the student with his

Fig. 81. Growing out fryers on a school farm in New Mexico. (*New Mexico State Department of Education.*)

task and assist him in making the necessary beginning plans. A few of the suggested units (jobs) are as follows:

1. Determining the importance of agriculture in the community.
2. Exploring the occupational opportunities in agriculture.
3. Getting more familiar with the training needs of people who plan to farm.
4. Getting better acquainted with the facilities of the local training program.
5. Deciding what type of farming to follow.
6. Selecting the enterprises for a type of farming.
7. Choosing the productive enterprises, improvement projects, and supplementary skills for each year.

The teacher will also be guided by each of the following principles:

1. Group instruction should occupy a major portion of the time for the first year and less time in the succeeding years.
2. Operative jobs of major importance should be taught early in the course of study.

3. Type jobs, such as preparing land for crops, planting, cultivating, harvesting, and feeding farm animals, should be considered early in the course.

4. Most farm jobs fit into a seasonal sequence and should be so taught.

5. The farm-shop jobs taught should be related to the crop and livestock jobs taught and follow the training needs of students as well as their farm needs.

6. Boys should be taught early in the course the study procedure to be followed, including keeping classroom notebooks and cost-account record books.

Fig. 82. Livestock enterprises vary in importance with the section of the country and the locality. (*Courtesy of R. J. Woodin, Ohio.*)

7. Boys need instruction the first year in how to help develop and participate in the F.F.A. or N.F.A. program of work.

Types of Course Organization. Since the passage of the Smith-Hughes Act in 1917, many different plans have been suggested for organizing the course of study based on local farming. These plans may be briefly described as follows:

1. The traditional type of course organization. In this plan different phases of instruction are followed each year. For example, the course may include instruction in field crops and soils the first year, animal husbandry the second year, vegetables and fruits the third year, and farm management the fourth year.

2. The major enterprise type of course. Following this plan, the teacher

would teach major enterprises first, contributory enterprises second, minor enterprises third, and farm management fourth. In this plan the teacher would integrate the program, having field crops, fruits, vegetables, farm mechanics, and animals in his course of study each year.

3. A modified cross-sectional plan. In this plan the teacher uses dairying, poultry, or farm crops as the central phase of his course, adding current problems as they arise each year from other agricultural enterprises.

4. The cross-sectional plan of organization. In this plan the jobs of one enterprise may extend over a number of years of instruction. For example, in the swine enterprise the first year may include such jobs as selecting

Fig. 83. Fruit is a crop with a variety of products. (*Courtesy of L. R. Stanley, Michigan.*)

a breed, purchasing foundation stock, building houses and equipment, and feeding young animals. The second year may include such jobs as breeding animals, caring for sows at farrowing time, registering pigs, and castrating pigs. The third year may include such jobs as butchering hogs, marketing hogs, and curing meat. The fourth year may involve such jobs as organizing a cooperative breeders association, holding an F.F.A. chapter sale of breeding swine, or similar community problems. The boy grows swine the four years of his training program. Since each boy may have a different type of farming for his training objective, the plan gives an opportunity for considerable individualized and small-group instruction.

Many leaders in the field of agricultural education today favor the cross-sectional plan for course organization for the following reasons:

1. The plan provides for flexibility in meeting the interests and needs of students in solving problems as they arise in the supervised farming development. The plan also stimulates a program that leads toward establishment in farming.
2. The plan provides for a distribution of subject-matter materials (jobs) in relation to the educational attainment levels of students as they acquire skill and information from year to year.
3. The plan provides for an organization of activities similar to the farm-as-a-whole approach of the farmer.

FIG. 84. Developing a dairy enterprise calls for careful instruction and follow-up on the part of the teacher.   (*Courtesy of T. L. Faulkner, Alabama.*)

4. The plan provides for instruction in community problems, cooperative and leadership activities, and for a review of any needed information.
5. The plan provides an ideal situation for the use of an advisory council.

Naturally, problems arise in using the cross-sectional plan; among them are the following:

1. In some departments the teacher is inclined to allow students to study much of what they please even though the jobs do not apply to their supervised farming.
2. No check is made to see that the decisions made in individualized study are put into practice.
3. In a department where a former teacher leaves poor records, the second

teacher may duplicate the jobs already taught, particularly if an advisory council is not used to develop the program.

4. The plan makes it difficult for a boy to enter the department any year after the first. For example, it may make a schedule problem for a tenth-grade boy in the first-year (ninth-grade) periods, and to enter the second year of the course, he is facing many problems that should have been solved previously by each other member of the class.

Analyzing Enterprises into Jobs. All enterprises and certain general subjects, like farm management and farm shop, should be analyzed into jobs. The jobs may be taught to the class or a group within the class or studied by individuals. A "farm job," used as a teaching unit, may be defined as a complete unit of work in the production and marketing of a farm enterprise. One job may be distinguished from another by the place where the work is performed, by the purpose of the work, and by the equipment used, if any.

In making analyses of enterprises, it is easy to see that some jobs involve only decisions, whereas others are largely operative in character. Skill jobs, involving manipulative operations, are known as "operative jobs." Jobs involving only decisions are known as "managerial jobs."

Boys just entering high school will often need help in making the proper analyses of agricultural enterprises. The enterprise analyses below illustrate the procedure to follow:

IRISH POTATOES

1. Determining the advisability of growing potatoes
2. Deciding the acreage to plant
3. Selecting the variety to plant
4. Deciding what fertilizers to use
5. Purchasing seed potatoes and fertilizers
6. Selecting the land for potatoes
7. Preparing the land for planting
8. Cutting potato seed
9. Treating potato seed before planting
10. Planting Irish-potato seed
11. Applying fertilizers to potatoes
12. Cultivating Irish potatoes
13. Controlling Irish-potato diseases
14. Controlling Irish-potato insects
15. Harvesting Irish potatoes
16. Storing Irish potatoes
17. Grading and packing potatoes
18. Marketing potatoes
19. Keeping and analyzing cost records

SWINE

1. Determining the possibilities of growing swine
2. Deciding on the number to raise
3. Constructing houses and equipment
4. Selecting the type and the breed
5. Selecting and purchasing breeding stock
6. Providing suitable pasture
7. Providing suitable feed crops
8. Breeding sows
9. Managing and feeding the breeding stock
10. Caring for sows at farrowing time
11. Feeding pigs
12. Castrating swine
13. Registering pigs
14. Controlling diseases of hogs
15. Controlling insect pests of hogs
16. Finishing hogs for market
17. Grading hogs for market
18. Marketing hogs—breeding and fat
19. Butchering hogs for meat
20. Cutting and curing meat
21. Canning and freezing meat
22. Keeping and analyzing cost records

Outlining a Teaching Program. Teaching programs set up in job form are of real assistance to either the inexperienced or the experienced teacher. They help him get his "mind around" the total teaching responsibility in so far as the day-school classes are concerned. The sample materials included here serve to illustrate this point.

A SUGGESTED TEACHING PROGRAM

I. Supervised farming
    1. Selecting the productive enterprises for the year
    2. Determining the improvement projects to be included in the program
    3. Selecting the supplementary farm practices or skills to be included for the year
    4. Preparing a long-time supervised farming program
    5. Revising the annual supervised farming program
    6. Making a job analyses of the enterprises in the supervised farming program
    7. Preparing the annual study calendar

8. Determining the cost of producing farm enterprises in the program
9. Estimating probable yields and receipts
10. Preparing enterprise budgets
11. Making business agreements for land and equipment
12. Keeping cost account records on production enterprises
13. Keeping records on improvement projects and supplementary farm practices

Fig. 85. Construction of needed farm structures should be included in the course of study. (*Courtesy of G. F. Ekstrom, Missouri.*)

14. Summarizing enterprise records
15. Analyzing and studying cost records

II. Farm mechanics
  A. Group-teaching jobs
  The group jobs may be taught in connection with the construction and repair of needed jobs on some farm, on the land laboratory, or at the school.
  1. Identifying and caring for tools
  2. Making working plans for a shop job
  3. Figuring the bill of materials for a shop job
  4. Identifying the kinds and sizes of nails, screws, bolts, pipe, and wire
  5. Cutting lumber to given dimensions
  6. Sanding wood projects

7. Gluing wood
8. Mixing and applying paints
9. Soldering metals
10. Lacing belts
11. Sharpening hand tools
12. Welding metals by using the forge
13. Tempering steel tools
14. Mixing concrete
15. Welding metals with oxyacetylene or an electric arc
16. Repairing and adjusting farm machinery
17. Repairing and adjusting farm motors and other farm engines
18. Sharpening saws
19. Adjusting power equipment
20. Determining the safety rules for a shop
21. Purchasing farm equipment
22. Treating fence posts
23. Constructing farm fences
24. Constructing farm roads
25. Constructing farm buildings
26. Fitting and laying water pipes
27. Selecting a heating system for a home
28. Designing a sewage system
29. Repairing electric appliances
30. Splicing rope
31. Tying knots in rope
32. Repairing and caring for leather
33. Shoeing horses
34. Fitting handles in tools
35. Laying out a drainage ditch
36. Leveling a building
37. Constructing an irrigation system
38. Sketching and reading blueprints
39. Establishing a farm water supply
40. Operating the machinery for a cannery
41. Planning a farm-mechanics shop for the home farm
42. Clearing land on the farm

B. Individual farm-mechanics jobs
1. Preparing a calendar of shop jobs to be done at school and at home based on a farm survey
2. Making working plans of jobs to be done
3. Figuring the bill of materials for each job
4. Constructing the various projects needed

    5. Repairing the necessary machinery and equipment

    6. Keeping records of shop jobs performed

III. Individualized study jobs on supervised farming

    1. Adopting a study procedure to follow and a system for recording notes and decisions

    2. Studying jobs and making plans for productive projects, improvement projects, and supplementary farm practices

    3. Executing plans that have been approved by the teacher

    4. Analyzing results of plans that have been executed

FIG. 86. Timber growing takes a prominent place in many agricultural courses.

IV. Farm forestry

    1. Determining the importance of forestry

    2. Choosing a farm-forestry program

    3. Collecting forestry seeds

    4. Identifying forestry trees

    5. Planting a forestry seedbed

    6. Managing a forestry seedbed

    7. Transplanting pine seedlings

    8. Identifying and making forestry tools

    9. Measuring trees and estimating timber

    10. Preserving timber

    11. Protecting forests from fire

    12. Using trees for windbreaks

    13. Thinning and managing a forest

    14. Farming pine trees for gum

15. Marketing pulpwood and sawmill timber
16. Keeping records of the farm-forest area

V. Future Farmers of America
    1. Becoming familiar with the main provisions of the F.F.A.
    2. Qualifying for the Green Hand degree
    3. Qualifying for the Chapter Farmer degree
    4. Qualifying for the State Farmer degree
    5. Qualifying for the American Farmer degree
    6. Preparing a chapter program of work
    7. Making an annual chapter-accomplishment report
    8. Planning and holding the F.F.A. banquet

Fig. 87. An F.F.A. chapter in session. (*California State Bureau of Agricultural Education.*)

    9. Preparing F.F.A. exhibits for fairs
   10. Financing the F.F.A. chapter
   11. Participating in the F.F.A. public-speaking contest
   12. Preparing a parliamentary-procedure team
   13. Planning and conducting cooperative chapter projects
   14. Determining the duties of chapter officers
   15. Planning for chapter publicity
   16. Planning and conducting chapter agricultural and educational tours
   17. Participating in various community activities
   18. Participating in all F.F.A. contests not named previously
   19. Selecting delegates to the state F.F.A. convention

VI. Conservation
    A. Soil and water
        1. Determining the land use of a farm
        2. Determining the program for water control and its use on a farm

      3. Determining the function and the sources of fertilizer elements
      4. Determining fertilizer formulas for major crops
      5. Mixing fertilizers on the farm
      6. Using composts, green manures, cover crops, and animal manures
      7. Producing soil-improvement crops
      8. Applying fertilizers to crops
      9. Securing assistance from the U.S. Department of Agriculture in conducting soil-improvement practices

  B. Wildlife and fish
      1. Developing a program for the proper utilization of wildlife on the farm
      2. Determining changes needed in the laws for wildlife in the nation
      3. Restocking wildlife on the farm
      4. Building farm fish ponds
      5. Restocking streams on the farm with fish
      6. Determining the state fish laws as they relate to conservation

VII. Acquainting students with the agricultural program
    1. Determining the importance of agriculture in the community
    2. Determining the occupational opportunities in the field of agriculture
    3. Deciding on the training needed for the different agricultural occupations
    4. Acquainting students with the program of vocational agriculture
    5. Organizing and keeping a classroom notebook

VIII. Type jobs
    1. Feeding farm animals
    2. Designing a program for livestock sanitation on the farm
    3. Slaughtering farm animals
    4. Cutting and curing farm meats
    5. Selecting soil for crops
    6. Preparing land for crops
    7. Cultivating crops
    8. Treating farm seeds
    9. Controlling biting or chewing insects
   10. Controlling sucking insects
   11. Planting farm crops
   12. Growing plants in the hotbed
   13. Transplanting plants
   14. Propagating fruits and ornamental plants
   15. Measuring land

16. Establishing permanent pasture for livestock
17. Selecting foundation stock for beef cattle, dairy cattle, hogs, and poultry
18. Grading and packing farm crops, fruits, and vegetables

IX. Live-at-home jobs
1. Determining the food requirements for a given family
2. Determining the feed-crop requirements for the animals on a farm
3. Planning and producing a home vegetable garden
4. Planning and establishing a producing home fruit orchard

Fig. 88. Raising farm animals shapes the course of study.   (*Courtesy of C. G. Howard, New Mexico.*)

5. Providing for a supply of milk on the farm
6. Producing poultry and eggs for the home
7. Producing a supply of farm meats
8. Producing home-grown farm seeds
9. Storing food on the farm
10. Storing feed crops on the farm
11. Canning fruits, vegetables, and meats
12. Freezing fruits, vegetables, and meats
13. Dehydrating fruits, vegetables, and meats
14. Producing honey on the farm
15. Producing sirup for home use

X. Farm management
   1. Balancing a farm business
   2. Determining a crop-rotation program
   3. Determining the need and use of farm credit
   4. Securing a loan for purchasing land
   5. Securing production credit
   6. Marketing farm products
   7. Hiring and managing farm labor
   8. Determining the steps to follow in becoming established in farming
   9. Selecting and purchasing a farm
   10. Keeping farm records
   11. Analyzing farm records
   12. Making farm-management surveys
XI. Miscellaneous group jobs
   1. Planning the use and management of a land laboratory or a school farm
   2. Working on the land laboratory or school farm
   3. Exchanging classes with the home economics teacher
   4. Landscaping the home grounds
   5. Producing pot plants and cut flowers for the home

Deciding What to Teach First. The teacher is faced with the problem of determining what to teach each year and each month of the course. Agricultural jobs that have a seasonal sequence must follow the growing season for that particular locality. Some farm jobs are more basic than others and this must be taken into consideration.

The teacher must also decide the length of his course of study in years. Circumstances may demand that he plan it to be two, three, or four years in length. He should always remember to allow time for examinations, holidays, and emergency problems. Below is a sample four-year course as planned for a given locality.

A SUGGESTED FOUR-YEAR COURSE OF STUDY

First Year

JOB	NO. OF PERIODS
September	
Registering students	3
Determining the importance of agriculture in the community	5
Determining the occupational opportunities in the field of agriculture	3
Organizing and keeping a classroom notebook	3
Identifying and caring for hand tools	3
Learning the main provisions of the F.F.A.	3
	20

A Suggested Four-year Course of Study (*Continued*)

JOB   No. of Periods

October

Deciding on the training needed for different agricultural occupations....... 2
Acquainting students with the program of vocational agriculture........... 2
Selecting the productive enterprise for the supervised farming program...... 3
Determining the improvement projects to be included in the farming program. 2
Selecting supplementary farm practices or skills to include for the year........ 1
Preparing a long-time supervised farming program...................... 3
Qualifying for the Green Hand degree.................................. 1
Making working plans for shop jobs................................... 3
Figuring the bill of materials for a shop job............................ 2
Miscellaneous.. 1
                                                                    ——
                                                                    20

November

Making a job analysis of the enterprises in the supervised farming program.... 5
Preparing the annual individual study calendar......................... 3
Determining the cost of producing farm enterprises in the program........ 3
Estimating probable yields and returns................................ 2
Preparing enterprise budgets... 2
Making business agreements for land and equipment..................... 2
Determining the size of nails, screws, bolts, pipe, and wire................ 2
Miscellaneous.. 1
                                                                    ——
                                                                    20

December

Keeping cost-account records on production enterprises................... 5
Keeping records on improvement projects and supplementary farm practices.. 2
Adopting a study procedure to follow and a system for recording notes in the
    notebook... 3
Feeding farm animals.. 3
Slaughtering farm animals.. 2
Measuring land... 2
Cutting lumber to given dimensions................................... 2
Miscellaneous.. 1
                                                                    ——
                                                                    20

January

Slaughtering farm animals.. 3
Cutting and curing farm meats.. 3
Treating farm seeds... 2
Preparing land for crops... 2
Growing plants in the hotbed... 2
Gluing wood... 2
Mixing and applying paints... 3
Preparing a calendar of shop jobs to be done at school and at home.......... 2
Miscellaneous.. 1
                                                                    ——
                                                                    20

A Suggested Four-year Course of Study (*Continued*)

JOB   No. of Periods

February

Job	No. of Periods
Soldering metals	3
Sharpening hand tools	3
Planning and holding the F.F.A. banquet	3
Determining the duties of F.F.A. chapter officers	3
Participating in F.F.A. contests	2
Studying individual jobs in the supervised farming program	3
Selecting soil for crops	2
Miscellaneous	1
	20

March

Job	No. of Periods
Splicing rope	2
Tying knots in rope	3
Figuring a bill of material for a shop job	2
Planting farm crops	3
Working on the land laboratory	3
Selecting foundation stock for beef, cattle, hogs, dairy cattle, and poultry	6
Miscellaneous	1
	20

April

Job	No. of Periods
Lacing belts for machinery	2
Fitting handles in tools	2
Performing individual shop jobs	3
Studying individual jobs in supervised farming	3
Preparing a parliamentary-procedure team	3
Cultivating crops	3
Transplanting plants	3
Miscellaneous	1
	20

May

Job	No. of Periods
Mixing concrete on the farm	3
Performing individual shop jobs	3
Studying individual jobs in supervised farming	3
Controlling biting insects	4
Controlling sucking insects	3
Making the annual F.F.A. accomplishment report	3
Miscellaneous	1
	20

Second Year
September

Job	No. of Periods
Revising the annual supervised farming program	3
Preparing the study calendar	3
Qualifying for the Chapter Farmer degree	2
Preparing a chapter program of work	3
Financing the F.F.A. chapter	2
Planning and conducting cooperative chapter projects	3
Propagating ornamental plants	3
Miscellaneous	1
	20

A Suggested Four-year Course of Study (*Continued*)

Job	No. of Periods

October

Performing individual shop jobs	3
Studying individual jobs in the supervised farming program	3
Summarizing enterprise records	5
Analyzing and studying cost records	3
Working on the land laboratory	3
Planning the publicity for the F.F.A. chapter	2
Miscellaneous	1
	20

November

Welding metals by using the forge	3
Tempering steel tools	2
Performing individual shop jobs	3
Studying individual supervised farming jobs	3
Shoeing and grooming horses	2
Determining the function and the sources of fertilizer elements	3
Determining fertilizer formulas for major crops	3
Miscellaneous	1
	20

December

Mixing fertilizers on the farm	3
Using composts, green manure, cover crops, and animal manures	2
Producing soil-improvement crops	3
Applying fertilizers to crops	2
Establishing permanent pasture for livestock	3
Performing individual shop jobs	3
Performing individual study jobs	3
Miscellaneous	1
	20

January

Repairing and caring for leather	2
Performing individual shop jobs	3
Performing individual study jobs	3
Sharpening saws	3
Laying water pipe	3
Securing Production and Marketing Administration assistance for soil-improvement practices	2
Propagating fruit trees by grafting	2
Working on the land laboratory	1
Miscellaneous	1
	20

A Suggested Four-year Course of Study (*Continued*)

Job	No. of Periods
February	
Repairing and adjusting farm machinery	3
Treating fence posts	3
Leveling a building	2
Participating in various community activities	2
Planning the F.F.A. banquet	3
Performing individual shop jobs	3
Performing individual study jobs	3
Miscellaneous	1
	20

March	
Determining the safety rules for a shop (also taught with each job)	2
Making and reading blueprints	3
Performing individual shop jobs	3
Performing individual study jobs	3
Working on the land laboratory	3
Participating in the F.F.A. public-speaking contest	3
Participating in the parliamentary-procedure contest	2
Miscellaneous	1
	20

April	
Designing a program for livestock sanitation on the farm	3
Grading and packing vegetables	4
Working on the land laboratory	3
Performing individual shop jobs	3
Performing individual study jobs	3
Producing pot plants and cut flowers	3
Miscellaneous	1
	20

May	
Constructing farm fences	4
Laying out a drainage ditch	2
Performing individual shop jobs	3
Performing individual study jobs	3
Making the annual F.F.A. chapter-accomplishment report	3
Selecting delegates to the F.F.A. state convention	1
Working on the land laboratory	3
Miscellaneous	1
	20

A SUGGESTED FOUR-YEAR COURSE OF STUDY (*Continued*)

JOB	NO. OF PERIODS
Third Year	
September	
Revising the annual supervised farming program	3
Preparing the annual study calendar	3
Qualifying for the State Farmer degree	2
Preparing a chapter program of work	3
Financing the F.F.A. chapter	2
Performing individual shop jobs	3
Studying individual supervised farming jobs	3
Miscellaneous	1
	20

October	
Determining the importance of farm forestry	2
Collecting pine seed	1
Identifying forestry trees	2
Preparing F.F.A. exhibits for fairs	2
Determining the land use of a farm	3
Planning a farm-water-control program	3
Performing individual farm-shop jobs	3
Studying individual supervised farming jobs	3
Miscellaneous	1
	20

November	
Choosing a program of forestry for a farm	2
Planting a forestry seedbed	1
Determining the food requirements of a given farm family	3
Determining the feed-crop needs of a farm	2
Constructing farm roads	3
Planning a farm-mechanics shop for a farm	2
Performing individual shop jobs	3
Studying individual supervised farming jobs	3
Miscellaneous	1
	20

December	
Constructing an irrigation system	3
Analyzing cost-account records	2
Clearing land on the farm	2
Producing a home fruit orchard	3
Storing feed crops	2
Producing a supply of farm meats	1
Performing individual shop jobs	3
Studying individual supervised farming jobs	3
Miscellaneous	1
	20

A SUGGESTED FOUR-YEAR COURSE OF STUDY (*Continued*)

JOB	No. OF PERIODS

January

Producing a home vegetable garden	4
Producing poultry and eggs	3
Measuring forest trees (saw and pulp timber)	2
Transplanting pine seedlings	2
Protecting forests from fire	2
Performing individual shop jobs	3
Studying individual supervised farming jobs	3
Miscellaneous	1
	20

February

Planning the F.F.A. banquet	2
Participating in F.F.A. contests	2
Preparing and adjusting farm motors and engines	5
Adjusting and servicing power equipment	2
Using trees for windbreaks	2
Performing individual shop jobs	3
Studying individual supervised farming jobs	3
Miscellaneous	1
	20

March

Thinning and managing a farm forest	2
Identifying and making forestry tools	2
Farming pine trees for gum	3
Marketing pulpwood and sawmill timber	2
Preserving farm timber	2
Keeping cost records for a forest	2
Performing individual shop jobs	3
Studying individual supervised farming jobs	3
Miscellaneous	1
	20

April

Canning fruits, vegetables, and meats	3
Operating and adjusting the machinery for a cannery	2
Welding metals (oxyacetylene)	3
Producing home-grown farm seeds	2
Freezing fruits, vegetables, and meats	3
Performing individual shop jobs	3
Studying individual supervised farming jobs	3
Miscellaneous	1
	20

A Suggested Four-year Course of Study (*Continued*)

Job   No. of Periods

May

Dehydrating fruits, vegetables, and meats............................... 4
Producing honey on the farm.. 2
Producing sirup for home use... 2
Storing food on the farm... 3
Preparing the F.F.A. chapter-accomplishment report..................... 2
Performing individual shop jobs....................................... 3
Studying individual supervised farming jobs............................ 3
Miscellaneous... 1
                                                                      ——
                                                                      20

Fourth Year
September

Revising the annual supervised farming program........................ 2
Preparing the annual study calendar................................... 2
Qualifying for the American Farmer degree............................. 2
Preparing the chapter program of work................................ 2
Preparing a cooperative chapter project............................... 2
Providing for a supply of milk for the farm home...................... 1
Performing individual shop jobs....................................... 3
Studying individual supervised farming jobs............................ 5
Miscellaneous... 1
                                                                      ——
                                                                      20

October

Analyzing cost-account records.. 1
Welding metals (electric arc)... 2
Selecting a heating system for the home............................... 2
Repairing electric appliances... 1
Developing a program for the proper utilization of wildlife on the farm...... 2
Balancing a farm business.. 3
Performing individual shop jobs....................................... 3
Studying individual supervised farming jobs............................ 5
Miscellaneous... 1
                                                                      ——
                                                                      20

November

Planning the utilization of a land laboratory or school farm............... 2
Landscaping the home grounds.. 3
Determining a crop-rotation program.................................. 2
Determining the need and the use of farm credit....................... 2
Designing a sewage system... 2
Performing individual shop jobs....................................... 3
Studying individual supervised farming jobs............................ 5
Miscellaneous... 1
                                                                      ——
                                                                      20

A SUGGESTED FOUR-YEAR COURSE OF STUDY (*Continued*)

JOB   NO. OF PERIODS

December

Purchasing farm equipment.. 2
Repairing and servicing farm machinery.............................. 2
Securing a loan for purchasing land.................................. 3
Securing production credit... 2
Participating in community activities................................ 2
Performing individual shop jobs...................................... 3
Studying individual supervised farming jobs.......................... 5
Miscellaneous.. 1
                                                                      ——
                                                                      20

January

Planning the F.F.A. banquet.. 1
Participating in F.F.A. contests..................................... 2
Cutting and curing farm meats.. 3
Canning and freezing meats... 3
Selecting and purchasing a farm...................................... 2
Performing individual shop jobs...................................... 3
Studying individual supervised farming jobs.......................... 5
Miscellaneous.. 1
                                                                      ——
                                                                      20

February

Making farm-management surveys....................................... 3
Keeping farm records... 2
Building a farm fish pond.. 2
Establishing a farm water supply..................................... 2
Planning a tour for the F.F.A. chapter............................... 2
Performing individual shop jobs...................................... 2
Studying individual supervised farming jobs.......................... 5
Miscellaneous.. 2
                                                                      ——
                                                                      20

March

Analyzing farm records... 5
Determining the steps to follow in getting established in farming.... 3
Landscaping the school grounds....................................... 3
Performing individual shop jobs...................................... 3
Studying individual supervised farming jobs.......................... 5
Miscellaneous.. 1
                                                                      ——
                                                                      20

April

Hiring and managing farm labor....................................... 3
Marketing farm products.. 3
Participating in community activities................................ 3
Participating in F.F.A. contests..................................... 2
Performing individual shop jobs...................................... 3
Studying individual supervised farming jobs.......................... 5
Miscellaneous.. 1
                                                                      ——
                                                                      20

JOB	NO. OF PERIODS
May	
Selecting and purchasing farm equipment	3
Planning farm buildings	3
Planning a lighting system for a farm home	3
Performing individual shop jobs	5
Studying individual supervised farming jobs	5
Miscellaneous	1
	20

Calendar for Individualized Study. Each student will need to prepare a course calendar for the time to be given to the study of individual jobs. The suggested course of study previously explained is for group instruction. In the suggested course the following time was given for individualized study: first year, 9 periods; second year, 24 periods; third year, 27 periods; and fourth year, 45 periods. Some of this time can be given to small groups having common problems.

After the student has decided on the type of farming he desires to follow, he will then start his long-time supervised farming program. Such a program will contain the enterprises and supplementary farm jobs added from time to time that he needs to include in his study calendar. The enterprises will have to be analyzed into jobs and the jobs arranged into months and years.

There should be no duplication of group jobs and individual jobs. The individual jobs to be studied can be listed on a form. An example of a usable form for this purpose is shown below.

YEARLY INDIVIDUAL STUDY CALENDAR: 19—

Jobs	Month to be studied	Number of periods
Purchasing baby chicks	March	3

Revising the Course of Study.   Experience from year to year in the same school will indicate many needed changes in the course of study.   It is well for the teacher to take time each summer to make the needed changes and adjustments.   The program must be kept abreast of farming conditions, which necessitates surveys being kept current or up to date.   It is also necessary for each student to revise his individual course calendar at the beginning of each school year.

SELECTED REFERENCES

COOK, G. C., and L. J. PHIPPS, "A Handbook on Teaching Vocational Agriculture," The Interstate, Danville, Ill., 1952.

Curriculum in Vocational Agriculture for Nebraska High Schools, *Bulletin* 431, State Department of Education, Lincoln, Neb.

Directing Vocational Agricultural Day-school Students in Developing Their Farming Programs, U.S. Office of Education, Division of Vocational Education, *Bulletin* 225.

Educational Objectives in Vocational Agriculture, U.S. Office of Education, Division of Vocational Education, *Monograph* 21, 1940.

HAMLIN, H. M., "Agricultural Education in Community Schools," The Interstate, Danville, Ill., 1949.

Instructional Guide for Improvement Projects in Dairying, *Bulletin* 260, State Department of Education, Lansing, Mich.

Teaching Techniques, *Bulletin* 290, State Department of Education, Lansing, Mich.

10. Preparing Schedules and Enrolling Day Students

S CHOOL ADMINISTRATORS sometimes feel that vocational agriculture is a difficult subject to work into the high school schedule of classes. Closely identified with this problem is that of enrolling the type of student who needs, wants, and can profit by such instruction. Both problems must be approached in the spirit of making the school really serve the people of the community.

The Agricultural Curriculum. Few high schools have separate curriculums for students with different vocational objectives. The average high school offers a list of courses from which each pupil must select enough to make 16 units. In most states the state board of education prescribes certain subjects for all high school pupils, and the local high school authorities may add to those required by the state. The following high school units are required by most states:

SUBJECT	NUMBER OF UNITS
English	3 or 4
Mathematics	1 or 2
Science	1 or 2
Social Science	2 or 3

In addition, nearly all the states have requirements for health and physical education. In most agricultural communities the course of study in vocational agriculture is three or four years in length. The credit usually allowed is $1\frac{1}{2}$ units. This credit is for the work done in class, in the farm-mechanics shop, and in connection with the supervised farming program. The Southern Association of Secondary Schools and Colleges prohibits the granting of more than four units toward graduation for any one subject.

Because of this regulation, any student who is given $1\frac{1}{2}$ units per year for agriculture can receive no credit for the fourth year toward graduation. A few states give separate credit for farm-mechanics work.

A high school boy who desires to enter the vocation of farming is continually asking: "What elective subjects should I take?" Any high school subject, properly taught, should be of some value to a person who is engaged in farming.   On the other hand, it stands to reason that some subjects may have more direct application to his needs than others.   Any student can profit by taking additional courses in science, mathematics, business, speech, or the social studies.

Fig. 89. There should be a close relationship between teacher and student.   (*Courtesy of J. K. Coggin, North Carolina.*)

The following curriculum is common for a boy who plans to be a farmer and includes the usual required units.

Subject	Number of Units
English	4
Agriculture	4
Science	3
Social Science	2 or 3
Mathematics	1 or 2
Business or Speech	1

English would be given for all four years.   Few rural boys can afford to miss any instruction in the use of the English language.   Agriculture would be given for three or four years (including farm mechanics). The three units in science would likely be general science or biology, chemistry, and physics. If physics would not be taught, the student could take general science, biology, and chemistry. In social science most states require one unit in American history. Other units recommended are world history, problems in democracy, or political science.

The units in mathematics might be one unit in general mathematics and one unit in business arithmetic or two units in algebra. Plane geometry

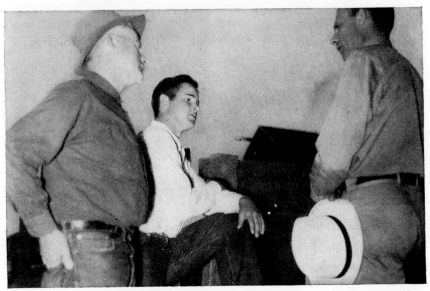

Fig. 90. The "right" combination in vocational agriculture—interested student, teacher, and parent. (*California State Bureau of Agricultural Education.*)

might also be a valuable subject. If any language is desired, the student will probably find he must take it for two years in order to receive credit. The one unit in business, if elected, may well be a half unit in bookkeeping and a half unit in typing. A unit in speech is also of value to any boy who is preparing to be a rural leader.

It is recommended that the teacher of agriculture be familiar with the list of high school units required by the state board of education and by the local high school before he assists boys in their selection of elective subjects.

Length of Class Periods. The length of the high school period has never been standardized. According to the Southern Association of Secondary Schools and Colleges, the period should not be less than 45 minutes.

For many years the approved period for vocational agriculture was 90 minutes per day. Complaints have been made that the 90-minute period was often difficult to schedule.   Recently plans have been modified and a state or school may select any one of the following plans:[1]

Plan A.   Two consecutive 60-minute periods of instruction, five days per week, for one year, and one 60-minute period of instruction, five days per week, for the other years.

Plan B.   Two consecutive 60-minute periods of instruction, two days per week, and one 60-minute period, three days per week, for each class, each year.

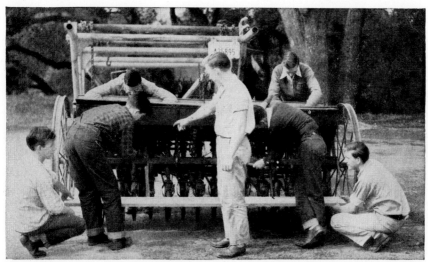

Fig. 91.   Schedules must be so arranged as to allow time for outside and field work.   (*California State Bureau of Agricultural Education.*)

Plan C.   Two consecutive 45-minute periods of instruction per day, five days per week, for each class, each year.

Plan D.   Sixty minutes of instruction per day, five days per week, for each class, each year, provided, that there is in operation a program of systematic group instruction for out-of-school young farmers and for adult farmers for not less than a total of 72 clock hours during the year.

Plan E.   Thirty clock hours of scheduled class instruction in agriculture during each school month for each class.

A given state may adopt one of the above time requirements or the responsibility may be passed on to the local departments.

Alternating Classes.   Because of the fact that the high enrollment is usually in the first year, it is recommended that first-year pupils always be

[1] From Administration of Vocational Education, U.S. Office of Education, Division of Vocational Education, *Bulletin* 1, General Series 1, rev. 1948, sec. II (Agricultural Education), p. 39—All-day Classes.

taught in a separate class. It is possible to alternate the third and fourth years, or the second and third years where only three years are offered. If any classes are alternated, the teacher must arrange his course so that no regular student repeats himself. Individual problems need to form the main core of the course of study each year.

The Teaching Schedule. The teacher of vocational agriculture often teaches four types of classes—all-day, day-unit, young-farmer, and adult-farmer. His teaching schedule at the high school should be prepared with the idea in mind that all four groups of citizens are entitled to instructional service.

Fig. 92. Students getting practical experience in selecting western ewes.

In some cases, a teacher of agriculture may teach in two high schools. This plan makes it necessary to schedule all his classes at one school in the morning and at the other school in the afternoon.

Since vocational agriculture is an elective subject, certain required subjects, like English, cannot be scheduled at the same time unless the school is large enough to have more than one section of English for a grade.

It is not because the teacher of vocational agriculture believes his subject is the most important one in the high school but because of the reasons already stated that it is best to schedule agriculture first in a small high school. The other subjects can then be easily adjusted and fitted into the schedule.

In preparing the teaching schedule, the high school principal is further limited by the subjects each teacher can teach, by the number of teachers on the faculty, by the available classrooms, and by the number of subjects he may wish to offer.

SAMPLE TEACHING SCHEDULE

Time	Teacher 1*	2	3	4	5	6	7	8
8:30–9:15	Agriculture I	Home Economics I	English IV		Social Science II	Chemistry III	Business III	Physical Education†
9:15–10:30	Agriculture I	Home Economics I	Speech IV	Algebra II		Chemistry III		
10:30–11:15	Agriculture II	Home Economics II	English III		Social Science I	Physics IV		
11:15–12:30	Agriculture II	Home Economics II	English I	Plain Geometry III	Social Science IV	Physics IV	Business II	
12:30–1:00	Noon Period							
1:00–1:45	Agriculture III and IV	Home Economics III and IV		Algebra I	French III	Biology II	General Mathematics I	
1:45–2:30	Agriculture III and IV	Home Economics III and IV		General Science I		Biology II	French IV	
2:30–3:15	‡		English II	General Science I	Social Science III		Business IV	

* The agriculture teacher will have to schedule his young-farmer and adult-farmer classes at night.
† Each pupil to schedule one period per day for physical education.
‡ A day-unit class to be taught once per week at "Shady Grove."

Suppose a high school has eight teachers and the principal and offers the following subjects:

NINTH GRADE		TENTH GRADE	
English	Agriculture	English	Agriculture
General Science	Home Economics	Biology	Home Economics
Social Science	Physical Education	Social Science	Physical Education
Mathematics		Mathematics	Business

ELEVENTH GRADE		TWELFTH GRADE	
English	Business	English	Business
Mathematics	Chemistry	Home Economics	Physics
Home Economics	Social Science	Agriculture	Social Science
French		French	Speech

From the suggested teaching schedule it can be observed that pupils actually have a choice of the following subjects:

NINTH GRADE	TENTH GRADE
Agriculture or Home Economics	Agriculture or Home Economics
General Science	Social Science
English	Algebra II
Algebra or General Mathematics I	Business II
Social Science	Biology
Physical Education	English
	Physical Education

ELEVENTH GRADE	TWELFTH GRADE
Chemistry or French and Business III	English
English	Speech
Plane Geometry	Physics or Social Science
Agriculture or Home Economics or French	Agriculture or Home Economics or French
Physical Education	Business IV
	Physical Education

It is to be expected that many problems will arise in making the schedule and many more in applying it to individual cases. Students in one grade desire to take subjects offered specifically for another grade, and a few students usually have to take subjects for the second time.

Selecting and Registering Students. There are a few rather definite limitations placed on the teachers of vocational agriculture in enrolling pupils. According to the Smith-Hughes Act, pupils must meet these qualifications:

1. Be fourteen years of age or older.
2. Have as their objective farming for a vocation.
3. Be able to follow some approved plan for obtaining supervised farming experience.

Quite a number of teachers who do not have school farms experience problems when they enroll town boys. Many times such students have had no previous experience in farming and have no facilities for conducting a satisfactory program of supervised farming. If town boys do want to enroll, the teacher should make it clear to them and to their parents that the course cannot be completed without meeting this requirement.

The teacher will find it to his advantage to get acquainted with boys when they are in the grade below the age for him to enroll them. Visits should be made to the homes of these pupils and definite conferences held with the parents. The teacher will find that there are many pupils he can wisely

FIG. 93. Teacher and boy discussing plans for growing out the pigs.

advise to take other subjects rather than agriculture. A group meeting with the parents of prospective students to explain the program is most helpful. This meeting should be held near the close of the school year prior to the enrollment of the students.

In some schools there seems to be a tendency to advise "slow" students to take vocational subjects, and the teacher of agriculture usually gets his share of them. It is true that many vocations need people of different levels of ability. A person may follow the vocation of farming and never be more than a day laborer, that is, do as he is told all his life. Such a student may be taught a few of the manual skills he may need. However, to finance a farm business, manage the production of crops and animals, recondition and service farm machines, and market farm products economically, a person needs marked ability—probably as much ability as it takes to manage a business. The teacher of agriculture, therefore, should try to secure students with as high mental capacity as is possible.

Experience has shown that it is unwise to admit girls to high school classes in vocational agriculture.   In the first place, few of them expect to actually manage a farm and would not be very much interested in the course of study organized for that purpose.   In the second place, there are many problems to be taught in livestock production that are difficult to handle where high school boys and girls are both present.   If a large group of girls desire to take agriculture and the teacher has the time, he may organize a special nonvocational section for them.   The course could follow their agricultural interests, such as flower growing, poultry, canning, vegetable gardening, and other similar enterprises and jobs.

SELECTED REFERENCES

Cook, G. C., and L. J. Phipps, "A Handbook on Teaching Vocational Agriculture," The Interstate, Danville, Ill., 1952.

Curriculum in Vocational Agriculture for Nebraska High Schools, *Bulletin* 431, State Department of Education, Lincoln, Neb.

The Program of Vocational Agriculture in Kentucky, *Bulletin* 8, vol. 13, State Department of Education, Frankfort, Ky.

Requirements and High School Students' Programs, U.S. Office of Education, Division of Secondary Education, *Circular* 300.

Selection of Students for Vocational Training, U.S. Office of Education, Division of Vocational Education, *Bulletin* 232.

Vocational Agriculture in Pennsylvania, *Bulletin* 250, State Department of Education, Harrisburg, Pa.

Vocational Education in Agriculture for Louisiana, *Bulletin* 587, State Department of Education, Baton Rouge, La.

11. Selecting Teaching Procedures

T HE PURPOSE of any type of teaching is to bring about growth in learners, to increase knowledge, to improve ability to make decisions or to perform skills, and to stimulate growth in character and personality traits, growth in the acceptance of social responsibility, growth in health and physical alertness, and growth in many other areas of capability. It is possible, however, with some subject matter, materials, and methods, to bring about the wrong type of growth so far as society is concerned. The desired growth in students is the kind which is best for society and also best for bringing about a higher level of attainment in each individual.

In vocational agriculture the teaching is directed toward growth in vocational efficiency and useful citizenship. The teacher of vocational agriculture understands that his program should bring about desirable growth in many areas of intelligent living.

The teacher should be anxious to see that the desired changes and growth take place in each student. Effective teaching is a process by which the teacher guides the learner in obtaining the desired growth. The following abilities are found in the successful teacher of vocational agriculture:

1. To develop and maintain the interest of the learner.
2. To plan with students to meet individual needs and to make assignments accordingly.
3. To maintain discipline.
4. To develop student understandings of technical information and skills.
5. To demonstrate manipulative skills.
6. To teach students how to discover and solve new problems.
7. To stimulate students to apply sound facts and information to the solution of problems.
8. To select and use effective methods and devices in teaching a specific job.
9. To deal effectively with the individual differences in students.
10. To evaluate his own teaching.

The remainder of this chapter is devoted to how a teacher may further develop and use the abilities just indicated.

The Four-step Procedure in Teaching

Many teachers of vocational agriculture follow four rather well-defined steps in the teaching of any job to either individuals or groups: (1) preparation, (2) presentation, (3) supervision of practice, and (4) testing and follow-up. The success or failure of teaching depends upon how well each step is handled. Before starting the instruction process in which these four steps are used, a teacher should have reviewed and analyzed the subject

Fig. 94. A job clearly and interestingly presented to young students in appropriate surroundings is usually effective. (*Courtesy of J. K. Coggin, North Carolina.*)

matter and materials involved, determined his teaching objectives, and blocked out a teaching plan to be followed.

Preparation Step. The purposes of the preparation step are as follows:

1. To find out what students already know about the job. The teacher must know at what level to begin the instruction. In skill jobs he can determine who, if any, can assist him in giving a demonstration or act as leaders during the supervision of practice step.
2. To create a desire on the part of each student to want to learn the job—to acquire new knowledge and skills and to apply this in his farming program.
3. To "set the stage" for the lesson.
4. To prepare the mind of the learner to receive. This is sometimes done by making an analysis of the job with the learners in order to determine the needed information or the various operations to be performed.

Keeping these purposes in mind, the teacher may use any combination of the following devices or methods:

Discussion. Ask questions. The experiences of each student will be reflected in the answers.

Demonstration. Ask some student who has had experience to demonstrate designated skills in the job.

Cite cases. Use cases from the local area if at all possible.

Illustrations. Pictures and samples of materials will often arouse curiosity and thereby stimulate interest.

Job Analysis. Determine what facts the learner will need. These facts may be outlined by a series of questions for both operative and managerial jobs. An operative job analysis should show the order for each step in the process of doing the skill. The method of making a job analysis will be given in another chapter.

Presentation Step. The purpose of the presentation step is to present new information and facts and to demonstrate the skills needed in performing the job properly. In carrying through this step, the teacher has a variety of excellent devices from which he may choose. He will usually find that the demonstration technique is appropriate for all operative jobs but that it is inappropriate for a managerial job. Among the many devices commonly used in this step are

1. Analysis and key points
2. Demonstration
3. Laboratory work
4. Field trips
5. Individualized instruction
6. Assignment and supervised study
7. Surveys
8. Discussion and modified conference procedure
9. Illustrations (visual aids)
10. Drills

Supervision of Practice Step. The purpose of this step is to make use of the facts and procedures presented and to practice skills. In an operative job the pupil should summarize the facts and then be given an opportunity to practice by performing the job under supervision. The teacher is responsible for correcting false impressions and redemonstrating as may be necessary for clarity. If the teacher is teaching the job of culling hens, each student must have actual practice in determining a good layer from a poor one. Without this practice under the supervision of the teacher, the value of the teaching job can be seriously questioned. Each learner should also make plans for using the skill at once at his home or on the school farm in order to "clinch" newly acquired knowledge and skill.

In a managerial job each student should summarize the facts and then decide on the procedure he plans to follow in applying the factors involved. For example, the job may be the selection of a breed of chickens to keep on the farm. The decisions made by the different students may be quite dissimilar, depending largely upon the individual objectives in keeping poultry and upon the personal likes and dislikes. Each student should make his own decision based on the information available and then prepare plans for putting his decision into action. The teacher must guide students in making their decisions and formulating plans. No plans on the part of students should be approved unless they appear to be the best for that particular farm and situation. Commonly used devices for this step in an operation job are

1. Group discussion and redemonstration
2. Laboratory or farm shop (to secure practice)
3. Field trip (to secure practice)
4. Supervised planning for the practice work to be done at home or at school

Testing and Follow-up Step. The purpose of this step is to enable the teacher to determine how successfully he has taught the job and to determine how well each student has learned it. The teacher has probably taught the job successfully if he can answer "yes" to such questions as the following:

1. Does each student understand the technical facts?
2. Can each student use the facts properly in making a decision on the farm?
3. In the case of an operative job, would you employ each student to perform this job on your farm?

Common devices a teacher may use in testing include:

1. Performance tests. How well can each student perform "on his own," under actual conditions, without supervision? The supervised farming program, including shop work, gives the teacher an excellent way to determine from time to time how well each student can work independently and how well he can perform the jobs he has been taught. Checking often reveals the need for reteaching certain parts or jobs on an individual-student basis as well as the need for strengthening the lesson plan being followed the next time the same job is taught.
2. Using appropriate oral or written questions.

The Individualized Instruction Method

In some instances, the need for individualized instruction is based upon the different mental-ability levels of students. Although boys taking vocational agriculture will vary as much in mental ability as they usually do in other subjects, that is not the main reason for using individualized instruction for at least part of the time in vocational agriculture.

Students in the same class are often training to enter quite different types of farming and farming situations. The teacher may have one student who

Fig. 95. Much of the individualized instruction is done on project visits. (*Courtesy of R. J. Woodin, Ohio.*)

is preparing to be primarily a dairy farmer, one a hog farmer, one a vegetable farmer, one a fruit farmer, one a nurseryman, and one a florist. Each boy in the class faces problems in his supervised farming program which must receive careful study at the right time. Under such conditions, the teacher must use individualized instruction in order to meet the differences in the need of each student. These differences in need, then, are not based on differences in mental ability but are based on differences in the kind of farming programs being developed by students and their vocational objectives.

When to Begin Individualized Instruction. Because first-year students do not have well-established study habits and because they do not know how to locate reference materials or how to make plans for their supervised farming programs, the teacher must spend much of his time teaching jobs to groups where these abilities are to be developed.   As students gain experience, establish their vocational objectives, and launch their farming programs, more and more time can be devoted by them to individualized study.

As a rule, a few periods per month during the spring of the first year are used to teach students the system to follow in individualized study.   During the second year, one period per week may be used; the third year, five to seven periods per month; and the fourth year, eight to ten periods per month.

A Study Calendar.   If each student is to do effective individualized study, he needs to prepare a study calendar to follow.   The study calendar indicates the jobs to be considered and the date for them to be studied.   It goes without saying that the study calendar will contain the jobs the student faces in his supervised farming program and the jobs he must do in farm mechanics.   Although the form of the study calendar will vary from one state to another, the form shown below should prove adequate.

INDIVIDUAL-COURSE CALENDAR

School year_____Month_____

Jobs	Number of periods	Date completed
Brooding baby chicks	2	Jan. 6
Building feed hoppers for chicks	1	Jan. 9
Feeding baby chicks	2	Jan. 15
Choosing a variety of sweet potatoes	2	Jan. 20
Purchasing sweet-potato seed	1	Jan. 24
Planting a sweet-potato bed	2	Jan. 28

It is well to have the course calendar on a separate sheet for each month of the school year.   The calendar is often made in the early fall for the school year.

Steps for the Student to Follow.   In individualized instruction the student needs to follow rather definite steps.   He may follow those indicated below.

1. Prepare the course calendar for the month.
2. Make an analysis of the job—things to do and know.
3. Have the instructor approve the analysis and offer suggestions as to reference materials.
4. Secure reference materials and begin the study.

5. Have the teacher check to see that the facts are understood.
6. Form conclusions or decisions based on the information and study.
7. Have the teacher approve the conclusions.
8. Make definite plans for putting the decisions into action.
9. Have the plans approved by the teacher.
10. Execute the plans.

The Teacher's Responsibility. The teacher's duties during individualized study are approximately the same as those he faces during supervised study. Among them are the following:

1. To see that each student has a monthly study calendar.
2. To assist in making proper job analyses.
3. To help locate suitable reference materials.
4. To assist students in understanding technical facts.
5. To approve plans made by students.
6. To evaluate (grade) the work done by each student.
7. To see that the physical conditions of the classroom are conducive to study.
8. To see that a working atmosphere is maintained.

Weakness of Teachers in Using the Individualized Study Method. A poor teacher will seldom guide students in learning activities no matter what method of teaching he may try to follow. Improper use of individualized instruction may include:

1. Students do not follow a study calendar.
2. Teachers often give too much time to this method and too little time to group instruction. Group instruction has values that must not be forgotten.
3. Often students do little more than ask and answer questions. If the information is not applied in solving problems or in understanding procedures for skill jobs, then the time may be largely wasted.
4. The student may fail to see the relationship of the facts to his particular problem.
5. Skill jobs are often poorly taught or not taught at all by teachers who use individualized instruction to the extreme.
6. Often good reference materials are not available, or the student is unable to locate them.
7. Some teachers fail to make any teaching plans for properly using this method or any plans whereby they know what each student should do next.

Notes to Keep. The procedure for keeping notes during individualized study should be the same as the procedure discussed later in this chapter.

There is little need for the teacher to adopt two systems for keeping notes. The system adopted should include a record of the essential facts and plans for applying the information to jobs to be done at home or on the farm.

The Assignment Method

The assignment method is often used to advantage. Job or topic assignments may vary as to the source of information. For example, some of the needed information may be obtained from reference materials, whereas individuals, including farmers and businessmen, are the best sources in other instances.

Fig. 96. Group assignment to secure up-to-date information on grades and packaging methods used in the grape industry. (*California State Bureau of Agricultural Education.*)

Assignment for a Group Job. During the assignment of a subject, each student must understand exactly what information he is expected to secure. It is possible to assign the same subject to all students or to give each one a separate subject. For example, if the group is deciding upon the best method of transportation to use in shipping string beans to New York City, one of the topics to consider would be the cost of each available method and the length of time involved. One student may be assigned to obtain the information from the railway freight office, one from the express office, one from a motor truck office, one from the ocean freight office, and one from the air transportation office. The information thus obtained is used to supplement other available information in making the final decision.

It is also possible for the teacher to make an assignment where the facts are to be obtained from reference materials. Specific jobs or topics may be assigned to all members of the class.

Assignments for Current Events. One valuable method of keeping the members of a class informed about new practices or facts in agriculture is through the use of the assignment. One day each month may be devoted to current events in agriculture. Specific areas may be assigned to each student. The topics may cover any field or phase of agriculture. As a rule, new information first appears in agricultural periodicals and bulletins.

The teacher will need to check current reference materials, decide upon a list of the most interesting items for the month, and then make the assignments. At other times, students may be told to review current reference materials and make their own selection of topics. When the latter plan is followed there is a possibility of a few duplications but that is not usually a serious problem.

Current agricultural topics, of course, will vary from month to month. The following will give a few examples:

1. The use of "Delsterol" in Poultry Feeds
2. Ceresan M Seed Disinfectant
3. New Developments in the Artificial Breeding of Farm Animals
4. Air-conditioned Plant for Mushrooms
5. Clearing Land with a Tractor Saw
6. Using 2,4-D to Kill Weeds in a Corn Field

Keeping Notes on Topic Assignments. Where students are assigned a definite topic in which facts must be obtained from business firms or farmers, it is desirable to have a list of guide questions to ask. If a system of this sort is not followed, a student may fail to obtain the necessary facts. When this method is used, the persons or firms called upon need to be informed in advance about the calls to be made by the students.

For making a report from reference materials, the student needs to make some usable notes.

Making Assignment Reports. The same principles should be followed in writing an assignment report as apply in the English class. The material should be stated in correct English and in logical order.

Often teachers require students to write their assignment report and then give the report orally. This plan will aid the student in learning how to speak before a class and, also, may aid other students. Usually students pay more attention to oral reports than to those that are read.

Reference Materials for Assignments. Bulletins, pamphlets, books, and magazines are excellent sources. The student should be encouraged to use the school and city libraries and to obtain facts from reference materials he may have at home.

Benefits of Using This Method. The use of the assignment as a method of teaching has the following values:

1. It acquaints students with many sources of information.
2. It aids students in learning how to locate desirable reference materials.
3. It helps students keep up with current agricultural developments.
4. It helps students learn how to organize and give a report.

The Supervised Study Method

After the assignment has been made for a given agricultural job, the students will profit by taking the time necessary to find the technical facts in reference materials.   Often the facts needed are to be located in a variety of

Fig. 97. Supervised study is a real aid to good teaching if properly conducted.   (*Courtesy of J. K. Coggin, North Carolina.*)

reference materials, such as up-to-date reference books, bulletins, magazines, and pamphlets.

"Supervised study," therefore, means a period of classroom study under the guidance of the teacher and participated in by students who feel the need of obtaining necessary information.   Few home-study assignments are usually made.   This makes it still more important that some time be given to a supervised study at school.   Among the purposes of supervised study are the following:

1. It gives students a period to study where available references can be found.
2. The teacher is present to explain and interpret information.
3. It maintains a businesslike atmosphere conducive to study because others are doing the same thing.

4. It gives the teacher an opportunity to teach students how to study.
5. It affords a good plan for meeting individual differences.
6. It teaches students how to think and how to solve problems.
7. It helps foster desirable teacher-pupil relationships.
8. It affords an opportunity to study for a purpose.
9. It teaches students how to solve individual problems.
10. It may be used as a period for the individual planning of supervised farming work.

When to Use Supervised Study. Supervised study can be used in the presentation step in teaching farm jobs. Managerial jobs require facts to assist in making decisions; with operative jobs facts and procedures are necessary to understand why the job is done in a particular way.

Supervised study is not for the purpose of merely keeping students busy. It is one of the best methods of obtaining facts from reference materials. There is no possible way for a teacher to specify any definite percentage of time to give to supervised study, but he should use the method whenever the need arises.

Length of a Supervised Study Period. The length of the time to use supervised study will depend upon the nature of the job, upon the amount of reference materials available, and upon the interest, age, and study habits of individuals. High school students easily tire if any one method of teaching is used continuously.

A short discussion period is desirable at the end of a period of study. For many jobs the teacher will find that 20 to 30 minutes is sufficient for study. Those who read rapidly will complete their work before others who read more slowly. In such cases, supplementary reference materials are suggested.

Duties of the Teacher during Supervised Study. Since the student is expected to learn during the study period, the teacher is responsible for directing the learning. He can never direct the study period seated at his desk doing other work and allowing students to read whatever they desire. Some of the instructor's responsibilities during a supervised study period are as follows:

1. Assist students to find the proper reference materials.
2. Counsel students as to the facts they are trying to secure.
3. Have the physical conditions of the classroom in a suitable condition for study; these include light, temperature, and ventilation.
4. Maintain order.
5. Keep each student busy with his assigned task.
6. Counsel with students and assist them in understanding the subject-matter materials.

7. Teach students how to study, such as showing them how to find facts in books and bulletins that are needed.
8. Teach students how to adjust for individual differences.
9. Call attention to information that may have been overlooked.
10. Teach students how to summarize facts and record them in their notebooks.
11. Move about from one student to another to determine the help each may need.
12. Determine when to end the study period or when to change to another method of teaching.

Handling Reference Materials.   The plan for handling reference materials may vary with the age and ability of the students.   First-year students may need to have the reference materials available at their seats.   Have the advanced students trained on how to find needed reference materials.

Often the teacher has enough duplicate copies of bulletins to provide one for each student or table.   These should be available on the teacher's desk before the class period begins.   Reference materials may also be exchanged by groups of students.   If a student is wasting time because he cannot find suitable reference materials, the teacher is responsible.   At the close of the supervised study period, provide sufficient time for all reference materials to be returned to its proper place.

Teaching Students How to Study.   Most students need help in finding facts.   It is usually necessary to help them with the following points:

1. How to use the table of contents and the index of a book.
2. How to make use of an appendix and its purpose.
3. How to use tables and graphs.
4. How to find important facts quickly.
5. How to follow a list of questions prepared through job analysis.
6. How to summarize and evaluate facts for use in making decisions.
7. How to determine what notes to keep and how to record these notes.
8. How to use the dictionary and encyclopedia.
9. How to use the filing system for bulletins and other reference materials.

Few students when they begin their work in vocational agriculture know how to use a library.   Previous experience usually includes only the use of a single textbook.   Therefore, the teacher will need to take time to acquaint the students with his way of teaching.   The keeping of proper notes by students will also be an important phase of his teaching.   First-year students seldom know how to keep notes.   Expect and demand that they learn how to record information and that they improve from month to month.

Determining the Help to Give Students. Beginning students in vocational agriculture will need more help than more advanced individuals. The ideal student is one who, at the close of his training period in high school, has learned how to find reference materials, how to study and summarize facts, and how to use facts in solving problems. Supervised study is often used in connection with individualized instruction, especially for planning jobs to be done in the supervised farming program.

Enterprise Study Guides. In reality, the so-called "enterprise study guides" are much the same as materials contained in well organized textbooks. They may be used to assist students in supervised study. However, study guides are usually designed to fit general conditions over a wide area and frequently fail to meet the specific needs of a boy in a given community. To follow study guides without first adapting them to the community may do the student more harm than good.

Because of the changes in economic conditions and world needs for agricultural products, a study guide prepared for or by a student one year would usually fail to fit the exact needs of another boy the following year, even if he were on the same farm.

The Laboratory Method

The laboratory method of teaching may be used to obtain facts for making management decisions or to give repetitive experience for skills. The method may follow inductive development, where the individual works alone under the supervision of the teacher and obtains knowledge new to himself. The student then uses these new facts he has learned to aid him in solving specific problems of his own.

The laboratory method may also be used by following the deductive method of thinking, where the student proves to himself that a given statement is true.

When to Use the Laboratory Method. The teacher can use the laboratory method in the presentation step of teaching a managerial job or in the supervision of practice step of an operative job. The teacher wastes time when he requires a laboratory exercise which has no relation to a definite farm job of his students. Use the laboratory method when time permits and when this method is necessary in teaching a farm job. Learners may be told the facts or have them demonstrated in a short period of time, whereas the discovery of the same facts by the use of a laboratory may take days. Facts gained by the laboratory method are usually better retained by the student.

The laboratory method is used for many operative jobs to allow opportunity to practice and develop skills.

The Laboratory Method to Discover Facts. In using the laboratory method to discover facts, the students will need to adopt an outline suggested by the teacher. A suggested outline would usually have the following divisions:

1. The purpose of the laboratory period. What is the student trying to find? Why is it desirable to obtain the facts in this manner?
2. The equipment that will be used. Often special attention must be given to the arrangement of the equipment.
3. The supplies needed in laboratory work. A list of the supplies needed should be given.
4. Steps to follow—directions and precautions. An outline of the steps to follow in doing the work needs to be given including what to do in each step. The precautions to take are to be mentioned.

Fig. 98. Laboratory work in the identification of farm seeds. (*Courtesy of J. W. Bunten, Nevada.*)

5. Observations to make. Special attention should be given to observations. Questions may be asked that can be answered only by careful observations.
6. Summary of the facts discovered. A list of the facts discovered is needed by the student in order for him to use the information in solving the decisions facing him in the job.
7. References used. It is well to list two or three of the best references that were used.

The Laboratory Method to Practice Skills. The laboratory method is often used in the classroom and farm-mechanics shop to allow students an opportunity to gain skills. The practice period may follow a demonstration which has been given by the teacher. The use of a demonstration is often desirable to speed up the training, to prevent unsafe practices, and to further assure the use of correct practices.

An outline for use in teaching skills by the laboratory method would be as follows:

1. The job specifications, such as drawings and sketches
2. The equipment and tools to be used
3. The materials (supplies) needed
4. Steps to follow—directions and precautions
5. Observations to make
6. Record of the cost of materials
7. Plans for using the skill at home
8. References used

Recording Results of Laboratory Work.   Although a well-organized notebook is necessary in recording facts that are discovered, it must not be made more important than the information.   If a student is just filling in blanks in a notebook, the work is artificial.   On the other hand, if he is recording facts that are to be used at once in solving a real problem, the work becomes a reality.

Students are expected to be accurate in measurements, observations, and statements.   No teacher, however, would expect beginning students to be as accurate as skilled mechanics or as research specialists.

Responsibilities of the Teacher.   In using the laboratory method a teacher must assume the following responsibilities:

1. Have enough equipment and supplies available for all students.
2. Have a definite outline for the students to follow in doing their work.
3. Discuss, demonstrate, and show by example the necessary safety rules.
4. Maintain discipline and order, keeping each student busy with assigned duties.
5. Determine that notes are properly kept and recorded.
6. Determine that the discovered facts or learned skills are in the plans of the students' supervised farming programs.

Examples of Laboratory Work in Agriculture.   Laboratory work is not an end in itself, and the following laboratory jobs illustrate this point:

1. Making a post-mortem of a fowl.
2. Testing milk for butterfat.
3. Operating a cream separator.
4. Cutting metal with an oxyacetylene torch.
5. Testing the fertility of farm seeds.
6. Determining the capillary rise of moisture in different soil types.
7. Testing the acidity of different soil samples.
8. Checking the solubility of different kinds of fertilizer materials.

9. Testing a sample of sand to determine if it is suitable for use in making concrete.

10. Cutting rafters for different pitches of the roof of a given structure.

Laboratory Books. There are many laboratory manuals available for agriculture, especially in the field of dairying, soils, and horticulture.

Since many books are written to be used over a wide area, the specific facts, even in laboratory manuals, have to be modified for any given school. The teacher may often get many valuable suggestions from these books, but it is highly necessary for him to adapt the outline to his community.

The Field-trip Method

The use of the field trip in teaching is the same as the use of the laboratory method except for a difference in the location. A field trip may be used for an operative job or for a managerial job although the purpose in the two

Fig. 99. On this field trip the students are comparing the values of various types of pasture grasses. (*Courtesy of J. K. Coggin, North Carolina.*)

cases is quite different. In a managerial job the teacher may use a field trip to determine farm practices and situations in order to have specific facts in making decisions. In operative jobs he often uses the field-trip method to provide practice experiences for members of the class. In addition to the uses or reasons just cited for field trips, the following may be given:

1. Boys learn more readily in a natural situation. Trees budded in the laboratory can never create the same interest as budding them in a nursery row.

2. Boys enjoy breaking the monotony of classroom routine.

3. Boys learn to do by doing.

4. Facts observed and collected on a field trip are remembered longer and better than facts obtained from books.

5. Some agricultural products cannot be brought to the classroom or farm-mechanics shop for study. Pastures and drainage systems are examples.

Transportation of Students. The teacher will need to have definite plans for transportation of his students. Because of the cost and liability involved in transporting students, it is best to have it furnished by the school. School busses are used to transport students to the majority of our rural high schools and are very suitable for field trips. If available, use a regular bus driver because he knows how to operate the bus and is usually licensed for the job. The teacher can be more effective in keeping order when he is seated in the rear of the bus.

Before school begins in the fall, the teacher should know approximately how many miles he will transport students on field trips during the school year. With these facts in mind, he should then obtain the approval of the school officials and have them notify the principal and the bus driver. In most schools such arrangements for bus travel can be made through the school principal or superintendent.

In some departments the county furnishes a truck and pays all operating expenses. This plan is satisfactory for small groups but will seldom accommodate a large class comfortably and safely. If such a truck is used, be certain that it is adequately insured and that it is operated by an experienced driver. Many F.F.A. chapters or vocational agriculture departments own and operate busses or pickups. The same facts should apply in such cases as those where the county furnishes the trucks.

Private cars are often used. In some cases, students may have cars at the school and would not object to using them. The teacher may also use his car. Discipline and safety is often a serious problem when students ride in a number of different cars.

Preliminary Planning for a Field Trip. A teacher who knows the agriculture of his area and knows when he should teach the various jobs can plan a field trip several days or weeks in advance. In making his plans, he has the following duties:

1. To determine where he should go on a field trip.

2. To make arrangements with the farmer or farmers concerned.

3. To outline for the class the exact facts to be secured or skills to be learned.

4. To give the class directions as to the transportation plan and precautions to take.

5. To see that the students return to the school on time.

Too much cannot be said of the importance of making advance arrangements with farmers for a field trip.   Often teachers who fail to make the necessary arrangements arrive at a farm to judge beef cattle and find that all animals are in a new pasture several miles in the opposite direction.   The teacher needs to know about the farm before taking the students there on a field trip.   On trips to collect information, the value of the time used depends upon the farmer's being available after the group arrives.

When to Take Field Trips.   It is best to take field trips when the weather is comfortable and the roads are in good condition.   The best time to take a field trip in connection with operative jobs is in the presentation or supervision of practice steps of teaching.   The purpose of the field trip is for demonstrations and for giving students an opportunity to practice skills.   It is best to complete the preparation step in teaching such a job before the field trip begins.

In a managerial job the trip should be made in connection with the presentation step in order that the students obtain the facts needed in the supervision of practice step for making plans and decisions.

Notebooks for a Field Trip.   Use the regular F.F.A. classroom notebook for making notes on field trips.   Information obtained on a field trip is recorded under a job in the same way it would be if obtained in any other manner.   Outlines for use on the field trip are a part of the notes.

Discipline on a Field Trip.   Students must remember that a field trip is being out of school only in place and not in time.   The conduct of all persons should be just as orderly during a field trip as during laboratory work in the classroom.

Special attention must be given to the conduct of students who visit dairy and poultry farms.   Exciting the animals may cause the farmer to lose part of his production for the day.   See that all gates are closed and that no damage is done to fruit trees or vegetable gardens.   Visiting a farm gives no liberty to obtain free food unless the farmer offers it.

Where students are visiting more than one livestock farm on the same day, it is desirable to clean and disinfect shoes after leaving each farm.   This avoids the possible spread of serious animal diseases.

Outline for a Field Trip to Secure Working Data.   Often the teacher desires to obtain local farming data to use in making decisions.   Suppose he is teaching the job of deciding on the type of tobacco barn to build.   He can obtain facts from books and bulletins, but the practical experience of local farmers is well worth considering.   In the preparation step of teaching this job, the teacher and students should agree on the information needed for the proper decisions to be made.   They may decide on the following outline, a separate copy of which would be used at each farm visited:

1. Date_____
2. Name of the farmer visited_____
3. Number of barns on his farm_____
4. Type of materials used in constructing the barns_____
5. Size of each barn: Width_____Length_____Height_____
6. Date each barn was constructed_____
7. Condition of repair of each barn_____
8. Cost of each barn when constructed_____
9. Probable life of each barn_____
10. Method of heating each barn_____
11. Danger of fire hazards_____
12. Arrangements of flue pipes_____
13. Arrangements for hanging tobacco_____
14. Location and size of doors_____
15. General comment made by the student or facts given by the farmer and not already recorded_____
16. Sketch of the interior of each barn.

The information obtained from a number of farmers may be summarized and used to advantage by each student in deciding on which type to build.

Outline for an Operative Job. The outline for an operative job can be similar to the procedure used in the laboratory method. If the job is budding citrus trees, the outline could be as follows:

1. Equipment needed_____
2. Materials to use_____
3. Steps to take in doing the job_____
4. Precautions to observe_____
5. Observations to make_____
6. Summary of facts learned
    a. What are the limits of budding?
    b. How is the incision made in the stock?
    c. State how the buds are cut from the bud stick.
    d. Sketch manner in which the bud is placed in the stock.
    e. What is the value of wrapping the bud?
    f. List the common wrapping materials
    g. Why is it necessary to insert a bud immediately after removing it from the bud stick?
    h. How long should the wrapping material be left on the bud?
    i. Why must budding be done at this season of the year?
7. What changes, if any, must I make in budding citrus trees at my home?_____
_____
8. References to be used in obtaining facts needed in performing this job._____
_____

Typical Jobs Involving Field Trips. A few examples of managerial jobs where valuable information may be obtained through field trips include:

1. Deciding on the type of tobacco barn to build.
2. Determining a variety of any crop.
3. Selecting a breed of livestock.

4. Planning a rotation system for a farm.
5. Planning a feeding program for animals.
6. Determining the best method of curing meat on the farm.
7. Deciding on the best method of managing turpentine faces on pine trees.
8. Selecting a method of marketing crops.
9. Determining the source of farm credit to use.
10. Determining the method to use in applying fertilizers to truck crops.

A few examples of operative jobs that are best taught by using field trips include:

1. Budding trees.
2. Judging beef cattle, dairy cattle, swine, sheep, and horses.
3. Milking cows.
4. Spraying or dusting plants.
5. Castrating animals.
6. Butchering farm animals.
7. Grading and packing fruit.
8. Preparing land for crops.
9. Constructing farm fences.
10. Establishing improved pastures.
11. Transplanting vegetable plants.
12. Cultivating crops.
13. Culling hens.
14. Constructing terraces.
15. Constructing fire lines in forests.
16. Applying fertilizers to crops.
17. Harvesting crops.
18. Storing sweet potatoes.
19. Curing a barn of tobacco.
20. Making sirup from sugar cane.
21. Landscaping home grounds.
22. Pruning fruit trees.
23. Preparing livestock for a show.
24. Treating livestock for screwworms.
25. Killing and dressing poultry.

Evaluating a Field Trip. If the teacher can answer "yes" to each of the following questions, the chances are the trip was successful as a method of teaching:

1. Did the students know the purpose of the trip?
2. Did they see the need of the trip in relation to the requirements of the job?

3. Did students assist in determining the observations to make or the skills to practice?
4. Were specific directions given to all before the trip was made?
5. Were preliminary plans made with the farmer?
6. Was good conduct maintained during the field trip?
7. Did students maintain interest and work in keeping with the objectives?
8. Did students use the skills (or facts) obtained on the trip in their supervised farming programs?
9. Did the teacher notify the high school principal that he was leaving the school building for a field trip?
10. Did the students return to the school on schedule?

The Demonstration Method

The use of the demonstration method of teaching is largely restricted to operative jobs. In conducting a demonstration for either an individual or

Fig. 100. A demonstration on the grading of sweet potatoes. (*Georgia State Department of Education.*)

group, the leader must "show" as well as "tell" how a certain skill or operating point is performed.

When to Use the Demonstration Method. Each teacher needs to use the demonstration method during the presentation step of any operative job. He may give the demonstration himself, use a student to give it, or bring in a qualified outsider. It would be rather foolish for the teacher to expect students to practice a technical skill before the skill had been demonstrated by a capable person.

It is often desirable to have students give a demonstration in the supervision of practice step of teaching. In fact, each learner should demonstrate, under supervision, that he knows how to do each step in a job before he performs it entirely independently.

Steps in Giving a Demonstration. Depending upon the nature of the demonstration, the teacher will usually follow these steps:

1. Have students in a correct position to properly observe what is to be demonstrated. It is usually best for them to stand behind or to the side of the person who is giving the demonstration. If they stand in front of the teacher, they do not visualize the proper movements of his hands—his right hand looks like his left hand to them.
2. Go through the demonstration without any explanations. Then repeat each step and tell why it is done as it is. Repeat the performance a third time and call attention to all "key" points in the job.
3. Request two or three students who may have had previous experience to repeat the demonstration for the benefit of the other class members.
4. Have the students who gave the demonstration assist in checking the performance of the other members of the class.
5. Allow students to go to work as soon as they have shown reasonable skill. Check them again in 15 or 30 minutes to see that the quality of the work being done is up to standard for beginners.
6. Check the quality of the work done later on the farm or in the farm-mechanics shop.

The Teacher's Responsibility in Giving a Demonstration. In the first place, the teacher must decide whether a demonstration should be given, what equipment will be needed, and what supplies will be necessary. Make definite plans for performing the demonstration. Some of the duties of the teacher in connection with a demonstration are as follows:

1. Decide at what point in teaching the job to give the demonstration.
2. Secure all necessary equipment and place it in the proper location.
3. Obtain all needed supplies and have them on hand.
4. Check the equipment to see that it is in proper working condition.
5. Have students get in proper positions to observe the demonstration.
6. See that each step in the demonstration is given in such a manner that all students can see and understand.
7. See that discipline is maintained.
8. See that the students keep essential notes, drawings, and plans.
9. Assist students in making their plans to utilize the skills learned.

10. Check the work performed by the students at the farm to see that it is up to standard for young workers.

Location for the Demonstration. In teaching an operative job, give the demonstration in the location best for learning. For example, the classroom is suitable for giving a demonstration on testing milk for butterfat, testing the germination of garden seeds, or making a rope halter. The farm-mechanics shop is the best location to demonstrate how to weld iron, to solder metals, and to cut rafters. A local farm or the school farm will probably be the best location to give such demonstrations as the following:

1. Preparing land with a tractor plow.
2. Dehorning cattle.
3. Butchering beef.
4. Running lines for terracing land.
5. Constructing a pit silo.

Use of Commercial Representatives. The teacher is not usually interested financially in any commercial firm, and he must guard against recommending one brand or product over another. Many commercial firms employ experts to demonstrate their particular equipment. Such individuals are often available to assist teachers of vocational agriculture in giving demonstrations. These representatives may demonstrate farm machinery of many types or the use of products to control plant diseases.

In making use of the services of individuals from commercial firms, be sure to arrange for them to be on time for the demonstration and to complete the demonstration in the allotted time. Also, be sure that they do not resort to unethical advertising.

Demonstrations on Farms. In the case of demonstrations to be given on a farm, the teacher should make prior arrangements with the owner. Such arrangements may well include the following:

1. The exact equipment and supplies to be used.
2. The exact time the members of the class will arrive.
3. The exact length of time to be used for the demonstration.
4. The part, if any, the farmer will be expected to take in the demonstration.

The Discussion Method

The discussion method of teaching is sometimes referred to as "socialized recitation." The teacher directs the discussion by making statements or by asking questions. Each student feels free to enter into the discussion at any point where he may make a contribution. The teacher may designate certain students to give their contributions, especially if they hesitate to enter into the discussion.

In leading a discussion, the teacher will usually do a better job if he stands in front of the class and near the blackboard. It is often necessary to summarize what has been said and write it on the blackboard for the benefit of the class or group.

Before the discussion gets under way, the teacher will do well to review the objectives of the job and state reasons for understanding the technical facts involved.

When to Use This Method. The discussion method may be used to advantage in the first three steps in four-step teaching. The teacher may

Fig. 101. Well-conducted group discussions on common farm problems are profitable. (*Courtesy of R. J. Woodin, Ohio.*)

use it in the preparation step to determine what students know already about the job, to create interest, and to make the analysis. In the presentation step, he may use discussion after a field trip, supervised study, laboratory work, or illustrations. The discussion should aid the student in properly understanding facts in their relationship to other truths. In the supervision of practice step, the discussion method is often used to find out whether or not the student can use the facts learned in solving definite problems.

The Use of Questions in Discussion. In leading a discussion, the teacher will want perhaps ten or twelve pivotal questions before him—the main points for consideration. Other appropriate questions can then be formulated during the discussion as the need arises.

The purpose of using a question in the discussion is not just to test the knowledge of the student or to emphasize facts he already knows.   Its main purpose, when properly used, is to stimulate thought.   In general, questions may serve the following purposes:

1. To determine the student's previous knowledge of the job.
2. To stimulate interest in wanting to learn.
3. To stimulate thinking so the student will be instructed.
4. To test the results of learning (and of teaching) after the job is taught.

These purposes may be further expanded into the following more specific aims of the teacher in using a question:

1. To help the teacher know where to begin his instruction by determining what students already know.
2. To stimulate thought.
3. To help the teacher discover individual interests.
4. To help the teacher discover individual problems in learning.
5. To help the teacher create in students the desire to learn.
6. To serve as a medium for practice or drill.
7. To direct attention in learning to the important facts of the job.
8. To test students on what they have learned.
9. To test the efficiency of the teaching.

Types of Questions to Ask in the Discussion.   There are a number of different types of questions and each type has a definite purpose.   The main types of questions used are

| Memory | Comparison | Thought |
| Drill | Contrast | "Yes" or "No" |

Memory.   A memory question calls for facts which the learner has been taught.   Such questions are valuable at all levels of teaching, especially in the elementary grades and secondary grades.   Facts must be retained, however, at all stages in life if they are to be used in solving problems.   Examples of memory questions in agriculture are

1. What is the formula for bordeaux mixture?
2. When were Hereford beef cattle first imported to America?
3. What is the average weight of a New Hampshire hen?

Drill.   Drill questions are actually memory questions asked in rapid-fire order.   Such questions are used largely in the elementary grades, where spelling and multiplication tables must be thoroughly mastered.

Comparison.   Comparison questions call for a discussion of a problem in which the students tell how two objects are similar in certain characteristics. Examples of this type of question are

1. How do the Hereford and Shorthorn cattle compare in rustling ability?
2. Compare the color markings of Berkshire and Poland China hogs.

Contrast. A contrast question is the opposite of a comparison question. Such a question calls for the students to tell how two things are unlike in specific characteristics. Examples are

1. Contrast the lasting qualities of white lead and barium sulfate as pigments in paint.
2. Contrast the rustling ability of Brahman and Hereford cattle.

Thought. Thought questions are used to make students think in order that they may solve a given problem. It is a very good type to use in high school and college teaching. Examples of thought questions are

1. Why should dairy cattle be inspected for tuberculosis?
2. Give the reasons why you selected New Hampshire chickens for your broiler project.

"Yes" or *"No."* The "yes" or "no" question has to be used when the teacher desires the student to face an issue. Many teachers use the question in such a way that the inflection of the voice indicates the correct answer. The "yes" and "no" or "true" and "false" question is often used in an examination. Such questions are not thought-provoking. Examples of such questions for discussion are

1. Is Holstein a breed of hogs?
2. Does the South produce the major part of the American corn crop?

Characteristics of a Good Question. All types of questions used in teaching should be adapted to the age, experience, and abilities of the students. Some of the specific characteristics of a good question are

1. It is stated in clear, definite language.
2. It is adapted to the age and ability of the student.
3. It is directed to the most important points in the job.
4. It is asked in terms that make a student think.
5. It is stated in terms that will cause a student to have to use related facts and information.
6. It is stated in terms that will not reveal the answer.
7. It is stated in terms that will demand the student to answer in sentences rather than in words.
8. It is stated in terms that will cause the student to reason and apply the facts.

The Mechanics of Questioning. Teachers inexperienced in questioning may profit from the following suggestions:

1. No special order should be followed during a discussion period in calling on students.
2. Ask the question and then designate some one pupil to answer it. In some instances, questions may also be addressed to the class and the teacher then allows any student who desires to respond.
3. The number of questions to ask during a specific discussion period will depend upon the type (or types) of questions being used. Drill questions are asked in rapid-fire order, whereas thought questions require ample time for reflective thinking.
4. Formulate at least eight or ten good questions to use in the discussion of the job.
5. Questions should follow a logical sequence.
6. Questions should be well distributed among the members of the class.
7. Questions, as a general rule, should not be repeated for students who have failed to pay attention.
8. Be as ready to answer questions as to ask them.
9. Encourage students to ask good questions.

Treatment of Student Response. The nature of the comment made by the teacher to the response of a student should vary with the individual. He should be guided by the following points in his treatment of responses:

1. Judge whether or not the comments need further emphasis. Often a teacher merely accepts what the student gave. In other cases, he will need to see that the contents of the response are modified.
2. Insist on accuracy of expression as well as of technical facts.
3. The teacher's attitude should not reveal his estimate of the value of the response unless he thinks it best to do so.
4. In certain cases, students who give excellent responses should be complimented, particularly if the individuals involved are seldom responsive.
5. The words "all right," "that's true," "well now," and "let's see now" add nothing to the value of the response. Their occasional use, however, helps "bridge" the discussion.
6. If a teacher receives no response to a question, the fault may lie at his own door. For example, he may have used a poor question or he may have not timed his question well.

Conclusions for a Discussion Period. After a field trip, a laboratory or supervised study period, or the acquiring of any other new information or skills, the teacher should give students an opportunity to present their findings. The discussion period should clear any points that students do not understand.

The final part of the discussion should make some rather definite conclusions. The conclusions reached will usually indicate improved practices on the farm. Each student will then apply the conclusions to his farm situation and adopt those improved practices that apply.

The Modified Conference Procedure in Teaching

The conference method of teaching is the name given to a procedure in which a group of people, each of whom has had some experience in connection with the job or problem at hand, come together to discuss situations they

FIG. 102. Outdoor discussion in connection with a demonstration on how to adjust a plow. (*Courtesy of C. L. Langdon, Michigan.*)

are facing. In teaching agriculture, the conference method is seldom used for all-day classes but is an excellent device for young-farmer and adult-farmer classes. The special purpose of the conference procedure is to provide, on the part of each individual, an opportunity for constructive thinking under the stimulus of contributions offered by each other member.

Steps in the Conference Procedure. In using the conference procedure, the leader should follow a definite plan of action. The following steps are recommended:

1. Define the job or problem under consideration.
2. Analyze the job or problem.
3. Select the functioning facts from the experiences given by members of the class.

4. Assemble these functioning facts either on a blackboard or a chart.
5. Evaluate the facts obtained in the light of the problem.
6. Submit any additional facts, such as experiment station data, to be considered.
7. Have each member of the group make a decision concerning the changes, if any, he can perform on his farm.
8. Have definite working plans prepared for carrying out desired improved farm practices.
9. Supervise the making of the plans and later visit each farm to check the results.

Points about the Use of the Conference Procedure

1. The conference leader (teacher) acts as a director of the discussion.
2. The conference leader helps the members formulate their thoughts and reactions.
3. The conference leader does not, except in rare instances, tell the group what to think, or decide controversial points.
4. The tone of the conference should be kept rather informal. There should be no textbook assignments followed by a recitation.
5. In some cases, prepared materials, especially charts, may be used to supplement the experiences of the members of the class.
6. The conference leader must try to keep the discussion going in the proper direction. Items not important to the job or problem should not take up time.
7. The success of the method will depend upon the amount of real thinking and planning done by the members of the group.

12. Preparing Teaching Plans and Teaching

THE PREPARATION of teaching plans is an essential step to successful teaching. Most superior teachers use carefully prepared teaching plans regularly, and any teacher can do better work if he has a definite plan of action to follow.

FIG. 103. Nothing equals the actual materials with which to do a teaching job.

There are many different forms, or outlines, for teaching plans. Some are in detail and others consist of a skeleton outline. Reasons that may be advanced for making teaching plans are

1. Definite objectives can be adopted.
2. Local situations in the community can be considered in advance.
3. The teacher has a better knowledge of the subject matter because he has reviewed it in preparing the plans.
4. Material is presented in a logical sequence.
5. Time is saved in the classroom.
6. Better student interest is promoted.
7. References and teaching materials can be ready when the period begins.

178

8. It is easier for the teacher to cover all important phases of a job.

9. A plan helps the teacher gain the respect of students, principal, and supervisors.

Before preparing a teaching plan, review the important technical information involved in the job. This means a check of books, bulletins, and magazines. Technical facts are constantly changing and a teacher must use only the best-known approved information. The following complete plans for jobs to be taught are typical as to organization and teaching procedure:

SAMPLE OPERATIVE JOB ANALYSIS

Job: Butchering Hogs

STEPS	HOW TO PERFORM
Secure the equipment....	Provide sticking knife, cutting knife, scoring knife, boning knife, scrapers, cleaver, saw, thermometer, file and whetstone, kettle or barrel for hot water, hook, twine, and equipment for suspending the carcass.
Heat the water.........	Check the temperature of the water. For scalding hogs, it should be from 145–155 deg. F. Water above 155 deg. F. will "set" the hair. Use a thermometer.
Stun the hog...........	Hit on the head with a blunt instrument or shoot with a rifle.
Stick the hog...........	Turn the hog on its back and direct the sticking knife at an angle toward but not into the chest cavity, thus severing the artery that leads to the heart. Allow the hog to bleed well.
Scald.................	Scald immediately after killing and bleeding. Scald the rear end of the carcass first and the head end second.
Clean the carcass.......	Remove the hair by using a bell-shaped scraper. Wash the carcass with warm water and then with cold water. Scrape to remove all possible dirt from the skin.
Suspend the carcass.....	Hang the carcass by means of a gambrel stick. Insert pointed ends beneath the tendons at the back of each hind leg between the hock and the foot. Elevate carcass until the nose is above the ground.
Remove the viscera.....	1. Cut from where the hog was stuck up through the breastbone.
	2. Cut between the hams in front and downward to hit the white membrane that marks the middle of the seam.
	3. Cut the hams apart.
	4. Cut, tie, and remove the "bung."
	5. Open the abdominal cavity by placing the left hand inside, using the fingers as a guide.
	6. Remove the intestines and internal organs.
	7. Cut off the head, leaving jowls on carcass if desired.
	8. Split the carcass down the middle of the backbone.
	9. Pull out the leaf lard.
Cool carcass...........	Place the carcass in a cool place, preferably in cold storage, at once. Leave it for at least 24 hr. at a temperature of 34–40 deg. F. Avoid freezing temperatures.

SAMPLE OPERATIVE JOB ANALYSIS (*Continued*)

STEPS	HOW TO PERFORM
Cut up the carcass......	1. Cut off the shoulders between the third and fourth ribs. Remove jowls if left on carcass when removing head.
	2. Cut out neck bone from the shoulder.
	3. Cut off hams just behind the rise in the pelvic arch, holding the saw at right angles to the shank.
	4. Cut loin from the thin side or bacon.
	5. Cut spareribs from the bacon.
	6. Remove back fat from the loin.
	7. Trim all cuts.

SAMPLE TEACHING PLAN FOR AN OPERATIVE JOB

Job: Butchering Hogs

Objectives:

1. To assist each student to develop the necessary skills and understanding in butchering hogs and in cutting up the carcass properly.
2. To produce meat products of a desirable quality according to market demands.

Preparation Step:

1. Secure the following information from each student:
    a. The experience he has had in butchering hogs.
    b. Whether or not he can name the cuts of meat.
2. Relate the following example:
    a. Mr. Brown had trouble last year in selling his cured meat to a government hospital because he had not made proper cuts.
    b. Mr. Jackson had to take 2 cents under the market price because he had made the same mistake.
3. Raise these questions with the students:
    a. What weight hog is best for meat?
    b. What equipment is needed for butchering hogs?
    c. What temperature should the water be for proper scalding?
    d. Which of the common methods used for stunning hogs is most satisfactory?
    e. Is stunning absolutely necessary?
    f. How should a hog be stuck?
    g. What is the best procedure to follow in scalding a hog?
    h. How is the hair removed after the hog has been scalded?
    i. How is the carcass cleaned?
    j. How should a carcass be suspended?
    k. How should the viscera be removed?
    l. Why should the carcass be chilled before cutting the meat?
    m. How should the carcass be cut to obtain the proper meat cuts?

Presentation Step:

1. Supervised study
    a. Have pupils read the references that will assist them in answering the questions.
    b. Outline steps in butchering a hog (see analysis).

2. Illustration

Use a chart to show the proper cuts of meat.

3. Demonstration

Butcher one hog and show the students how to perform each operation.

4. Discussion

The discussion will involve the key points in the analysis and those suggested by the demonstration.

Supervision of Practice Step:

1. Take a field trip to the farm of Mr. J. D. Smith.   Under supervision each student is to kill, dress, and cut the meat of one hog.
2. Each student will make the necessary plans for butchering hogs at home.

Testing and Follow-up Step:

Test students by each of the following plans:

a. Check the results of the work done at home.

b. Give a written quiz at the end of the month and include questions on key points in this job.

Equipment and Materials Needed:

(See analysis of the job.)

References:

1. Butchering and Curing Pork on the Farm, *Bulletin* 120, Florida Agricultural Extension Service, 1943.
2. Butchering the Family Pork Supply, *Bulletin* 501, New York Agricultural Experiment Station, 1942.
3. Deyoe, G. P., and J. L. Krider, "Raising Swine," McGraw-Hill Book Company, Inc., New York, 1952.
4. Farm Dressed Pork, *Circular* 239, Pennsylvania Agricultural Extension Service, 1942.
5. The Farm Pork Supply, *Bulletin* 448, Georgia Agricultural Extension Service, 1948.
6. Hog Killing and Cutting and Curing the Meat, *Circular* 458, Kentucky Agricultural Extension Service, 1948.
7. Pork and Carolina Farmers, *Bulletin* 77, South Carolina Agricultural Extension Service, 1940.
8. Pork on the Farm, U.S. Department of Agriculture, *Farmers' Bulletin* 1186, 1932.
9. Pork for the Farm Family, *Circular* 195, Maine Agricultural Extension Service, 1944.
10. Pork Production in California, *Circular* 15, California Agricultural Extension Service, 1938.
11. Pork Slaughtering, Cutting, and Curing, *Circular* 155, North Dakota Agricultural Extension Service, 1937.
12. The Slaughtering and Curing of Home-grown Pork, *Circular* 466, New Jersey Agricultural Experiment Station, 1943.
13. Southwell, B. L., J. T. Wheeler, and A. O. Duncan, "Swine Production in the South," The Interstate, Danville, Ill., 1940.

SAMPLE MANAGERIAL JOB ANALYSIS
Job: Buying Baby Chicks

Decisions to make	Factors to consider in making decisions	Working data
When to purchase chicks	Use to be made of chicks Equipment available Climatic conditions Price of chicks	If chicks are purchased for pullets, they should be obtained at a time so that the pullets will be in production when egg prices are high—fall More equipment for heating is needed in winter months In warm climates the winter months are desirable for growing chicks Fryers usually bring a higher price in winter and early spring The price of chicks is usually high in March and April Place order for chicks early
The grade of chicks to buy	Use to be made of chicks Price of the different grades	For growing pullets, high-grade chicks are usually best. Fryers may be produced just as well from lower-grade chicks. See that the hatchery grades chicks according to national standards
Whether to buy sexed chicks	Cost of chicks Use to be made of chicks Space available Breed of chicks	Pullet chicks are higher in price than straight-run or cockerel chicks Cockerel chicks cost less and are just as good for fryers for a given breed Where space is limited and the grower wants pullets, sexed pullet chicks are usually obtained In the egg breeds the cockerel chicks are not very desirable to grow for fryers
Price to pay	Grade of chicks Location of the hatchery Season	Grade of chicks will largely determine the price Other things being equal, it is best to purchase chicks locally to prevent dangers in transportation Chicks cost more during the spring months when the demand is high Obtain prices from a number of hatcheries If purchased cooperatively, the price may be reduced because of the number bought at one time
Where to purchase chicks	Cost of chicks Reliability of the hatchery Location of the hatchery Breeds available	The cost of chicks is of less importance than grade Purchase chicks only from reliable hatcheries It is best to purchase chicks locally, especially during cold weather Certain hatcheries may not sell the breed or the grade of chicks you want and you will have to buy from another source

SAMPLE TEACHING PLAN FOR A MANAGERIAL JOB

Job: Buying Baby Chicks

Objectives:

1. To assist each student to decide the number, grade, and sex of chicks to buy.
2. To assist in determining when and where to purchase chicks.
3. To develop the ability in students to produce chicks of high quality according to market demands.

Preparation Step:

1. Determine from each member of the class the following facts:
    a. Whether or not he has ever purchased chicks.
    b. Where the chicks were bought, price paid, and success in growing them.
2. Cite the case of Mr. Holmes, who ordered chicks last year in February from a distant hatchery and lost all of them because of weather conditions.
3. Analysis (pupils to assist in formulating these questions):
    a. What months do hatcheries have chicks available?
    b. What is the price each month?
    c. What is meant by straight-run chicks?   Sexed chicks?
    d. How are national grades of chicks determined?
    e. Why is it important to get high grades of pullet chicks to be used for egg production?
    f. How do cockerel chicks and pullet chicks differ in price?
    g. What is meant by a state-approved hatchery?
    h. Why is it best to purchase chicks locally?
    i. How may the reliability of a hatchery be determined?
    j. What is meant by blood testing?
    k. When should chicks be purchased?
    l. What price can I afford to pay for chicks?
    m. Determine the difference in price if chicks are purchased cooperatively in lots of 10,000.

Presentation Step:

1. Field trip
    Visit a local hatchery and study the grades of chicks and observe how they are sexed.
2. Illustration
    Use a filmstrip to show the grades of chicks.
3. Supervised study
    Assign references for the pupils to study that will cover the needed information.
4. Discussion
    Use questions in the analysis as a basis for the discussion.

Supervision of Practice Step:

1. Have each student make a decision covering each of the following points:
    a. When he plans to purchase chicks.
    b. The breed and grade of chicks to buy.
    c. Whether or not to buy sexed chicks.
2. Make plans to purchase chicks from a hatchery and send the deposit.

Testing and Follow-up Step:

1. Check the results obtained by each pupil in purchasing chicks.
2. Give a written quiz by using several questions about this job.

Equipment and Materials Needed:

Filmstrip machine, screen, and film.

References:

1. Brooding Chicks, Producing Broilers and Raising Pullets, *Bulletin* 154, Florida Experiment Station, 1952.
2. Chicks, Brooding, Feeding and Rearing, *Circular* 382-R, Wisconsin Agricultural Extension Service, 1952.
3. Commercial Chick Hatcheries in South Carolina, *Bulletin* 392, South Carolina Agricultural Experiment Station, 1951.
4. Cooper, J. B., "Poultry for Home and Market," Turner E. Smith and Co., Atlanta, Ga., 1950.
5. Jull, M. A., "Successful Poultry Management," McGraw-Hill Book Company, Inc., New York, 1951.
6. The Problem of Distinguishing the Sex of Day-old Chicks, *Circular* 433, New Jersey Agricultural Experiment Station, 1942.
7. Rice, J. E., and H. E. Botsford, "Practical Poultry Management," John Wiley & Sons, Inc., New York, 1940.
8. A Simple Farm Brooder and Finisher, *Circular* 82, Florida Agricultural Extension Service, 1950.
9. Winter, A. R., and E. M. Funk, "Poultry Science and Practice," J. B. Lippincott Company, Philadelphia, 1941.

Teaching Agricultural Subjects

Use of Teaching Plans. An experienced teacher uses his teaching plan only as a guide. He will often have to modify the original plan, as his teaching results will indicate after he begins. A teaching plan, however, should guide the teacher and prevent him from rambling.

Teaching plans that were made during the previous year or summer should be checked for needed modifications. Most good teachers make notes on their teaching plans immediately after giving instruction regarding changes or additions that need to be made. Check new reference materials and review the technical subject matter before starting to teach any job. A further check just prior to teaching is also essential.

Induction and Deduction as Modes of Thinking. In arriving at correct conclusions, both for operative and for managerial jobs, the student uses both inductive and deductive methods of thinking.

In the inductive method of thinking, the student determines the facts he believes he needs, secures the facts, and then proceeds to form a generalization. He is stimulated to make discoveries for himself and to be unsatisfied with information handed down to him. After he has made his generalizations, they must be checked by the teacher before he uses them in formulating plans for their execution. This may require more time than the teacher cares to devote for a given job.

In the deductive method of thinking, the student takes a certain generalization (either his own, from another person, or from a book) and proceeds to test its validity in connection with a specific problem. The method is economical of time and equipment. It enables the student to take advantage of the vast storehouse of agricultural facts already discovered by scientists.

Fig. 104. A great deal of careful instruction was required to bring these animals, on exhibition by F.F.A. members, to the proper degree of finish. (*Courtesy of J. K. Coggin, North Carolina.*)

Classroom Management. The teacher is employed to lead and direct students in learning activities; therefore, little time should be lost in attending to class-routine matters. In general, classroom management involves the following:

1. Checking physical conditions of the classroom, such as light and ventilation.
2. Providing materials and equipment to be used by students.
3. Planning and handling the movement of students.
4. Eliminating all possible distractions.
5. Keeping attendance records.

Often it is possible for the agricultural teacher to check the physical conditions of the classroom before the students arrive. It is well to check the following items:

1. Adjust shades as much as possible to give correct lighting.
2. Turn on artificial lights on dark days.
3. See that the classroom is aired out.
4. See that the temperature is maintained at a comfortable level.
5. See that the room is arranged properly and kept clean.
6. See that the blackboard is cleaned.
7. See that important notices are posted on the bulletin boards.

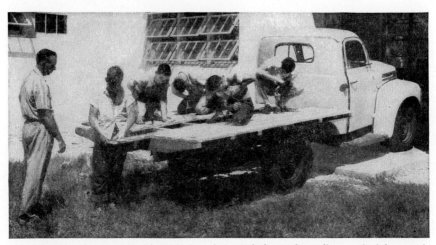

FIG. 105. The classroom may be either outdoors or indoors, depending on the job or project. (*Courtesy of Otis Bell, Florida.*)

In the handling of materials and equipment, it is well for the teacher to establish a routine to include such things as

1. Have students secure their notebooks each day before taking their seats.
2. Designate certain individuals weekly to pass out equipment or supplies and to collect them at the close of the period.
3. Have materials to be used by the teacher on the desk before the teaching period begins.
4. Standardize the classroom notebooks and paper. Also, use a system for written papers that includes where to put the name, whether or not to fold them, etc.
5. Have any maps, charts, pictures, and the like to be used either properly displayed or on your desk.
6. Check all visual-aid machines to be used to see that they are ready for operation with the minimum loss of time.

In handling the movement of students, the following recommendations are offered:

1. Require students to be orderly when they enter the classroom and to take their seats immediately. It is usually best for them to have definitely assigned seats.
2. Go to students needing individual help during the study period rather than have them come to you.
3. Let students remain seated during a discussion period.
4. Let students obtain any needed reference materials without asking you.
5. Have students leave the room in an orderly manner.

Distraction can be caused by such conditions as these:

1. Material on the blackboard not related to the job.
2. Equipment in evidence not needed for the job.
3. Clothing not needed by pupils left in the room.
4. Textbooks in other areas or subject matter left in the classroom.
5. Excessive and continued unnecessary noise. This does not mean that students can never speak to each other, but that noise that distracts attention is never tolerated.

Concerning attendance, the teacher may well think of such items as the following:

1. Check attendance at the beginning of class. When students are assigned seats, absentees can be determined without a roll call.
2. Report absent or tardy students according to the regulations of the school.
3. Do not admit students in the class who have been absent and who have no re-admission slip from the office.
4. Report sick persons to the office.

Discipline. Good discipline is usually the direct result of good organization, businesslike management, and effective teaching. Poor discipline is commonly caused by one or more of the following conditions or situations:

1. Weakness in classroom management.
2. Jobs selected that do not meet the needs of the learners.
3. Poor methods of teaching.
4. Inadequate provisions made to meet individual differences.
5. Students taking agriculture having little background or interest in the subject.
6. Weakness in the personality and leadership of the teacher.
7. Weakness in the method of enforcing good conduct by the whole school.
8. Students not knowing what is expected of them.

Punishment for violating the rules and customs of behavior at school has to be administered for the following reasons:

1. To see that the group (school) disapproves of the wrong acts performed.
2. To deter others from doing the same thing.
3. To try to bring about a change in the offenders.

No set of rules for discipline can be followed in all cases. The teacher must remember that each student is a different individual and his case must be

Fig. 106. Discipline problems tend to be few and unimportant when every student is kept busy and interested. (*U.S. Office of Education.*)

dealt with separately. The following suggestions are offered as applying to discipline problems:

1. All behavior activities, both good and undesirable, are a part of the environment of students and have influence upon their growth.
2. No two students are alike; therefore, punishment should follow no set rules.
3. The teacher should never show partiality.
4. Treat each student as if he were honest, truthful, and a gentleman. If he proves otherwise, never tell other people about the happening.
5. Be positive—"no" should mean no.
6. The teacher should never show anger before the class.
7. Punishment is not for revenge—the student is entitled to know why he is being punished.
8. If something amusing happens, let everyone enjoy it briefly.
9. Give a clear assignment and enough work to keep pupils busy.

10. The teacher should watch his speech, dress, health, and manners.
11. Assign responsibility to students who seem to give trouble.
12. If certain students are inclined to laugh or make noise, ask the class to pay attention while the offending pupils come to the front and demonstrate their achievements.
13. Little or no good is accomplished by sending a student to the principal. The teacher may often seek advice from the principal in methods of coping with specific cases, however.
14. Study each individual, his home conditions, his motives, his interests. Such facts may often reveal what you need to know in helping him.

The Student's Notebook. A classroom notebook is not a method of teaching. A properly kept notebook, however, does add materially to success in teaching. No argument should be necessary in favor of keeping a classroom notebook. It should aid the teacher in teaching and the student in learning and should prove a ready reference for either.

Notebook Covers. Most teachers agree that a three-ring notebook to carry $8\frac{1}{2}$- by 11-inch paper is the best size and type. It goes without saying that the notebook should be well constructed and of long-wearing materials because each student will need it for years. Each sheet of paper should be reinforced with gum reinforcements available for that purpose. If this is not done, sheets will soon tear out at the rings. F.F.A. notebooks with the emblem on the front cover are available. A cheap notebook cover of any design is usually a poor value. Because of the fact that the notebook is to have a system of guides adapted only to agriculture, the same notebook should not be used for other high school subjects.

Contents of a Classroom Notebook. Many teachers ask the question: "What should a student keep in his notebook?" The answer is "all the essential facts he has learned during the year." As a rule, most states have a record book of some type for keeping cost accounts and other records involved in supervised farming programs. The classroom notebook should contain all other forms of information the student has used. In general, the classroom notebook should contain the following items:

1 Dividing cards with tabs—preferably Celluloid tabs glued to both sides of the dividing cards.
2. A table-of-contents sheet for each section of the notebook.
3. A list of the enterprises to be taught in the course of study.
4. A job analysis of the different enterprises.
5. A calendar of activities (jobs) for individualized study.
6. Assignments made by the teacher.
7. Printed or mimeographed sheets of information given by the teacher.
8. Supervised-study notes.

9. Individualized-study notes (project planning).
10. Notes made on field trips.
11. Notes made during a laboratory period or in the farm-mechanics shop.
12. Clippings from newspapers or magazines.
13. Pictures of agricultural activities.
14. Farm surveys.
15. A list of supplementary farm jobs and skills learned.

Divider Sheets for the Notebook.   Divider sheets should be of medium-weight cardboard.   The number of these sheets will depend upon the system fol-

Fig. 107. Careful note taking is a matter of training and habit.   (*Courtesy of T. L. Faulkner, Alabama.*)

lowed by a particular teacher.   Some states recommend a division for each farm enterprise, whereas others use such divisions as Supervised Farming, Live-at-home Jobs, F.F.A., Farm Mechanics, Farm Management, Forestry, Conservation, and Miscellaneous.   Since it will take a large number of division sheets for each separate enterprise, some teachers classify the divisions somewhat as follows: Animal Husbandry, Dairy Husbandry, Poultry Husbandry, Bees, Forage and Pasture Crops, Field Crops, Vegetable Crops, Fruit Crops, Ornamentals, Forestry, Conservation, F.F.A., Farm Mechanics, Farm Management, Soils, and Miscellaneous.

Tabs that come on the division sheets soon bend and wear so badly that they are practically useless. Celluloid tabs can be purchased, cut into the desirable widths, and glued to the division sheets. Typewritten slips to indicate the divisions are placed in the tabs. The tab for the first division is placed at the top, the last one at the bottom, and the others so adjusted from top to bottom that the tabs will be like a thumb index of a dictionary. These tabs can be purchased in packages of different colors, and students may exchange the tabs so that each tab is a different color.

Notebook Table of Contents. The division sheets may be used for the table of contents of that particular section or separate sheets may be used. When a job has been completed, it is possible to enter it in the table of contents and give the page numbers. Each section usually begins with page one and is numbered consecutively as additional notes are added to the section. The table of contents may be used as shown below.

TABLE OF CONTENTS

Tab division   F.F.A.

Job completed	Page number
Qualifying for the Green Hand degree	1–5

Form of Student Notes. Some teachers require their students to copy paragraph after paragraph from reference materials, and others require their students to prepare practically no notes at all. The notebook is certainly not another textbook. It is true that the notebook should prove to be a priceless reference if facts are summarized and the index kept so that the facts may be easily found. The following form has been used and is satisfactory for information needed in operative jobs.

JOB: *Treating Seed with Bichloride of Mercury*

THINGS TO KNOW	STANDARD PRACTICE AND CONCLUSIONS
What seed to treat?	Bean, cabbage, cauliflower, celery, tomato, pepper, eggplant, watermelons, etc.
When to treat?	Immediately before planting time
How to prepare solution?	Dissolve 1 part of bichloride of mercury in 100 parts of water
What equipment is needed?	Wooden tub or crock
Amount to prepare?	Use enough bichloride of mercury solution to cover the seed
Length of time to treat?	Five to eight minutes
Value of the treatment?	Kills fungus spores on the seed coat
Can other materials be used?	Semesan and other dust materials are available on the market
How to dry the seed?	Spread seed thinly on a cloth or on a newspaper to dry
When to plant after treatment?	As soon as the seed are dry
Number of times to use the bichloride solution?	It is safe to use it as many as three times
How to dispose of the solution after using it?	Solution is poisonous so it is better to dig a hole and then cover with soil
What are my plans for treating seed at home?	I plan to purchase bichloride of mercury tablets at the local seed store for treating my cabbage seed. I have a wooden tub at home that is suitable for the solution. I shall treat the seed for 5 min. and then dry them before planting. Since we have a number of farm animals, I shall dig a deep hole in the soil to destroy the used solution, and refill the hole with soil and pack it
What were the best-used references?	Give a list of the most important references used. The student can later check these if he desires to secure the details

The above outline will have to be modified for managerial jobs. A managerial job might well be divided as follows for the classroom notebook.

JOB: *Purchasing Baby Chicks*

DECISIONS TO MAKE	FACTORS TO CONSIDER AND WORKING DATA
When to purchase chicks?	Time depends upon climate, use to be made of chicks, price of chicks, and equipment available. If chicks are to be used for pullets, purchase so they will be laying when egg prices are high. Fryer prices are usually higher in the winter months and early spring
Grade of chicks to buy?	High-grade chicks are best for pullets. Fryers may be produced from lower grades. Buy chicks graded according to national standards
Shall I buy sexed chicks?	Pullet chicks are higher in price than cockerel chicks of the same grade. Cockerel chicks are just as good for fryers. Pullet chicks are best if space is limited and if the cockerels of that breed do not sell as well as fryers

Price to pay?................ Grade of chicks will determine price as well as general economic conditions. Chicks usually cost more in March and April, when the demand is heavy. Secure prices from a number of hatcheries

Where to purchase chicks?..... The cost of chicks is a minor factor compared to grade. Purchase only from reliable firms. It is preferable to purchase locally. Some hatcheries do not sell all breeds or strains, so you may have to purchase chicks from more distant hatcheries to obtain exactly what you want

What I plan to do?........... I plan to grow fryers for the market, beginning to sell them the middle of January and weekly thereafter until the first day of May. I shall sell them at ten weeks of age. I shall need to purchase the first 100 the first day of November and continue getting 100 each week until the middle of March. Cockerel chicks are better for fryers than straight-run chicks, so I shall purchase New Hampshire cockerel chicks. I have made arrangements with a reliable local hatchery to secure the chicks weekly

References used?............. Give a list of the best references used

Most teachers find that students should use scrap paper to keep notes during the supervised study period. The final notes are placed in the notebook after the class discussion and when the pupil is certain they are accurate.

The same plan should be followed when the student is doing individualized study. No material should be copied in the classroom notebook until the information meets the approval of the teacher.

Where to Keep Classroom Notebooks. Since students do practically all their study at school, there is seldom a need for them to take the notebooks home at night. Teachers have found it best to construct a cabinet in the classroom for the purpose of filing the notebooks. The cabinets are usually of the post-office type and made of plywood or some other similar material.

At the close of the school year each student should be encouraged to take his classroom notebook home. Seniors, especially, should be expected to take their notebooks home and use them as a handy reference for many farm problems.

Teaching Farm-mechanics Subjects

Farm-mechanics jobs are both managerial and operative. The planning and decisions that a student must make involve the managerial aspects of farm mechanics, whereas the skills that are needed form the operative jobs. A managerial job in farm mechanics should be taught in about the same

Fig. 108. A student painting his farm-wagon project with a spray gun. (*Courtesy of R. W. Roberts, Arkansas.*)

manner as one in farm management. The major part of the teaching in this field, however, usually involves skills or operative jobs.

Job Sheets. The teacher may save time by having on hand job sheets for students to follow in performing the different farm-mechanics jobs. The sheets need to be properly filed and revised from time to time. A cabinet makes a satisfactory place in which to place the job sheets when they are not being used. Such sheets may be prepared by the teacher or purchased from companies which sell tools.[1]

Job sheets usually include the following information:

Job specifications (drawings, etc.)

Job applications

The materials needed for the job

The equipment and tools to be used

Steps or procedures to follow

Key points to observe

Cost of materials and labor

The job sheet on pages 196 to 197, with necessary modifications, may be used as a record for various mechanics jobs.

Teaching Shop Skills. All good teaching will follow the four main teaching steps of preparation, presentation, supervision of practice, and

---

[1] Stanley Rule and Level Plant, New Britain, Conn.

FIG. 109. Every student to his own shop task.   (*Courtesy of H. C. Fetterolf, Pennsylvania.*)

testing and follow-up.   For shop jobs the four basic steps usually include
the following:

Step 1.   Prepare the student (preparation step)
   a. See that the student is in correct position.
   b. Secure the complete attention of the student.
   c. Determine what the student already knows about the tools and
    the job.
   d. Point out the importance of the job.
   e. Explain what is to be learned.
Step 2.   Present the operation (presentation)
   a. Demonstrate how the job is done.
   b. Demonstrate the job again, step by step.
   c. Demonstrate again and stress key points.
   d. Illustrate special points in the job.
   e. Indicate danger points or safe work habits.
   f. Ask questions about the job and the manner in which it is done.
Step 3.   Tryout performance (supervision of practice)
   a. Have the student perform the job under supervision.
   b. Have the student perform the job and explain each step.
   c. Have the student explain key points and safety precautions.
   d. Correct any errors in procedure.
Step 4.   Follow-up (testing and follow-up)
   a. Put the student on the job on his own.
   b. Advise the student what to do in the case of emergency.
   c. Check the kind of work being done by the student from time to
    time.

JOB SHEET

Job:_____

Date work was started:_____Date completed:_____

Number of hours required to do the job:_____
Bill of materials for the job:

1. Lumber:

Number of pieces	Kind	Dimensions	Board feet	Total cost

2. Other materials:

Kind	Quality	Price	Total cost

Total hardware cost............. $_____
Labor cost..................... _____
Lumber cost................... _____
Total of all costs............... _____
Estimated market value.......... _____

Diagram of the job:
  Front view
  End view
  Top view
Procedures to follow:_____

_____

_____

_____

Observations to make:_____

_____

_____

_____

Teacher's remarks:_____

_____

_____

_____

_____

References used:_____

_____

_____

_____

_____

Grade made on the job:_____

Group Instruction. The teacher may often save time if he uses group instruction in teaching fundamentals of farm mechanics; the following jobs serve to illustrate:

1. Identifying tools and their use.
2. Sharpening and adjusting tools.
3. Filing a saw.
4. Soldering metals.
5. Painting, finishing, and glazing.
6. Mixing concrete.
7. Welding metals.
8. Splicing rope.

Since time is often not available for each student being taught by group instructions to become fully proficient in the skill being taught, the teacher will need to give individual instruction to a student when he desires to apply the skill to some other particular construction or repair job. The main problem in group instruction is to be certain that each learner can observe the demonstration and that he is allowed time to practice the skill until he can perform it satisfactorily.

Most teachers use group instruction for teaching the fundamental farm-mechanics skills. As a rule, many of these skills are taught the first year of the course. The management problems, such as selecting a system of running water for the home, can also be taught by means of group instruction. In managerial farm-mechanics jobs each student may plan his own application to his home farm. In that sense, the application step is individual instruction.

Individual Instruction in Farm Mechanics. Because of the limited number of farm-mechanics tools and because of the special jobs needed on

FIG. 110. Teacher giving individual instruction in the use of the acetylene welding tip. (*Vocational Division, Georgia State Department of Education.*)

the home farms of various students, the teacher must have a plan for individualized instruction in farm mechanics. After studying the needs for farm-mechanics jobs in his supervised farming program and on his home farm and after discussing them with the teacher, the student decides on the actual jobs to be undertaken. He then prepares a farm-mechanics calendar for the year.

Shop Management. Discipline in the shop is little different from that demanded in the laboratory or during a field trip. It would not be expected, however, that a class would be as quiet in the shop, nor is it necessary. Students should be allowed to confer with each other provided it is done in an orderly way and concerns shop problems.   Discipline problems usually arise because of the failure of the teacher to do the following:

1. To see that each student has a job to perform.
2. To see that each student has the proper instructions for doing the job before he begins work.
3. To see that a student does not kill time in the shop.
4. To check on each pupil weekly to see what jobs he has completed.
5. To see that pupils stay in the shop and work during the entire period.
6. To make the grade given in shopwork a part of the grade given for class-work in agriculture.
7. To keep shop noise to a minimum.
8. To see that all tools and supplies are returned to their proper places at the close of the period.

Shop Clothes.   Many teachers do not require any special type of shop clothes.   It is true, however, that clothes worn to other classes may often be soiled during the shop period.   Loose clothing often causes shop accidents.   Special shop clothing includes shop coats, shop aprons, and coveralls.   Coveralls are excellent for the winter months but too warm for late spring and early fall. Shop caps are desirable for work at the forge, welding, farm machinery, and similar jobs.   If special clothing is required, a definite place should be provided for each student to keep his outfit.   A special locker to keep his street clothes in while he is in the shop may also be necessary.

Securing Tools.   Where a central toolroom is maintained, the teacher often uses one student to check out individual tools as needed by members of the class.   Although

FIG. 111. Appropriate clothing is essential for good farm-shop work.   (*U.S. Office of Education.*)

conducive to better shop operation, it does not duplicate a natural farm situation.

Probably the best method of storing tools is in cabinets or on panels. Tools used for any specific job or group of jobs are assembled together.   For example, tools for blacksmith work are kept in a cabinet near the forge. Boys are placed on their honor to secure tools as they are needed and to return them as soon as the job is completed or at least by the close of the period.

In any system it is highly desirable to have a student designated to check to see that all tools are returned to the proper place at the close of the period. This is an easy matter if tools are stored in cabinets where silhouettes indicate the place for each tool. It is also a good idea for the teacher to give special attention to this problem.

FIG. 112. The right tools and proper space in which to work are conducive to learner safety. (*U.S. Office of Education.*)

All tools should be inventoried and a record made of any that are broken during the year. Students need to be taught to take pride in keeping tools in place and to see that none are taken from the shop.

Supplies. The teacher will need to keep a reasonable amount of supplies for the shop. Materials used in many types of demonstrations and for making equipment for the school should be purchased by the school board.

Where students are making or repairing things for the home farm, they should pay for all the materials and supplies they use. This can be done in either of two ways: (1) The student may purchase his own supplies as he needs them from local merchants, or (2) he may purchase them from the school. If the second method is followed, a complete record, signed by the boy, must be kept on file. The school can often purchase supplies at wholesale prices and save money for students. On the other hand, boys gain valuable experience in the responsibility of selecting and purchasing their own supplies.

Safety Rules. Accidents occur in farm-mechanics shop and on farms every year. The teacher should do everything possible to prevent accidents and know what to do in case of accidents. Accidents can be reduced by observing the following general rules:

1. Ground all electric machines and motors.
2. Use safety guards on all machines where they are supposed to be used.
3. Paint all danger points on machines with a bright red paint.
4. Insist that students wear proper clothing.
5. Demonstrate the safety rules to follow before allowing individuals to use a machine.
6. See that a respirator is worn when a pupil is using a paint spray gun; wearing a pair of goggles used for a grinder, etc.
7. Teach safety rules to the class.
8. Post safety rules in the shop.
9. Do not allow anyone to use a machine or tool if he will not follow safety rules.
10. Keep the shop clean.
11. Keep small amounts of gasoline and other flammables in red cans.

Caring for Accidents. The teacher will need to secure some first aid equipment and supplies to use in case of accidents. He should take time to teach the class the proper use of the equipment and supplies.

As a rule, the shop will need the following safety equipment and supplies:

1. Fire extinguishers, buckets for sand, several packages of soda
2. A first-aid kit and all approved supplies
3. A Red Cross manual of first-aid instructions
4. Some means of getting a victim to the doctor or to the hospital

Cleaning the Shop. The teacher is expected to see that the shop is kept in order. The best way to keep it clean is for each class to leave it in order. It will usually take about ten minutes at the close of the period to get all tools put back in place, supplies placed in the proper storage place, and the floor swept. Some teachers follow the plan of assigning two boys each week to sweep the floor and two to see that all tools and supplies are left in place. The teacher will need to check to see if the boys are doing their work in a satisfactory manner.

Standards of Workmanship. Students are expected to do their work in a satisfactory manner. A beginning worker, however, should not be expected to show perfection. If the job is done in such a manner that it will answer the purpose, a teacher may accept it from a first-year student. As boys gain more experience, they should be expected to do better-quality work.

It is best to have all projects made at school painted or finished in some other manner before the student takes them to his farm. Projects should be well constructed and completely finished in order that they may be durable.

Record of Jobs Completed.   Many teachers keep a complete record, with a grade on every shop project that each student completes.   This may be done by using a file card for each student, by a sheet in a class notebook kept by the teacher, or by means of a large wall chart posted in the shop.   Each student's name is placed on the wall chart and to the right of the name all projects completed are listed.   The wall chart has the value of creating healthy competition among the various class members since each one can see what the others have accomplished.

Fig. 113. Standards of workmanship in farm mechanics are as important as they are in many of the trades.

Evaluation of Teaching Farm Mechanics.   It is necessary for the teacher to make some type of evaluation for the work done by each student because practically all schools require grade assignments.   The teacher may appraise the progress of a given student through application of a combination of the following factors:

1. The number and type of projects completed at school.
2. The projects made on the home farm.
3. The type of workmanship shown on the projects completed.
4. The number of skills developed.
5. Abilities developed in planning a farm-mechanics job or project.
6. Results made on performance tests.
7. The type of notebook kept by the student.
8. Oral and written examinations.

SELECTED REFERENCES

Baxter, B., "Teacher-Pupil Relationships," The Macmillan Company, New York, 1941.

Bossing, N. L., "Progressive Methods of Teaching in Secondary Schools," Houghton Mifflin Company, Boston, 1942.

Burton, W. H., "The Guidance of Learning Activities," Appleton-Century-Crofts, Inc., New York, 1944.

Coggin, J. K., Farm Shop Activities and Equipment, Bulletin 4, North Carolina State College, Raleigh, N.C.

The Conference Procedure in Teaching Vocational Agriculture, U.S. Office of Education, Division of Vocational Education, Bulletin 147.

Cook, G. C., and L. J. Phipps, "A Handbook on Teaching Vocational Agriculture," The Interstate, Danville, Ill., 1952.

———, C. Walker, and O. L. Snowden, "Practical Methods in Teaching Farm Mechanics," The Interstate, Danville, Ill., 1952.

Farm Shop Work, Bulletin 261, Michigan State Board for Vocational Education, Lansing, Mich.

Hamlin, H. M., "Agricultural Education in Community Schools," The Interstate, Danville, Ill., 1949.

Knight, Ewart, and Dickinson, Handbook for Students of Vocational Agriculture, Bulletin 8, vol. 39, University of Missouri, Columbia, Mo.

Lancelot, W. H., "Permanent Learning," John Wiley & Sons, Inc., New York, 1944.

Methods of Teaching Applied to Vocational Education in Agriculture, U.S. Office of Education, Division of Vocational Education, Bulletin 103.

Organization and Management of Classes for Farmer Veterans, Bulletin, Illinois State Board of Vocational Education, Springfield, Ill.

The Program of Vocational Agriculture in Kentucky, Bulletin 8, vol. 13, State Department of Education, Frankfort, Ky.

Safety Education in the School Shop, Bulletin, National Safety Council, Inc., Chicago, Ill.

Schorling, R., "Student Teaching," 2d ed., McGraw-Hill Book Company, Inc., New York, 1949.

Teaching Farm Credit, U.S. Office of Education, Division of Vocational Education, Bulletin 178.

Teaching Techniques in Vocational Agriculture, Bulletin 290, Michigan State Board for Vocational Education, Lansing, Mich.

What Is the Discussion Leader's Job? U.S. Department of Agriculture, Bureau of Agricultural Economics, Bulletin D-3.

Wrinkle, W., and W. Armentrout, "Directed Observation and Teaching in Secondary Schools," The Macmillan Company, New York, 1932.

13. Developing and Using Visual Aids

VISUAL AIDS are excellent helps in teaching. The United States Armed Forces during the Second World War found that visual aids were effective in getting more factual material learned in a given period of time and that information thus obtained was retained longer.

Agricultural teachers may secure and use a number of different types of visual aids. There are some types, such as flash cards and posters, however, that are used largely by teachers in elementary grades. The most important types of visual aids used by agricultural teachers are

1. Objects, samples, specimens, and models
2. Pictures and photographs
3. Maps, charts, graphs, drawings, mock-ups, and a shadow box
4. Opaque projector
5. Lantern slides
6. Strip films
7. Motion pictures
8. Blackboard illustrations

Locating Sources of Visual-aid Materials. The teacher of vocational agriculture may secure such materials of educational value from the following sources:

1. Machinery companies
2. Commercial companies
3. U.S. Department of Agriculture
4. Agricultural colleges
5. State departments of agriculture
6. Associations of various kinds
7. U.S. Department of Labor
8. U.S. Office of Education

It is his responsibility to see that the materials used are adapted to his particular use. The teacher must guard against the recommendation of products from any one commercial firm.

Objects, Samples, and Specimens. The teacher of agriculture may often use actual animals and crops in his teaching. He may use the field-trip method and visit farms in the community or make use of his land laboratory or school farm. Actual materials are better than any other visual representation of them.

FIG. 114. Visual aids intelligently used at the right place are an important factor in instruction. (*Courtesy of J. K. Coggin, North Carolina.*)

Samples of teaching aids commonly used are

1. Fertilizer materials
2. Feeds for animals
3. Wood grown locally
4. Paint materials
5. Local soils
6. Farm seeds
7. Weed and grass seeds
8. Spray and dust materials
9. Different types of nails, screws, and bolts
10. Aggregate for making concrete

Other things being equal, it is best to secure samples locally. Use the proper glass containers for the samples. Many teachers use wide-mouth glass bottles with screw tops. After the samples are placed in the containers, accurate labels are necessary. A few samples, like feeds, will not last more than a year, whereas others, like soils, will last many years.

Mounted or Preserved Specimens. Mounted or preserved specimens of various kinds may be purchased or prepared from local materials. The kinds of most value are

1. Insect specimens
2. Plant-disease specimens
3. Animal-disease specimens
4. Internal-parasite specimens
5. Specimens of fruit varieties

Insect specimens have to be collected at the proper stage, placed in a bottle which has either potassium cyanide or sodium cyanide to kill them quickly,

Fig. 115. Specimens, such as this growth of pine, always create interest among students. (*Vocational Division, Georgia State Department of Education.*)

and then mounted in a box. The mounted specimens must be labeled and then fumigated by placing a small amount of carbon bisulfide or paradichlorobenzene in the bottom of the box and sealing the box. Keep the box in a dark place to help preserve the color of the insects. Liquid preservatives may also be used for some insects and parasites.

Plant-disease specimens are usually preserved by placing them in glass jars that are filled with a 5 or 6 percent solution of 40 percent formaldehyde. A little practice will determine the exact strength to use for each type of plant.

Animal-disease specimens may also be preserved by using one part of 40 percent formaldehyde to nine parts of water. Some specimens can be kept best by using a solution of 45 percent ethyl alcohol containing 10 percent formaldehyde.

After specimens are placed in any solution, the containers should be sealed with paraffin, wax, or some other method to keep them airtight.

Pictures and Photographs. Pictures and photographs are used to arouse interest, to illustrate specific steps in an operative job, to develop appreciation, to teach facts, and to test the student's knowledge.

Agricultural teachers are fortunate in being able to secure many pictures without cost. Many livestock breeders associations are glad to furnish pictures of ideal animals of a given breed. Animal paintings are available from farm magazines and from commercial firms. Many firms furnish pictures showing the use of their products. Actual photographs of prize animals are available from a number of commercial firms. Also, teachers often take timely pictures. Instructions for taking pictures can be obtained from photographic companies.

It is best to either mount or frame pictures in order to preserve them. Mount pictures on a thin, durable cardboard. Use rubber cement to paste the pictures to the cardboard. Label the pictures and give them a thin coat of a mixture containing equal parts of shellac and denatured alcohol.

It is well to have some method of filing the pictures in order for them to to be found easily when they are needed for use in teaching a job.

Maps, Charts, Graphs, and Drawings. Maps of many kinds are used in teaching agriculture. It is possible to enlarge maps for more effective use by any one of the following methods:

1. Maps may be enlarged by proportional squares. Draw squares of 1-inch dimensions on the original map and number horizontal and vertical lines. Rule your paper for 2-inch squares and number lines similar to the ones on the original map. Draw the second map by observing where the outline crosses the vertical and horizontal lines of the first one.
2. Maps may be enlarged by tracing the original map with a pantograph that has been set as desired.
3. Maps may be enlarged by projection. Use an opaque projector for the original map. By moving the screen nearer to or farther from the projector, the desired size of map may be secured. It is then traced on paper that is placed on the screen.

Fig. 116. Well-prepared, reliable charts focus attention on key points.   (*Courtesy of G. F. Ekstrom, Missouri.*)

Fig. 117. A chart on which program progress in the F.F.A. chapter is recorded.   (*New Mexico State Department of Education.*)

Charts of various types are available from commercial firms and from many other sources.   The teacher may prepare his own charts.   The following topics for charts are examples:

1. The Yields of Different Varieties of a Given Crop
2. Results of Supervised Farming

3. F.F.A. Chapter Program of Work
4. F.F.A. Accomplishment Report
5. A List of Farm-shop Jobs Completed by Each Student
6. A Scholarship Chart of All Students
7. Fertilizer Tests on Crops
8. Feed Tests on Animals
9. Livestock-breeding Improvement Charts
10. Loss of Animals by Diseases

FIG. 118. Good exhibits are an effective means of catching and holding attention. (*Courtesy of H. C. Fetterolf, Pennsylvania.*)

Charts may be made from the following types of materials:

1. Light-colored wrapping paper
2. Sign cloth
3. Unbleached muslin
4. Vellum cloth
5. Cardboard

Wrapping paper is inexpensive and good for making charts to be used only a few times. A large pencil can be used on the paper or lettering pens and ink. Ordinary chalk can be used if the paper is given a coat of equal parts of white shellac and denatured alcohol followed by a second coat of blackboard slating paint. The chalk may be treated to give a more permanent effect. Take soft chalk and dip it in a saturated solution of granulated sugar. Allow the chalk to remain in the solution until the bubbles quit showing and then remove it and drain. Use the chalk as soon as the surface moisture has evaporated.

Sign cloth is good for charts that are to be used a few times; however, it is much more expensive than ordinary wrapping paper.

Unbleached muslin is comparatively cheap and will take india ink. Stamping letters may be used on this cloth.

Fig. 119. An idea is clinched through the use of easily read charts. (*Courtesy of R. J. Woodin, Ohio.*)

Vellum cloth, used for covering books, is very good for making charts but much more expensive than the other materials already mentioned.

Cardboard, especially light-colored, is very good for chart making. The only objection to its use is the cost.

The size of the letters in the title of a table, in the subtitles or headings, and in the body should be in the ratio of $3:2:1$ or $2:1\frac{1}{2}:1$.

The most common graphs used in teaching vocational agriculture are

1. The bar graph
2. The line graph
3. The pie graph
4. The pictorial graph

Drawings or diagrams are especially valuable in teaching farm-mechanics jobs and many of the operative, or skill, jobs on the farm.

The Opaque Projector.   Opaque projectors make it possible to present 6 by 6 inch or larger flat objects on a screen without the necessity of making the picture into slides or films.   Pictures, drawings, or printed materials may be shown on the screen.   The pictures and drawings may come from magazines, books, or bulletins as well as from special photographs or pictures.   If the pictures are to be used from year to year, it is desirable to mount them on medium-weight cardboard.

Before the class period the teacher should set the projector and screen in place and test the projection to determine that it is satisfactory.   The pictures or printed materials should be arranged in the order they are to be presented to the class.

Specific directions for operating a given make of opaque projector come with the machine.   Follow them carefully.

The Use of Lantern Slides.   Lantern slides are made from negatives of pictures taken with a camera.   These slides are valuable to use because the teacher is certain that all members of the class observe the same thing.   Also, these slides are excellent to use if the teacher wants to discuss the picture in detail.

Lantern slides that are $3\frac{1}{2}$ by 4 inches may be obtained in black and white or in kodachrome, but smaller slides are less expensive and take less storage space.   They may be purchased in sets for given agricultural topics or they may be made from photographs.

Pictures may be taken with a 35-millimeter camera, the negatives developed, and the selected frames sent to a processing company to be made into positive frames.   Slide binders can be purchased and each positive frame cut and mounted between the two pieces of glass, bound, and labeled.   Old filmstrip frames may be cut and mounted between glass slides in the same way.   Cellophane slides may be made on a typewriter and the tables or written materials bound for use.

In order to secure the best results with slides, a good screen is necessary and the classroom must be properly darkened.

To operate the lantern-slide machine, follow the directions that came with it.

Filmstrips.   This type of visual aid is often preferred by teachers because it is light in weight, easily stored, reasonable in cost, and effective.   Pictures may be taken of local agricultural products in black and white or in Kodachrome with a 35-millimeter camera and filmstrips made from them.   Filmstrips have certain limitations.   In the first place, they are usually less easily illuminated than slides, and, in the second place, they are arranged in a fixed sequence.

Sound slide films are very similar to filmstrips except all explanations and titles are given by sound instead of reading printed materials.   A slight sound of a bell indicates when the next frame should be shown.

The use of equipment for filmstrips is about the same as for lantern slides. In order to use the equipment properly, check the following items:

1. See that the room is dark.
2. Use a suitable screen.
3. Set the projector in place and operate it before class time.
4. Change the needles at regular intervals for the sound attachment of the sound slide film.
5. Check the ventilation of the room.
6. Follow the manufacturer's instructions in operating the machine.
7. Prepare a brief script to use for each frame.

Motion Pictures. Motion pictures are a valuable means of presenting information of an educational nature and are often used with a companion filmstrip serving as an interest developer. Practically all educational films are the 16-millimeter size, silent or sound, and in color. There are home films available in the 8-millimeter size, or for theatrical use there are films available in the 35-millimeter size.

In some cases, the silent films are desired, especially if the teacher wants to give explanations during the picture. The sound films often attract more attention.

In purchasing a machine for 16-millimeter film, it is desirable to select one where you can use the sound if you so desire or run the picture without sound. Specific directions for threading the film and operating the machine come with the equipment. Different makes vary in this respect.

To use a motion picture machine during the day, some method of darkening the room is necessary. Sliding black curtains have proved to be very effective.

Motion-picture films may be secured from the U.S. Department of Agriculture, commercial firms, and rental companies. (See Appendix XIV, pages 383 to 386, for list of films and for sources of motion pictures.)

The Use of a Blackboard. Properly used, the blackboard has an important place in teaching many jobs. It may be used for any one of the following purposes:

1. To illustrate any job by using drawings, sketches, maps, graphs, or diagrams.
2. To make the assignment for a job:
   a. Analysis of the job.
   b. Daily problem assignments.
3. To aid in teaching new facts:
   a. Giving definitions.

    b. Explaining technical words.
    c. Using key words—point clinchers.
    d. Giving directions for operative jobs.
4. To give notice of important events:
    a. Announcements of F.F.A. meetings.
    b. Community meetings.
    c. Rules and policies of the school.
5. To test pupils:
    a. Review questions.
    b. Test questions.
    c. Training records of individual pupils.

Fɪɢ. 120. Simple blackboard sketches are a valuable teaching aid. (*Courtesy of J. K. Coggin, North Carolina.*)

Recommendations on the proper use of a blackboard include the following:

1. Clean the blackboard before the class meets.
2. Have chalk, ruler, and erasers handy.
3. Make short, simple statements.
4. Print headings or captions for emphasis.
5. Use chrome yellow or pale green chalk for more emphasis.
6. Prepare blackboard layouts ahead of the class period.
7. Check the light in the room to avoid glare.
8. Write or print legibly and straight across the blackboard.
9. Stand to one side of the blackboard so the class can have full view of the board.

SELECTED REFERENCES

Cook, G. C., and L. J. Phipps, "A Handbook on Teaching Vocational Agriculture," The Interstate, Danville, Ill., 1952.

———, C. Walker, and O. L. Snowden, "Practical Methods in Teaching Farm Mechanics," The Interstate, Danville, Ill., 1952.

Haas, K. B., and H. Q. Packer, "Preparation and Use of Visual Aids," Prentice-Hall, Inc., New York, 1950.

Henderson, M., and H. F. Witt, "Free Illustrative Materials for Courses in Vocational Agriculture," The Interstate, Danville, Ill., 1949.

14. Supervising the Farming Programs of Day Students

THE SMITH-HUGHES ACT states that each person who is enrolled in vocational agriculture must have at least six months of directed, or supervised, farming each year. Even before the passage of this act, a num-

FIG. 121. Assisting all-day students in planning their farming programs is an important teacher responsibility. (*Courtesy of J. K. Coggin, North Carolina.*)

ber of states were requiring practice work as a part of the course of study in agriculture. The specific form, or type, of farming program is not stated in the Smith-Hughes Act, but any one of the following plans will satisfy the requirements of the law:

1. A supervised farming program conducted on the home farm.
2. A supervised farming program conducted on the school farm.
3. Group projects conducted on a farm or on the school farm.
4. Supervised practice work done on a farm, for which the student received wages.
5. Supervision and management of a farm.
6. A combination of any two or more of the above plans.

215

Home Projects. The word "project" will be found to mean to design, to scheme, to plan, or to plan and undertake work. The construction of the Hoover Dam was an engineering project. A person who produces a field of Irish potatoes or who grows fryers for the market is conducting a project. In vocational agriculture a project involves planning and doing all jobs connected with the cycle of producing and marketing any given farm crop, such as vegetable, fruit, flower, tree, or animal.

The name "home project" means that the student is doing the work for his project on the home farm. The idea of conducting projects on the home farm probably started in 1908 in Massachusetts. After the passage of the Smith-Hughes Act in 1917, the states quickly adopted the home-project plan for meeting the legal requirements for farm-practice work.

Types of Projects. States have used a number of different ways to classify projects in vocational agriculture. The following list includes the types usually found:

1. Home projects
2. Group projects
3. Chapter projects
4. Demonstration projects
5. Production projects
6. Improvement projects
7. Continuation projects
8. Major projects
9. Minor projects
10. Contributory projects
11. Supplementary farm practice

Home Projects. These have already been defined. A home project forms a unit in the supervised farming program of the student.

Group Projects. These are conducted by two or more students. Several students may jointly produce crops, such as watermelons, Irish potatoes, or cabbage, on a large enough scale to make it possible to ship the produce to market in carlots. Group projects are used also for boys who do not have the proper farming facilities at home.

Chapter Projects. These are conducted by the members of local F.F.A. or N.F.A. chapters for any one of several purposes such as:

1. To earn money to finance the chapter.
2. To grow products to serve at the annual parent-and-son banquet.
3. To produce materials for teaching purposes.

Demonstration Projects. These are designed to stimulate students and farmers in the use of improved farm practices. Examples are the use of nitrate of soda as a side dressing on corn or the use of winter cover crops in soil improvement.

Production Projects.   These may be thought of as business ventures for profit involving a series of farm jobs usually following a production cycle in a farm enterprise.

Fig. 122.   An F.F.A. member enters the open-class competition at the San Francisco Grand National Livestock Show.   (*California State Bureau of Agricultural Education.*)

Improvement Projects.   These are undertakings involving a series of jobs designed to improve the appearance and real-estate value of the farm and the efficiency of the farm business as a whole and to contribute to the comfort or convenience of the farm family.

Continuation Projects.   These go on from year to year and give considerable repetitive experiences in a given enterprise.

Major Projects.   These include enterprises which normally yield the major income in a student's supervised farming program.

Minor Projects.   These are enterprises in the supervised farming program which ordinarily yield less income than a major project but which may be fitted into the program to utilize and balance labor more effectively and yield a quick cash return on a small investment.

Contributory Projects.   These are productive projects in a supervised farming program, the products of which are consumed or utilized in the conduct of major or minor projects.

Supplementary Farm Practice.   This means small farm jobs performed for additional experience, skill, and efficiency lying outside the jobs included in the student's production or improvement projects.

Values of a Supervised Farming Program.   Projects of various types conducted on the home farm offer the best-possible setting for both teaching and learning.   Among the many values claimed for supervised farming are[1]

1. To the student
    a. Provides an excellent avenue to satisfactory establishment in farming.
    b. Develops a sense of values.
    c. Prevents costly errors and failures in later life when responsibilities are greater.
    d. Provides opportunity to learn how to earn, save, spend, and invest money.
    e. Provides exploratory experience that will assist in deciding what type of farming to enter.
    f. Provides opportunity to accumulate livestock, equipment, and land and to build up gradually and "grow into" a farming business.
    g. Provides challenging real-life situations in which judgment, abilities, skills, habits, and attitudes are developed.
    h. Provides unusual opportunity to develop pride of ownership, self-confidence, initiative, and responsibility.
    i. Leads to better understanding and cooperation between parents and son.
    j. Provides desirable motivation for the learner.
2. To the instructor and school
    a. Makes the supervised farming programs logically the core of courses of study and instruction.
    b. Gives definite purpose and direction to the study of agriculture.
    c. Serves as a basis for selection of material appropriate for instruction.
    d. Provides subject-matter material from real-life situations for more practical instruction.
    e. Keeps the instructor in closer touch with farmers and the farm life of his community.

[1] Directing Vocational Agriculture Day-school Students in Developing Their Farming Programs, U.S. Office of Education, Division of Vocational Education, *Bulletin* 225, Agricultural Series 56, p. 5, 1944.

3. To the home and community
   a. Contributes to the efficiency of the home farm and other farms in the community.
   b. Introduces standard approved practices on farms in the locality.
   c. Provides a valuable contact linking school, home, and community.
   d. Provides for more practical results in schoolwork.
   e. Makes it possible for the school to serve better the people of the community.

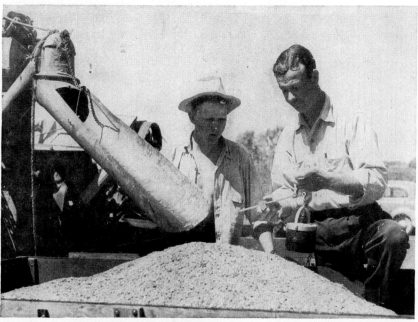

FIG. 123. Teacher checking the weight of certified oatseed produced by a student of vocational agriculture. (*Courtesy of M. J. Peterson, Minnesota.*)

Scope and Components of a Supervised Farming Program. As already stated, a student will usually have several types of projects in his supervised farming program. The scope of such a program will depend largely upon the following factors:

1. The age and experience of the boy.
2. The type of projects.
3. The number of hours per week the boy has available for work.
4. The number of hours of labor required per unit to produce each enterprise.
5. The cost per unit of each enterprise.

Various standards of scope have been suggested. In general, the standards are approached from the following standpoints:

1. The supervised farming program should be large enough in scope to give the student a chance to earn a specified labor income.
2. The total program should be large enough to take at least a minimum number of about 240 hours of labor.

FIG. 124. Supervision of student work on the home farm offers an excellent opportunity for on-the-job teaching.   (*Courtesy of J. K. Coggin, North Carolina.*)

Under most conditions, the supervised farming program should have the following components:[2]

1. At least one major cash project started early in the student's career, continued, expanded in scope, and improved in quality over a period of several years.

[2] Directing Vocational Agriculture Day-school Students in Developing Their Farming Programs, U.S. Office of Education, Division of Vocational Education, *Bulletin* 225, Agricultural Series 56, p. 8, 1944.

2. One or more minor cash projects fitted into the long-time program as needed and as opportunity arises.
3. One or more contributory projects, increasing in number, scope, and quality in keeping with major and minor projects.
4. One or more improvement projects started or continued each year for the purpose of improving the farm or the farm home.
5. Sufficient supplementary farm jobs carried out under the supervision of the instructor to develop the desired skills and managerial ability.

Examples of Improvement Projects. Although there is some difference of opinion as to what improvement projects include, the following are examples:

1. Landscaping the home grounds
2. Providing a permanent pasture
3. Stumping a field
4. Draining a wet field
5. Terracing and contour furrowing
6. Renovating an old orchard
7. Budding and top-grafting an orchard
8. Installing a water system in the home
9. Rebuilding the farm fences
10. Painting farm buildings
11. Planting and maintaining windbreaks
12. Providing an irrigation system for the farm
13. Practicing controlled breeding of livestock
14. Controlling erosion on the farm
15. Planting soil-improvement crops
16. Mapping the farm and relocating fields
17. Installing a heating system in the home

Supplementary Farm Practice. Supplementary farm practice has no direct relationship to the production projects. It improves efficiency, increases skill, and creates general interest in many needed experiences not covered otherwise.

Supplementary farm practice may include culling hens, budding fruit trees, castrating pigs, and building a farm gate. The practices selected should be of general value to the boy and be useful to the farm or farm home. Boys are usually asked to perform 10 or more of these supplementary-farm-practice jobs per year.

Placement for Farm Experience. This plan may be followed for six or more months each year to satisfy the requirements for directed and supervised practice work. Care should be exercised to prevent the farm operator from using the boy for only a few jobs, thus preventing him from receiving all types of skill experiences. It is probably best to have a written agreement with the farm operator and the various skills to be learned listed in it. In this type of work the boy is paid a certain rate per hour for his labor but receives no part of any labor income.

Little or no managerial experience is usually possible in placement situations. The boy often has little interest in the profits and is seldom able to correlate properly his class instruction with his practice work.

Farm-management Experience. In many of our rural communities there are boys who desire definite training for farm managers rather than for farm operators. Often a boy knows that he will inherit a farm, or he may prefer to secure a position as a farm manager for another person. It

FIG. 125. Proof of good work greets the teacher here. This lad won corn-growing honors in his county.

may be possible, especially during the fourth year of the course, for a boy working under adult supervision to assume the full management of a farm in order for him to secure the needed educational experiences.

Steps in Determining the Supervised Farming Program. The student will want, first, to make a decision as to the type of farming he wishes to follow and, second, to select the specific enterprises he desires to include in that type of farming.

Since the home farm will be the student's laboratory, he should know it in detail. One satisfactory way to make this study is by means of a farm survey. Farm-survey blanks are usually available from the state department of education or from the department of agricultural economics at the agricultural college in each state.

After determining the enterprises for his type of farming and after studying the facilities of the home farm, the boy is ready to start a supervised farming

SUPERVISED FARMING PROGRAM

Livestock-type Farm

Production project	Classification	In school				Out of school	
		1st year	2d year	3rd year	4th year	1st year	2d year
Swine	Major	2 head	10 head	15 head	20 head	20 head	
Beef cattle	Major	2 head	3 head	4 head	6 head	8 head	
Sweet potatoes	Minor	1 acre	1½ acres	2 acres	2 acres	2 acres	
Peppers	Minor		½ acre	1 acre	1 acre	3 acres	
Corn	Contributory	2 acres	3 acres	3 acres	4 acres	5 acres	
Peanuts*	Contributory Minor		1 acre	2 acres	2 acres	3 acres	
Improvement projects........		Constructed barn, 1 acre permanent pasture	Landscaped home grounds; Erected a new fence; Drained a wet field	Painted a barn; Planted cover crops; Installed running water	Seeded 5 acres of pasture; Stumped 5 acres of land	Constructed a poultry house; Built a permanent hotbed; Installed an irrigation system for 5 acres	
Supplementary farm practices......		Mixed fertilizers; Pruned trees; Culled hens; Caponized cockerels; Repaired screens	Made toolbox; Sharpened tools; Treated seed; Canned fruit; Dressed poultry	Tested milk; Built steps; Sprayed trees; Sheared sheep	Baled hay; Inoculated legumes; Tested seed oats; Operated mowing machine	Built poultry appliances; Painted shelves in kitchen; Sprayed vegetable garden; Adjusted cream separator; Built trap nests; Prepared a fair exhibit	

* Some used for feed and some for market.

SUPERVISED FARMING PROGRAM
Poultry-type Farm

Production projects	Improvement projects	Supplementary farm jobs
First Year		
300 baby chicks for fryers 300 baby chicks for pullets 1 acre of green feed 1 acre of corn 1 dairy calf	Landscape the home grounds Set out a home fruit orchard	Sharpen farm tools Plant a forestry seedbed Repair window screens
Second Year		
100 laying hens 600 baby chicks 1 acre of green feed 4 acres of corn 1 heifer 1 gilt	Set out 2 acres of pine seedlings Improve 1 acre of pasture Continue landscaping home grounds and establishing home orchard	Grow a home garden Propagate ornamental plants Build steps for the home
Third Year		
250 laying hens 600 baby chicks 3 acres of green feed 5 acres of corn 1 dairy cow 1 breed sow and pigs	Improve 1 acre pasture Drain 2 acres lowland Grow 2 acres winter cover crops Plant 3 acres pine trees	Repair water pump Repair front gate Put handles in farm tools Grow home garden
Fourth Year		
350 laying hens 750 baby chicks 4 acres of green feed 10 acres of corn and peanuts 1 brood sow and pigs 6 hogs for meat 1 dairy cow and calf	Clear 5 acres of land Install running water and electric lights on the farm Protect planted pine acreage	Hive 5 colonies of bees Cure 100 bushels of sweet potatoes Repair broken windowpanes Grow home garden

program for his period of training. On the preceding pages examples of such programs are given on different forms; however, certain modifications will have to be made during each year of operation. The boy should develop and formulate his general plans for four or five years in advance but be willing to modify them when experience and economic conditions make it advisable.

Cooperative Relationships in Connection with the Students' Supervised Farming Programs. The teacher of agriculture can best secure the proper cooperation by seeing that parents are acquainted with the aims and purposes of the supervised farming program. Early contacts should be made with parents during the summer months and before the boy actually enrolls. Instructors should never depend upon students to explain to their parents the requirements for this important phase of instruction.

Parents of a beginning student should be given a complete picture of the need for adequate facilities for the student so that the problems can be solved as they arise. The projects should be the responsibility of the student as far as both management and labor are concerned. Parents, as a rule, desire

Fig. 126. A fine combination in the supervision of a student's farming program—the teacher, the high school principal, and the county superintendent of schools. (*Courtesy of J. K. Coggin, North Carolina.*)

to cooperate with the teacher in providing the best practical learning situation for their son.

Project tours often acquaint some parents with the supervised farming programs being conducted by other students.

The agricultural teacher may plan a series of meetings with the parents of his students. At some of these meetings he may have former students who are now established in farming explain how they developed their farming program. Also, at these meetings the following topics may be discussed:

1. The Objectives of a Supervised Farming Program
2. Examples of Good Supervised Farming Programs
3. Supervised Farming Programs Necessary to Be a State Farmer or an American Farmer in the F.F.A.
4. Project Agreements

5. Financing Supervised Farming Programs
6. The Course of Study and How It Should Be Determined by the Supervised Farming Problems
7. Cost-account Records

It is the responsibility of the teacher of agriculture to acquaint the principal and superintendent of schools with the necessity for a good program of supervised farming for each student who enrolls. That the course of study is based on the farming programs should be well understood. It is important for the teacher to ask these school officials, including members of the board of education, to visit the classroom, farm-mechanics shop, and school farm and to see the supervised farming programs being conducted by students at their homes.

The local F.F.A. or N.F.A. chapter usually has a committee to assist members, especially new ones, with their supervised farming programs. The chapter is rated on the work done by each member. The committee tries to develop pride in meeting chapter standards on supervised farming. In many cases, the local chapter may make financial loans to worthy members or may assist them to secure loans from the local bank, from the local production credit association, or from other lending agencies.

Helping the Individual Start His Farming Program. The instructor is responsible for helping launch each student in his farming program as early as possible. In explaining the program to a beginning student, the teacher should present the idea of "growing into farming." This idea allows a boy to start with a small program and gradually increase it as time and money will warrant.

The teacher should also present the idea that a student's progress depends, to a large degree, upon his own interests, initiative, and aggressiveness in making and developing plans.

Often the teacher assists students by having them analyze the records of former students before a final selection of a type of farming is made. The permanent follow-up record cards of all former students provide valuable information.

Making farm surveys can also give each student assistance in deciding on the type of farming to enter. Often a number of surveys are taken at the same time and summarized, and graphs are made of the important items. The various types of farm surveys are discussed in Chapter 8, Making and Using Surveys, pages 94 to 114.

After the surveys have been made and summarized, the student should be ready to select a type of farming. The major project or projects in the type of farming selected comprise the foundation for the development of the program and the instruction for that particular student. After the major projects are selected, minor projects, contributory projects, improvement projects, and supplementary farm practices are added to complete a well-planned educational program.

Essential Records to Keep. A farmer who keeps no records may be able to tell at the end of the year whether or not he has made an annual profit, but he cannot accurately tell which specific enterprises were the most profit-

FIG. 127. The best motivation for learning is pride in ownership and possession. (*Courtesy of R. A. Manire, Texas.*)

FIG. 128. Learning to harvest persimmons for market. (*Courtesy of R. A. Manire, Texas.*)

able. Cost-account records showing the results of supervised farming must be furnished by each agricultural teacher to the state department of education.

In keeping records on supervised farming, the student has to determine what records are essential. In general, the following records are usually kept by students:

1. An inventory
2. A labor record
3. A record of all costs
4. A record of all receipts

5. Special records
      a. Feed records for animals
      b. Breeding records for animals
      c. Production and loss records
      d. Monthly summary records
      e. Financial summary records
      f. Analysis of records

The Inventory. An inventory may not be necessary for a first-year student. The student, however, should have something to inventory at the close of the year. The inventory should include all items on hand at the beginning of the year and all items not sold at the close of the year. These items should be listed at their actual value at the farm.

The following example of an inventory record will indicate the method to be used in recording an inventory:

INVENTORY RECORD

Date	Amount and items	Scope	Beginning value	Closing value
Jan. 1, 1953	Bred gilts	2	$20.00	$ 42.50
	Hog houses	2	10.00	8.50
	Corn on hand	60 bu.	36.00	
Dec. 31, 1953	Pigs	12	......	60.00
	Corn on hand	25 bu.	......	18.75
	Total...............		$66.00	$129.75

If the following items are owned by the student at the close or at the beginning of the year, he should inventory them:

1. Farm
2. Farm equipment
3. Livestock on hand
4. Feed, seed, fertilizer
5. Farm products other than livestock

The Labor Record. All items of cost for labor are usually charged by the hour, except contract labor, which is charged by the job. In most cases, it is best to estimate the number of hours for labor even if contract labor is used. This information is needed in the analysis of the records.

The charge per hour for labor should be at the rate common to the community. The rate varies from one section of any state to another section.

The rate ranges from 25 to 50 cents per hour; however, it makes no difference in the final labor income what the student charges for his own labor. Hired labor should be recorded at the rate that is actually paid.

Traded labor is recorded as self-labor if there is no difference in the number of hours.

The charge for horse and tractor labor should be at the local rate.

FIG. 129. Patience and a love of animals were necessary on the part of this student to train his Brahman calf.   (*Courtesy of R. A. Manire, Texas.*)

The cost of farm machinery should be charged by the hour. The rates for such machinery might well be calculated by all members of the class. In setting the rates, consideration must be given to the interest on the investment, to the amount of depreciation, and to the number of hours the machine is used each year.

The cost of a truck for hauling or a tractor for plowing must include the driver, the fuel, and the expense of the machine being used. These expenses are usually recorded by the hour.

RECORD OF LABOR
(Sample for one month)
Irish-potato Project

Date	Kind of work	Self hours	Hired hours		Horse hours		Equipment hours	
			No.	Cost	No.	Cost	No.	Cost
Jan. 3	Breaking the land.......	..	10	$5.50	..	.....	10	$5.00
Jan. 5	Hauling fertilizer.......	5	..	......	..	.....	5	2.00
Jan. 6	Laying off rows.........	10	..	......	10	$0.50	10	0.20
Jan. 9–10	Putting out fertilizer.....	15	..	......	15	0.75	5	0.15
Jan. 20	Hauling seed potatoes....	1	..	......	1	0.05	1	0.05
Jan. 26–28	Cutting seed potatoes....	18	26	10.00				
	Subtotal.............	49	36	$15.50	26	$1.30	31	$7.40

The Expense Record. All items of cost are recorded as they are paid. The beginning inventory is entered as a cost at the close of the year.

1. Rent (land, buildings)
2. Interest on investment
3. Seeds and fertilizers for crops
4. Feeds for livestock
5. Fees for services (inspection, breeding, registration, treatment of sick animals)
6. Transportation (truck, wagon, freight, express)
7. Crop or animal insurance
8. Labor
9. Farm machinery hired
10. Commission charges for marketing
11. Storage charges if not listed as rent
12. Containers (bags, bottles, crates, barrels, baskets)
13. Livestock, farm machinery, or similar items purchased
14. Miscellaneous

EXPENSE RECORD
(Sample for one month)

Date	Expenses			
	Items	Amount	Unit price	Total price
Jan. 5	Commercial fertilizer 5-7-5	2 tons	$41.00	$82.00
Jan. 20	Seed potatoes	10 sacks	6.50	65.00
	Subtotal.............	....	......	$147.00

The Receipt Record. All items sold or used at home are listed in the receipt record. Credit products used at home are at the wholesale farm value and not at the retail value at the grocery stores in town.

In addition to products marketed or used at home which were obtained from the enterprise, there are usually a few miscellaneous receipts, such as feed sacks and fertilizer bags.

At the close of the year, the closing inventory is also entered as a receipt.

RECORD OF RECEIPTS
(Sample for one month)

Receipts

Date	Items	Amount, sacks	Unit price	Total price
May 1	No. 1 potatoes	75	$2.75	$206.25
May 1	No. 2 potatoes	30	2.50	75.00
May 1	No. 3 potatoes	8	1.00	8.00
	Subtotal......	..	.....	$289.25

Special Records. A breeding record is usually kept for every type of animal where such a record is desirable. For poultry, a special feed record is often kept as well as a daily egg-production record. The same general type of record is needed for a dairy project. Often a loss record—especially for livestock or poultry—is essential.

A financial summary is made at the close of the year. It is also essential to make a complete analysis of the records in order to plan improvements for the future. The outline for such an analysis is found in the back of most record books.

The Teacher's Supervision of Student Farming. The teacher is responsible, under the provisions of the Smith-Hughes Act, for the proper supervision of each student who is enrolled.

According to most of the monthly reports now in use, a teacher visits a student for the following purposes: to acquaint himself with the local situations, to inspect the work done by the student, to teach the student new facts or skills, and to inspire the student to greater effort.

The following recommendations should prove valuable to teachers when they are supervising projects:

1. Take the project record book with you and check it for accuracy and completeness. See that records are recorded to date and then make recommendations on the project-visitation page.
2. Recommend improved or needed practices on productive enterprises.

3. Be on the alert to discover practical and necessary farm-shop jobs. These jobs may be done either at school or on the farm.
4. Look for needed supplementary farm practices and improvement projects which may be included in the student's program.
5. Try to get the student to recognize new potential productive enterprises which may be started.
6. Check on the work already done on supplementary farm practices and improvement projects.
7. Help student to keep one or more productive enterprises in operation each month of the year.
8. Meet parents or guardians to gain their confidence and to secure their cooperation.
9. Where necessary, provide needed technical information and teach skills.
10. In the case of some disaster in connection with a project, or the lack of proper interest, try to inspire the student to go ahead and do his best.

No one can say exactly how often a teacher should visit a given student. In general, it may be said that he should visit the student at each vital step in the supervised farming program. The visits should commence when the supervised farming program is being planned and continue as long as the student takes vocational agriculture, which should be as long as he farms in the community. The number of times that a teacher should visit the student during the year will depend upon the following factors:

1. The kind of projects being conducted
2. The age and experience of the student
3. The stage of development of the projects
4. The general weather conditions
5. The number of projects being conducted by the student

As a general statement, each student should be visited a minimum of once each month. Some projects—baby chicks, for example—may need a number of daily visits at the beginning. The harvesting and curing of tobacco may also call for a number of visits at frequent intervals. In reality, the teacher needs to make service calls, not visits.

Teacher's Notebook for Supervision. Teachers of vocational agriculture find that a notebook is very essential in project supervision. A student may lose his project record, and then the teacher faces a problem in securing a final report. The main purpose, however, in keeping a notebook is for the teacher to know what is being done by each student and to make a record of the jobs needed to be performed.

A loose-leaf notebook with letter tabs, which facilitate the entering of each name alphabetically, is handy.   The notebook may be used to record costs, receipts, and the condition of the projects.

School Credit for Practice Work. The supervised farming program is a vital part of the training in vocational agriculture.   School credit is given for the completed classroom work and the supervised farming. No credit should ever be allowed for class instruction without the experience obtained in supervised farming. The same statement is true concerning the supervised farm-practice work without the class instruction.

It is a good plan for the teacher to grade a student after he has completed each farm job.   In other words, a grade is given for the type of work done in the classroom on a specified job and a second grade is given on the proficiency shown by the student in putting the job into actual practice on a specified project. A number of teachers are using a plan for grading similar to the following:

Fig. 130. Gum-production projects are common among the boys of the southern pine belt.

1. Give 25 percent of the final grade for work done in the classroom.
2. Give 35 percent of the final grade for work done in the supervised farming program.
3. Give 15 percent of the final grade for participation activities in F.F.A. work.
4. Give 25 percent of the final grade for farm-mechanics shopwork.

If such a grading system is followed, no student can pass and receive final credit unless he has a satisfactory supervised farming program.

Establishing Students in Farming.   The teacher of agriculture should have as his final goal the successful establishment of students in farming. Often the student may have to work for a number of years after he completes high school before he is able to purchase a farm.   In fact, he may use one or more of the following interim steps in finally becoming established in farming:

1. Working on the home farm with no definite allowance
2. Working on the home farm with definite wages
3. Working on the home farm with an allowance from specific farm enterprises
4. Working on the home farm as a partner
5. Working on a farm away from home for wages
6. Managing a farm for a salary
7. Sharecropping with some landowner
8. Renting and operating a farm
9. Owning and operating a farm

FIG. 131. Poultry production starts many a student toward his goal of establishment in farming. (*Courtesy of Otis Bell, Florida.*)

It would be well for the teacher of agriculture to keep in touch with each farmer in the community who may want to employ a student. He should also know who has land to be rented and the price, who desires a renter, and who has land for sale. A current list of the farms for sale may also be secured from local real-estate dealers, from the Federal Land Bank, and from surveys.

Most young men need assistance in getting established in farming. They will need help in selecting the proper farm and in securing finances. The teacher of agriculture has a wonderful opportunity to render outstanding service in this respect. He should be able to assist the student in making the following decisions:

1. Is the farm the proper type and size?
2. Is the land worth the price for agricultural purposes?
3. Is the title to the property clear?
4. Is the interest rate satisfactory?
5. Are the terms of payment satisfactory?

SELECTED REFERENCES

COOK, G. C., and L. J. PHIPPS, "A Handbook on Teaching Vocational Agriculture," The Interstate, Danville, Ill., 1952.

DEYOE, G. P., "Supervised Farming in Vocational Agriculture," The Interstate, Danville, Ill., 1947.

Directing Vocational Agriculture Day-school Students in Developing Their Farming Programs, U.S. Office of Education, *Bulletin* 225, Agricultural Series 56, 1944.

Father-Son Farm Operating Agreements, U.S. Department of Agriculture, *Farmers' Bulletin* 2026.

Improvement Projects in Dairying, *Bulletin* 260, State Board of Control for Vocational Education, Lansing, Mich.

POLLOM, L. F., and L. HALL, The Farming Program as a Means of Developing Farm Boys, *Bulletin* 1, Kansas State Board for Vocational Education, Topeka, Kan.

————, and ————, Guiding Farm Boys in Developing Farming Programs in Vocational Agriculture, *Bulletin* 11, Kansas State Board for Vocational Education, Topeka, Kan.

SAUNDERS, H. W., Supervised Farm Practice, *Department Mimeograph* 36, Virginia Polytechnic Institute, Blacksburg, Va.

SPANTON, W. T., "Teacher's Manual for Use in Teaching Project Record Keeping and Accounting," The French-Bray Printing Company, Baltimore, 1932.

Supervised Farming Programs in Illinois, *Bulletin*, University of Illinois, Urbana, Ill.

Supervised Practice in Agriculture, U.S. Office of Education, Division of Vocational Education, *Bulletin* 112.

15. Teaching Young Farmers and Adult Farmers

NOT ALL instruction in vocational agriculture is designed for the student in high school. A local department of vocational agriculture is also responsible for meeting, to some extent, the training needs of young farmers and adult farmers who are residents of the community.

Teaching Young Farmers

Young-farmer classes are designed for farm boys and men who have left the public school and who are between the ages of sixteen and thirty. These

FIG. 132. Young farmers discussing problems of production credit. (*Courtesy of H. S. Johnson, Farm Credit Administration.*)

individuals must be engaged in farm work and interested in becoming established in a farming occupation.

Classes for young farmers may meet either during the day or at night, but they must be under public supervision and control. Such classes must not be confused with institutional or farm classes for veterans.

Young Men Out of School. Included in the young-farmer classes are boys who have dropped out of school and those young men who have completed high school or college. It has been estimated that less than 25 percent of our farm boys who graduate from high school attend college. Even if a young man does attend college, he can profit from being a member of a young-farmer class. The fact is that most young men who are trying to become established in farming are in need of some kind of educational assistance.

The majority of the young men on the farm above eighteen and under thirty years of age are out of school. In practically any rural community where farming is important, the teacher will find more young farmers than he can properly serve. Often he could use an assistant teacher for this responsibility.

Locating the Young Men. Teachers of vocational agriculture use various methods to locate young men who are available as students. The plans given below or modifications thereof are usually followed:

1. Securing names from school records
2. Obtaining the help of the local F.F.A. or N.F.A. chapter
3. Making a farm-to-farm survey
4. Using key young men to supply information and help recruit
5. Securing the aid of businessmen and farmers
6. Securing the aid of adult-farmer classes

Because tenant farmers move often, the only accurate way to obtain the names of all young men in the area who are farming is to make a farm-to-farm survey. The following form is suggested for that purpose:

SURVEY FORM FOR YOUNG-FARMER CLASSES

1. Name_____Address_____
2. Age_____Single or married_____
3. Grade completed in school_____Date of leaving school_____
4. Why did you leave school?_____
_____
5. Did you take vocational agriculture in high school?_____
6. What have you done since leaving school?_____
_____

7. What is your present farming status?
   a. Owner and operator of a farm_____
   b. Renter and operator of a farm_____
   c. Manager of a farm for someone else_____
   d. In partnership at home_____
   e. At home with a definite allowance_____
   f. At home with an indefinite allowance_____
   g. At home with specified enterprises_____
   h. Farm laborer_____
8. How do you spend your leisure time? Reading_____
   Athletics_____Music_____
   Hobbies_____

9. Do you play a musical instrument?_____If so, what kind?_____

_____Do you sing?_____

10. What were your approximate earnings for the past year?_____

11. Occupation of your father_____Does he own a

farm?_____If so, state type and size_____

_____

12. Is your homestead landscaped?_____

Is your home screened?_____Painted?_____

13. Number of boys in your family?_____Ages?_____

14. What are your vocational plans for the future?_____

    a. If you plan to farm: Where?_____What type of

    farm?_____

    b. Will you inherit land?_____

    c. Do you plan to purchase land?_____

    d. Are you planning to rent a farm or sharecrop?_____

15. Would you be interested in attending a young-farmer class?_____

16. If you are interested in attending a young-farmer class, what problems would you

be most interested in?

    a. Becoming established in farming_____

    b. Production of farm enterprises: Crops_____

    Livestock_____

    c. Farm mechanics_____

    d. Business English_____

    e. Citizenship_____

    f. Farm mathematics_____

    g. Related sciences_____

    h. Health protection_____

    i. Social customs_____

17. Do you have the proper facilities for developing a farming program?_____

18. Class meeting time best suited to your needs:

    a. Time of day_____

    b. Day or days of the week_____

Types of Classes. Young-farmer classes are sometimes classified on the basis of how often the class meets. Three such classifications are:

1. The intensive class

2. The slack-season class

3. The long intermittent class

The intensive class usually meets daily for a specified time. In most states a young-farmer class must meet at least fifteen times for a minimum of 30 clock hours per year.

The slack-season class is held during that part of the year when there is a minimum amount of farm work. The class usually meets from two to five times per week.

The long intermittent type of class usually meets once or twice each month of the year. This type of class gives the teacher an opportunity to consider seasonal problems as they are faced on the farm.

Fig. 133. Young-farmer class checking growth in an improved pasture.

Fig. 134. This young farmer built the post hole digger in the school farm shop. (*Courtesy of R. A. Manire, Texas.*)

Characteristics of Young Men. Since the age group ranges from sixteen to thirty years, those enrolling vary in education and farm experience.

Reasons for leaving school, as given by the young men, may include:

1. Not interested in the subjects being taught.
2. Had to repeat grades and was put in the room with younger students.
3. Had trouble with a teacher.
4. Desired to earn money.
5. Had to go to work to help support the family.

As a general rule, young farmers know farm skills or operative jobs better than high school boys. They are often interested in farm-mechanics skills, such as electric arc or oxyacetylene welding, soldering, rafter cutting, and concrete construction. These young men are usually interested in becoming established in farming. In fact, the satisfactory establishment in farming is the chief objective of a young-farmer class.

Where to Hold the Class. The class usually meets in the agricultural classroom or shop of the high school. It is possible for the class to meet at any central place in the community where suitable space and facilities are available. Farm-mechanics courses, however, can be offered only where such facilities are available, which is usually only in the high school farm-mechanics shop.

Who Should Teach the Class. The regular agricultural teacher has the responsibility of organizing and teaching classes for young farmers. He may obtain the assistance of specialists or technicians for certain phases of the course, or assistant teachers may be assigned to handle the class. Special teachers or technicians may be used for teaching young men who need further instruction in related subjects or in specific farm-mechanics skills. Many educational leaders believe that in the near future agricultural teachers will need an assistant who gives all his time to the instruction of out-of-school young and adult farmers.

The Course of Study and Subjects. The two main objectives of young-farmer classes are

1. To assist young men with their educational and production problems in becoming established in farming.
2. To increase the vocational, civic, and social intelligence of members of the class.

To meet the above objectives, the teacher will need to use both group and individual instruction. No two young men will face exactly the same problems, and the course of study should be designed to help solve individual problems. A special committee for the young-farmer class, which includes a member from the advisory council, can be very helpful to the teacher in setting up a course of study.

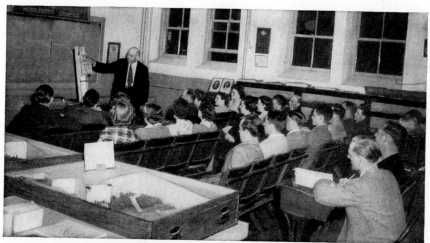

Fig. 135. Joint young-farmer and homemaker class held at the high school building. (*Courtesy of C. D. Watson, Vermont.*)

Agricultural Subjects. Production problems for each farm enterprise are usually taught on an individual basis. Typical group jobs desired by most young men include:

1. Determining the possibilities of becoming successfully established in farming
2. Deciding on whether to rent or purchase a farm
3. Deciding on the type of farm to buy
4. Determining the acreage needed for a given type of farming and for a given family
5. Securing the finances for purchasing a farm
6. Purchasing a farm
7. Laying out a farmstead
8. Purchasing farm equipment
9. Purchasing livestock for the farm
10. Securing and using production credit
11. Balancing a farm business
12. Rotating crops on the farm
13. Conserving fertility of the soil
14. Landscaping the farmstead
15. Hiring and managing labor
16. Insuring farm animals, crops, and farm buildings

17. Registering farm animals
18. Controlling farm insects
19. Controlling crop and fruit diseases
20. Determining the commercial fertilizers to use on the farm
21. Managing the farm-forestry plot
22. Servicing and maintaining farm machinery
23. Constructing farm buildings and equipment
24. Marketing farm products
25. Keeping farm records
26. Analyzing farm records
27. Improving farm crops
28. Improving livestock on the farm
29. Improving the farm home
30. Providing ample food for the farm family
31. Conserving food for the family
32. Cooperating with farm organizations
33. Improving pastures for livestock

The above group jobs are only suggestive. The teacher will have to design a course in agriculture to meet specific needs. He will also have to teach many individual production problems on the job.

English. Practically every study made of young men on the farm indicates that few of them read extensively, few know how to lead a discussion or how to speak effectively, and few know how to write a good business letter. To meet such situations, the following partial outline is worthy of study:

1. Writing
    a. How to write a check
    b. How to write a receipt
    c. How to write a telegram
    d. How to write an advertisement
    e. How to write a business letter
    f. How to write an article for the press
2. Speaking
    a. How to be at ease before an audience
    b. How to speak effectively
    c. How to lead a discussion
    d. How to conduct a meeting according to parliamentary rules
3. Reading
    a. How to develop speed and skill in reading
    b. How to select reading materials
    c. How to find and use reference material

Farm Arithmetic. All problems selected for the course should be obtained from the actual farms of the area. The ability of each class member must also be taken into consideration. The following activities are suggestive:

1. Locating a farm
2. Determining land areas
3. Balancing a ration for livestock
4. Computing the formula of a given fertilizer mixture
5. Computing the cubic contents of a truck body or a bin
6. Computing the capacity of a water tank
7. Computing interest on money
8. Computing the amount of timber on a given area
9. Computing the board feet of lumber
10. Computing the materials needed for a given volume of concrete
11. Computing the amount of taxes a farmer would have to pay on a given farm
12. Computing the cost of producing farm enterprises
13. Computing the various costs of marketing farm products
14. Figuring and comparing the costs of different forms of insurance
15. Computing farm labor income

Citizenship. The following special problems are suggested:

1. Determining the services performed by our national, state, and local governments
2. Making our laws
3. Enforcing laws
4. Registering and voting
5. Determining the basis and purposes of taxation
6. Determining how the tax dollar is spent
7. Determining the duties and qualifications of state and local officers
8. Deciding on the merits of a given bond issue
9. Deciding on the personal duties of an individual in community projects
10. Inventorying the advantages of a democratic government
11. Preserving our democratic institutions

Social Customs. Surveys indicate that young men between the ages of sixteen and twenty-five are very much interested in following accepted social customs. In this age group young men are associating with young women and they desire to do the correct thing. A few of them may not have had an opportunity to learn certain accepted practices. Among the most important problems in this area are

1. How to act as an escort
2. How to introduce people
3. How to make dates
4. How to extend invitations to various types of social functions
5. How to accept invitations
6. How to dress for different social functions
7. How to act at a formal dinner party
8. How to make and keep friends
9. How to plan for marriage
10. How the man should assume his responsibility in the home

Health. The following problems are examples of what may be included:

1. Deciding on the proper amount of rest and sleep
2. Selecting a proper diet
3. Building good bones and teeth
4. Securing and using health certificates
5. Preventing and controlling common diseases
6. Using certified or pasteurized milk
7. Giving first-aid treatments
8. Making use of hospital and health insurance
9. Planning a safe home water supply and adequate sewage disposal system

Science. The science of agriculture is the practical application of science to the production and preservation of farm products. A teacher will not have the time to call attention to all the principles of science involved in the agricultural jobs taught. However, he may profitably call the attention of his students to some of the most important principles as they apply to agriculture. Among the most common principles are

1. The use of centrifugal force in separating cream from milk
2. Principles of inheritance as applied to breeding plants and animals
3. The life history of insects
4. The methods nature uses in the pollination of plants
5. The limits of plant propagation
6. The proper use of disinfectants
7. Why a balanced ration is important
8. How plants and animals are classified
9. The causes of soil erosion
10. Methods of correcting the acidity of soils
11. Principles of science used in food preservation
12. How seeds germinate
13. The spread of plant diseases

14. The control measures for plant diseases
15. The irrigation of crops
16. The operating principles of farm machinery

The above list of topics could be greatly expanded. There are usually many principles of related science involved in any farm skill.

Farm Mechanics. Young men are usually much interested in farm mechanics. The available use of power tools is often the main factor in bringing them into the class. The following outline indicates the kind of mechanical jobs young men are commonly interested in:

1. Planning farm buildings
2. Painting farm buildings
3. Sharpening farm tools
4. Reconditioning and servicing farm machinery
5. Adjusting and operating farm machinery
6. Reconditioning gasoline engines
7. Welding metals (forge, electric arc, and oxyacetylene)
8. Tempering metals
9. Soldering metals
10. Making a livestock trailer
11. Making and using concrete feed troughs
12. Lacing a belt
13. Constructing farm roads
14. Constructing farm fences
15. Construcing farm terraces
16. Constructing a water system for the farm
17. Installing a heating system for the farm home
18. Repairing plaster and brickwork
19. Draining land
20. Installing a sewage system
21. Doing individual construction and repair jobs

Recreational Activities. The teacher will find that many types of recreational activities are desired for young-farmer classes. Such a program may include any one or a combination of the following activities:

1. Organizing a string band
2. Conducting group singing
3. Organizing a quartet
4. Organizing a basketball, volleyball, or baseball team
5. Holding banquets, parties, and picnics
6. Conducting fishing trips, tours, or other outings

7. Organizing and giving plays and pageants

8. Sponsoring the building of a community library, playground, or park

Young men who are married should be encouraged to bring their wives and single men to bring their "dates" to any of the planned recreational activities. It is often possible for the home economics teacher to meet with the women

Fɪɢ. 136. Checking the grading and packing of tomatoes grown by a young farmer. (*Courtesy of L. R. Stanley, Michigan.*)

while the men attend class with the agricultural teacher.   A social period can be arranged at the close of some class periods.

Supervised Farming.   According to the Smith-Hughes Act, each individual who enrolls in a class in vocational agriculture must have a supervised farming program.   Since the young men are already working on farms, it is no trouble to meet this requirement.   Young men who are working at home with a definite or indefinite allowance or those who are working at home for wages can usually arrange to have productive projects.   Those who are renting, sharecropping, or managing a farm may take the farm as a unit for their supervised farming.   Young men who work for farmers in the area can arrange for work that can be designated as placement for farm experience.

Definite records should be kept on these supervised farming programs. The teacher will need to visit each young man frequently in order to give him needed instruction and guidance on the job.

Methods of Teaching Young Farmers.   Teachers find it necessary to use different approaches and devices for instructing young-farmer classes.   Some

Fig. 137. The proof of the quality of instruction offered young farmers is in the quality of the product produced.   This young farmer and his family are packing tomatoes.   (*Courtesy of L. R. Stanley, Michigan.*)

of those used in teaching all-day classes are not satisfactory.   For example, supervised study is far less appropriate with young-farmer classes than with high school students.   Young men often have acquired many farm skills and need to be taught largely from the managerial standpoint.   Few of them are interested in reading a large number of references.

The actual devices to use will often depend upon the type of job taught. Skills will demand a demonstration by the teacher and a period of practice for the student, whereas decisions will require discussion and the pooling of experience.   The following procedures have been successfully used in teaching young-farmer classes:

Preparation Step

PURPOSE	DEVICES
1. To determine what young men already know.	1. Questions on the experiences of students.
2. To create a desire to learn.	2. Illustrations.
3. To outline the learning procedure to be followed.	3. Stories and jokes.
	4. Exhibits to create interest.
	5. Citing local situations.
	6. Job analysis.

Presentation Step

PURPOSE	DEVICES
1. To teach new facts or skills.	1. Demonstration.
	2. Discussion.
	3. Field trip.
	4. Survey.
	5. Visual aids.
	6. Topic assignment.
	7. Supervised study.
	8. Lecture.

Supervision of Practice Step

PURPOSE	DEVICES
1. To provide an opportunity to make plans and to practice skills.	1. Individual planning.
	2. Group discussion.
	3. Field trip to practice skills.
	4. Farm-mechanics shop to practice skills.
	5. Demonstrations given by students.

Testing and Follow-up Step

PURPOSE	DEVICES
1. To determine what the individual knows about facts.	1. Check the quality of work done on the farm.
2. To determine what the individual can do without supervision.	2. Check results of work done in the farm shop.

LESSON PLAN FOR A YOUNG-FARMER CLASS

Job: Purchasing a Farm

Objectives:

1. To acquaint the young men with the list of available farms.
2. To help the young men consider all the facts which are essential in purchasing a farm.
3. To assist young men in actually selecting and purchasing farms.

Preparation:

1. You have all seen large well-constructed buildings. What did the builders actually do before they started the construction work?
2. Why was it necessary to have definite plans?
3. It is agreed that plans are essential in constructing any good building. Is it as desirable to have definite plans for purchasing a farm?
4. Last year a farmer came to our county from another state and purchased a farm through a local real-estate firm. Then he came to the office of the county agricultural agent for assistance in planning a farm program. He learned that the farm was absolutely worthless from a production standpoint. Would a few well-made plans have helped him avoid this great mistake?

5. How many of you already own land or expect to inherit land?
6. Who is interested in purchasing a farm?
7. If you are interested in purchasing a farm, what factors should you consider? Write the suggested factors on the board: size of farm, fertility of soil, location of farm, cost, topography of soil, available water supply, type of farm, improvements on the farm, healthfulness, roads and markets, neighbors, taxes, community improvements, prospective development, and farm layout.

Presentation:

1. Lead the young men in a discussion of the suggested factors as applied to a specific farm in the community.
2. Present local data in graphic form showing labor income of the major types of farms, sizes of successful farms of each type, and other available data.
3. Present a list of farms that are for sale in the community. List these on the board and give the following factors: size of farm, fertility of soil, type, cost, terms, and present improvements.

Supervision of Practice:

1. Have each learner make definite plans for purchasing a farm, giving considerations to the factors listed, his personal characteristics, and financial status.
2. Assist each learner in making the necessary business arrangements in purchasing a farm.

Testing and Follow-up:

1. Check the results of each young man's decision and note his success.
2. Later check farms that were actually purchased.

References:

1. Business Problems in Farming, U.S. Department of the Interior, Office of Education, *Vocational Education Bulletin* 183, pp. 10–12, 1936.
2. Selecting a Farm, U.S. Department of Agriculture, *Farmers' Bulletin* 1088.

Evaluating the Young-farmer Instruction. It is always difficult to evaluate outcomes from instruction. The evaluation has to be attempted largely in terms of the aims or objectives of the teacher. The real test of the value of the instruction for young-farmer classes is the actual progress made by each individual—progress toward the ultimate goal of satisfactory establishment in a farming business. However, if "yes" can be given to such questions as the following on achievements, the work of the teacher must have been satisfactory:

1. Was labor income from farming increased?
2. Were farm inventories increased?
3. Was more land rented and worked?
4. Was the use of improved farm practices increased?
5. Was more purebred livestock acquired?
6. Were farm homes improved?
7. Were more permanent pastures established?

8. Were more soil-improving crops grown?

9. Were more memberships taken out in farm organizations?

10. Did those enrolled want another class conducted next year?

FIG. 138. Following up on improved practices taught in a young-farmer class. (*Courtesy of C. D. Watson, Vermont.*)

Teaching Adult Farmers

Farmers always have new problems and many old ones occur in new ways. The production and marketing of farm products call for new methods. The farmer must know the facts relating to agricultural conditions in the rest of the world in order to react intelligently to such matters as crop allotments. He must also know in detail the provisions of the Production and Marketing Administration and the Farm Credit Administration if he takes the proper advantages of the help that is available. Constant change makes it necessary for each farmer to decide what he should do for that particular year.

The Problem of Adult Learning. In the early period of our history many people claimed that adults were slow to learn. The old adage "You cannot teach an old dog new tricks" was often quoted and many believed it. The First World War period of 1917 to 1918 really gave birth to what is now known as "adult education" in America. The movement was brought about by leaders who were amazed at the results which intelligence tests and standardized subject-matter tests taken by servicemen revealed. Not only were certain procedures used in public schools questioned, but people began to wonder if something could not be done to assist generally those who no longer attended public schools.

The Smith-Hughes Act, signed on February 23, 1917, contained definite provisions for a program of adult vocational education. Many individuals in general education and in vocational education have contributed to the movement for adult education.

FIG. 139. Teaching adult farmers to run terrace lines. (*Courtesy of J. K. Coggin, North Carolina.*)

Dr. E. L. Thorndike made a rather complete study of adult learning.[1] In general, his conclusions were as follows:

1. Individuals reach their greatest mental vigor at about twenty-one years of age.
2. This high level of mental vigor is maintained for a period of approximately ten years.
3. The loss of mental vigor tends to go backward rather slowly.
4. Experience is a vital factor in learning. It tends to more than offset the loss due to deterioration of mental vigor, making a man's best years for learning to solve the real problems of life to be from forty-five to forty-nine years of age.
5. Adults of thirty to fifty years of age can probably learn better than children, provided the adult wants to learn.

[1] THORNDIKE, E. L., *et al.*, "Adult Learning," The Macmillan Company, New York, 1928.

According to all reliable information, a teacher of vocational agriculture may expect adult farmers to profit just as much from instruction as high school students who have been given the same amount of time.   Farmers are in a position to put into practice new procedures and practices they learn about farm management, whereas high school students may have to wait years before they actually face such problems of their own.

General Requirements for Evening Classes.   Most state plans for vocational education state that evening classes in agriculture are a vital part of the agricultural teacher's program.   The following recommendations are given as requirements in many state plans:

1. A minimum of 10 meetings per class and at least 20 hours of instruction per year.
2. A minimum of 90 minutes per meeting.   Most teachers find that a two-hour period is better.
3. A minimum enrollment of 10.   Fifteen to twenty members is preferred, except in farm-shop classes.

Where and When to Hold Class.   Evening classes may be taught at any time or any place where the teacher can get the physical facilities and the

Fig. 140. This adult group is meeting in the vocational agricultural room at the high school for a soil-testing demonstration.   (*Courtesy of L. R. Stanley, Michigan.*)

enrollment.   The regular high school classroom and shop for vocational agriculture are usually the best equipped to take care of the needs for evening-class instruction, but any rural school may afford a more convenient place for farmers to meet.

The physical equipment required, except that for farm-mechanics classes, can often be transported by the teacher. Visual aids and a portable blackboard are necessary teaching facilities which can be carried from place to place. The exact time for the class to meet will depend upon the season of the year and upon the distance the farmers have to travel.

Many adult evening classes meet once each week. The night most suitable to the majority of the prospective students should be selected. An effort should be made to avoid conflicts with the regularly scheduled meetings of any lodges, churches, and civic clubs that members are likely to attend.

Plans for Enrolling Adults. Agricultural teachers find it desirable to use a number of different ways to get farmers to attend evening classes. The more common methods are

1. Personal visits made to each farm.
2. The aid of "key" farmers or businessmen.
3. Individual letters or cards sent to farmers.
4. Telephone calls.
5. Newspaper announcements.
6. Posters placed in public places.
7. Announcements made at public meetings (school, church, or farmers' meetings).
8. Calls from members of a special committee or from members of the advisory council.

Studies have been made to determine the relative value of each of these methods. Each study indicates that personal visits and calls are by far the most effective method known.

The Course of Study. The content for the course of study is usually determined by the economic problems of the community. In visiting farmers from time to time during the year, the teacher has an opportunity to learn the main problems that are facing them.

In a few instances, the teacher may want to help introduce a new cash crop and teach the skills and operative jobs connected with it; however, the main problems are often of a managerial type. In selecting the managerial problems, the teacher may select the ones that pertain to specific types of farming or problems that are facing the farmers in various types of farming. For example, the problems may relate to dairy farming and be of such a nature that general-type farmers may not be interested. Problems relating to soil conservation may apply to all farmers in the community. It is well to have a special committee of farmers to advise on the course of study. Usually a member of the advisory council is on this committee.

The agricultural teacher using a special committee will more likely organize courses of study that will fit different types of farmers, or he will select a

cross section of the main farming problems.   In other words, the evening
course may be designed for dairy farmers, for poultry farmers, for truck
farmers, or for beef-cattle farmers.   The teacher may try to find common
managerial problems where each of the above types of farmers may come
together and study their solution.   It is also possible for him to spend the

FIG. 141. A well-attended adult meeting on production credit.   (*Courtesy of H. S. Johnson,*
Farm Credit Administration.)

entire time during an evening course on one main economic problem or
enterprise.   In order to clarify the various procedures, an example of each
plan is given.

EVENING COURSE FOR SWINE GROWERS

1. Determining the best farm organization for swine growers
2. Standardizing the breeds of swine for the community
3. Planning a feed-crop program for swine
4. Deciding on the proper breeding dates for swine
5. Controlling swine diseases and parasites
6. Finishing swine for the market
7. Marketing swine by individual methods and by cooperative methods

EVENING COURSE FOR ALL FARMERS OF A COMMUNITY

1. Determining the grasses best suited for improved pastures
2. Purchasing commercial fertilizers cooperatively
3. Feeding hens for winter egg production
4. Organizing a cooperative association for the marketing of vegetables

5. Cooperating with the program sponsored by the U.S. Department of Agriculture
6. Repairing farm machinery

EVENING COURSE ON ONE PROBLEM FOR ALL FARMERS OF A COMMUNITY
The Live-at-home Program

1. Determining the food needs for a given farm family
2. Estimating the foods that are now being produced
3. Setting up a program that will meet the food needs of the family
4. Conserving food for the farm family

Methods of Teaching Adult Farmers.   The conference method has been accepted by workers in the field of vocational education as the best procedure to use in evening-class instruction.   In general, this procedure consists of informal but systematic group discussion carried on by experienced farmers under the direction of a leader.   The special value of this method is to provide on the part of each individual an opportunity for constructive thinking under the stimulus of the contributions offered by each other member.

In the ideal conference procedure, all the facts needed to solve a problem may be drawn from the experiences of the members of the group.   In practice, however, we frequently find that new or additional information is needed.   The new information should not be supplied until after a clearly recognized need for the facts has been developed with the group.

The teacher, as the leader in the conference method, should follow certain well-defined steps.

1. Outline the job to be considered.
2. Select the functioning facts from all those given.
3. Assemble all needed facts from the experiences of the group.
4. Evaluate these functioning facts in the light of the problem.
5. Have each member of the class make a decision as to what he can do about the job on his particular farm.
6. Have each member of the class make definite working plans for carrying out any decisions reached.
7. Assist in supervising the making and carrying out of the plans.
8. Check the results.

In using the conference method of teaching, the instructor has work to do in preparing for the class meeting.   He must anticipate the reactions of the group and secure the new or additional information which will be needed.   It is certainly necessary for him to prepare a teaching plan.   Such a plan may include a demonstration.

Fig. 142. A field demonstration for adult farmers. (*Courtesy of J. W. Bunten, Nevada.*)

Preparing a Teaching Plan for the Conference Procedure. In order to illustrate the work of a teacher in getting ready for an evening class where he expects to use the conference procedure, a teaching plan is given for a specific job.

CONFERENCE LEADER'S TEACHING PLAN

Job: Deciding the kind and the amount of food to produce for the farm family in the live-at-home program.

Situations:

1. Many farmers do not produce enough food for their families.
2. Many farmers do not have cash for purchasing food supplies.
3. Many farm families are living on unbalanced diets.

Objective: To assist farmers to think through this job and reach the following decisions for their particular farms:

1. The kind of food enterprises to undertake.
2. The acreage (amount) of each enterprise to produce.
3. Plans for conducting these food enterprises.

Procedure:

A. Outline the job.

　　1. Explain the importance of producing all the food possible on the home farm and also its importance to children, especially in terms of balanced diets. State that the purpose of the discussion is to assist each member of the class in making the proper adjustments on his farm. Mention that you have no cut-and-dried plan but that each man will make a plan to suit his own farm.

　　2. Assist in keeping a record of the facts as they are brought out in the discussion for this is the main function of the teacher.

B. Analyze the job.

Have the members of the class assist in making the analysis.

SAMPLE ANALYSIS

Decisions	Factors	Information needed
What food crops to grow	a. Body requirements b. Adaptability of the soil and the climate c. Cost of production d. Labor requirements e. Likes and dislikes of the family f. Pests present	a. Facts on the biological food requirements of man b. Crops and varieties of each best adapted to the local soil and climate c. Cost of production of each of the food enterprises d. Labor distribution for each of the food enterprises e. Foods which the family likes f. Insect and disease pests common in the community
Amount of food to grow	a. Food requirements per individual b. Size of the family c. The number of different food enterprises grown	a. The amount and kind of food needed for an individual per year b. The size of family to be fed c. The number of the different food enterprises selected to grow which will meet the family needs

C. Secure from the members of the class a list of food enterprises being grown by each member.

AMOUNT OF FOOD PRODUCTS PRODUCED

Farmer: H. Brown

Size of family: 5

Corn...................	30 bu.	Milk...................	200 gal.
Sweet potatoes..........	20 bu.	Butter.................	100 lb.
Sirup..................	25 gal.	Eggs...................	30 doz.
Meat..................	700 lb.	Poultry...............	50 birds
Lard..................	200 lb.	Etc.	

D. Have overhead questions for discussion.

1. How may we tell how much food a person should eat in a year?
2. There are standard tables available for use in feeding horses and other animals. Where could we find such a table for human beings? (Present a standard food chart for a farm family.)
3. What food enterprises can be produced economically in this community? (Place the list on the blackboard.)
4. Classify food enterprises according to their dietic value.
5. What is the value of fresh fruits and vegetables in the diet?

    6. Why do children need more milk per day than adults?
      (Many other questions may be used.)

E. Have each member of the class select food enterprises.
    1. Name of the enterprises.
    2. Acreage or amount of each enterprise needed for his family.

F. Have each member of the class prepare a definite program for producing the food
enterprises selected.
    1. The list of food enterprises.
    2. The amount of each to produce.
    3. The variety or breed.
    4. When and how to plant.
    5. Fertilizers to use.
    6. Feeds to use.
    (Many similar items can be added to the list.)

G. Supervise the practice work.
    Supervise the practice work of each student in order to see that plans are properly
executed.

H. Check results obtained.
    Check the results accomplished at the close of the year. Calculate with the indi-
vidual student concerned the value to the farmer of the improved practices followed
for the year.

Fig. 143. The conference procedure is the best device yet discovered for pooling the
experiences of individuals interested in agricultural subjects. (*Courtesy of W. G. Hoag,
Farm Credit Administration.*)

Supplementary Information on the Conference Procedure. In using
the conference method, the teacher will often need to secure additional information to assist the group in making decisions. This additional material
usually consists of data from experiment stations properly organized. Probably the best way to present this additional information is in the form of charts.
It is possible to use mimeographed sheets or data placed on visual-aid slides
of different types.

In teaching the job as just outlined, the teacher will need to present a standard food chart. Information for such a chart may be secured from colleges and experiment stations an example is;

STANDARD FOOD CHART FOR THE FARM FAMILY
Food Items and the Amount Needed per Person per Year

Corn	7¼ bu.	Butter	50 lb.
Sweet potatoes	8 bu.	Eggs	2 per day
Meat	50 lb.	Poultry	17 fryers
Lard	50 lb.	Fruit	2 kinds per day
Milk per person per day.	1 pt. (adults)	Vegetables	2 kinds per day
	1 qt. (children)	Sirup	10 gal.

The teacher will find that a good variety of visual aids—charts, filmstrips, and motion pictures—add interest to his teaching methods. In certain cases, he may find it desirable to invite some experienced individual to lead the discussion for the evening. In so doing, the teacher is responsible for giving the visiting conference leader definite instructions concerning the facts he would like considered.

The Use of the Panel Method for Discussions. The panel method is often used in adult group discussions. The teacher selects six or eight students, usually the individuals that have had the most experience, and seats them around a table in front of the class. As a rule, the teacher acts as chairman of the group, directing questions so that different members of the panel will give their reactions to specific problems. The teacher will need to make a list of questions ahead of time in order to have them as a guide for the discussion. He has to be able to determine when enough discussion time has been given to a specific phase of the problem and when to move on to the next phase without any drag.

The chairman usually makes a summary at the close of the discussion, suggesting methods that should be used in applying the information brought out in the panel discussion. Each individual present is left to make the proper application to the problems he has on his farm.

The Use of Visual Aids. Various types of visual aids are valuable for use in teaching adult-farmer classes. Charts can be used to advantage in presenting many types of statistical information. In some cases, samples, models, and mock-ups built up on flannel boards can be used to advantage. Probably the most effective visual aids for adult classes are pictures—photographs, lantern slides, filmstrips, and motion pictures. The teacher should give attention to the selection of visual aids that are suitable. Farmers usually want more than entertainment.

Be sure to check visual aids, such as filmstrips and motion pictures, before using them to determine whether or not they will be desirable teaching aids for the job at hand.

FIG. 144. Good charts are very effective in teaching adult farmers. (*Department of Agricultural Education, Virginia Polytechnic Institute.*)

Tours and Field Trips. The teacher will find that well-planned and well-organized tours and field trips are valuable for obtaining facts upon which decisions are to be based. Field trips are usually held in the afternoon rather than at night. Field trips may be made to local farms, to local markets, or to agricultural experiment stations. These trips often give farmers the inspiration to do the very thing in improved practices that the teacher has in mind. "Seeing is believing" is still a true saying with adult farmers.

FIG. 145. Field trips help keep the instruction on a practical basis for adult farmers. (*Courtesy of J. K. Coggin, North Carolina.*)

Special Teachers. It is the responsibility of the local teacher to see that adult farmers are given the opportunity to attend an evening class. In some fields or areas of agriculture, the teacher may not be as well prepared as other people he may secure. No one should expect him to be a specialist in all lines. Special teachers or specialists are often used for part or for all of a technical problem.

In the past years special teachers have been used for teaching certain phases of repairing farm machinery and for canning and quick-freezing foods. If directed by the local teacher, these special teachers can do very satisfactory work.

Often the teacher of agriculture will have far more work than he can do and an assistant teacher is necessary for adult classes.

Special teachers or assistant teachers will need the close supervision of the teacher of agriculture. Especially is this true for special teachers who have had little professional training.

Supervised Farming. Each farmer who attends an evening class already has a real farming program in operation. The course of study is designed to consider improved practices which will make phases of that program more efficient. In the application step in the conference procedure, each farmer has the opportunity to make his decision as to what he can do about the improved practices. He makes his plans for putting the improved practices into action on his farm. The performing of these improved practices in his farm program constitutes his supervised farming program. Wherever possible, it is desirable for the farmer to keep a cost record of the improved practices. A final evaluation has to be made of the financial status of the completed improved practices.

The agricultural teacher will need to visit each farmer from time to time to assist him in putting many of the practices into operation. He will also need to visit the farmer to make a check of the completed improved practices. If no cost-account records have been kept, the teacher and the farmer will have to calculate the final value of the improved practices. As already indicated by the suggested courses of study, it is possible for a farmer to include improved practices in many different enterprises, different improved practices in one enterprise, or improved practices relating to the farm as a whole.

Records of Meetings. In addition to the preliminary and final reports of supervised farming, it is very desirable for the agricultural teacher to keep a record of the attendance at each meeting and an outline of what he teaches.

SELECTED REFERENCES

Adult Evening Classes in Oklahoma Department of Agricultural Education, *Mimeographed Bulletin* 1, Oklahoma Agricultural and Mechanical College, Stillwater, Okla.

Adult Evening Classes in Vocational Agriculture, *Vocational Education Bulletin* 6, Purdue University, Lafayette, Ind.

Adult Farmer Education, *Bulletin* 10, Agricultural and Mechanical College of Texas, College Station, Tex.

The Advisory Council for a Department of Vocational Agriculture, U.S. Office of Education, Division of Vocational Education, 1947.

Agricultural Occupations and Opportunities in West Virginia, *Bulletin*, State Board for Vocational Education, Charleston, W. Va., 1950.

COOK, G. C., and L. J. PHIPPS, "A Handbook on Teaching Vocational Agriculture," The Interstate, Danville, Ill., 1952.

Developing Young Farmer Programs in Ohio, *Bulletin* 100, Ohio State University, Columbus, Ohio.

DEYOE, G. P., "Supervised Farming in Vocational Agriculture," The Interstate, Danville, Ill., 1947.

EKSTROM, G. F., and J. B. McCLELLAND, "Adult Education in Vocational Agriculture," The Interstate, Danville, Ill., 1952.

Father-Son Farming Arrangements, *Bulletin* 219, Ohio State University, Columbus, Ohio.

Father and Son Partnerships, *Special Bulletin* 330, Michigan State College, East Lansing, Mich.

Fundamental Education, U.S. Office of Education, *Bulletin* 13.

Group Discussion and Its Techniques, U.S. Department of Agriculture, Bureau of Agricultural Economics, *Discussion Series* 4, 1942.

HAMLIN, H. M., "Agricultural Education in Community Schools," The Interstate, Danville, Ill., 1949.

Junior Partnerships for Rural Youth, *Bulletin* 231, Minnesota Extension Service, Minneapolis, Minn.

NICHOLS, M., "Young Farmers," The Interstate, Danville, Ill., 1952.

Out-of-school Rural Youth in Pennsylvania, *Bulletin* 374, Pennsylvania State College, State College, Pa.

Shop Courses for Adults, *Bulletin* 41, North Carolina State College, Raleigh, N.C.

U.S. Office of Education, Division of Vocational Education, *Bulletins* 89, 129, and 147.

Young Men in Farming, U.S. Office of Education, Division of Vocational Education, *Bulletin* 188.

Youth: Education for Those Out of School, U.S. Office of Education, *Bulletin* 18–111.

16. Handling Youth Organizations in Vocational Agriculture

YOUTH ORGANIZATIONS for students of vocational agriculture were a natural development in the steady growth and advancement of vocational education. Member activities since 1928 have enriched and improved instruction, developed the finest of public relations, and provided a most outstanding pattern of citizenship training for farm youth and young men.

Future Farmers of America

After the passage of the Smith-Hughes Act in 1917, a number of agricultural teachers organized their all-day pupils into local clubs known by various names in various parts of the country.

The national F.F.A. organization was formed in November, 1928 at a meeting in Kansas City, Missouri. It was patterned largely after the Future

Fig. 146. The emblem of the F.F.A. (*National Future Farmers of America Office.*)

Fig. 147. The emblem of the F.F.A. Foundation. (*National Future Farmers of America Office.*)

Farmers of Virginia and other state-wide associations of students of
vocational agriculture in operation at that time.   The George-Barden Act
of 1946 provided for the supervision by the vocational agriculture teachers
of the activities of the F.F.A. and the N.F.A. relating to vocational education in agriculture.   In 1950 Congress granted a charter to the F.F.A. which
is known as "Public Law 740."

The members of the F.F.A. and N.F.A. are boys enrolled in agricultural
classes in the public schools.   An approved supervised farming program is
also mandatory for membership in either organization.

Aims of the F.F.A.   The chief aims of the F.F.A. are as follows:

1. To develop competent, aggressive, rural, and agricultural leadership.
2. To create and nurture a love of country life.
3. To strengthen the confidence of farm boys and young men in themselves
   and their work.
4. To create more interest in the intelligent choice of farming occupations.
5. To encourage members in the development of individual farming programs and establishment in farming.
6. To encourage members to improve the farm home and its surroundings.
7. To participate in worthy undertakings for the improvement of agriculture.
8. To develop character, train for useful citizenship, and foster patriotism.
9. To participate in cooperative effort.
10. To encourage and practice thrift.
11. To encourage improvement in scholarship.
12. To provide and encourage the development of organized rural recrea-
    tional activities.

F.F.A. Colors.   The colors of the organization are national blue and
corn gold.

F.F.A. Motto.   The motto of the F.F.A. has attracted nation-wide
attention.   It consists of four meaningful lines:

> Learning to do
> Doing to learn
> Earning to live
> Living to serve

Degrees in the F.F.A.   The constitution provides for four types of active
degree membership.

1. The Green Hand degree
2. The Chapter Farmer degree
3. The State Farmer degree
4. The American Farmer degree

The first two degrees may be conferred by a local chapter, but the State Farmer degree may be conferred only by a state association and the American Farmer degree conferred only by the national F.F.A. organization.

Achievement is the only method of advancing from one degree to the next higher one.   Refer to the "Official Manual for Future Farmers of America" for the specific qualifications required for each degree.

Fig. 148. F.F.A. members salute the flag during each chapter meeting.   (*U.S. Office of Education.*)

The local chapter, state association, and national organization may each elect honorary members.

Organization of the F.F.A.   A chapter is composed of the eligible boys in a local school.   All the chapters in a state join to make a state association, and the various state associations join to form the national organization. Duties of the officers on a local, state, and national level are enumerated in the F.F.A. manual.   At the present time there are 50 associations, of which 48 are in the continental United States and the other 2 are in Hawaii and Puerto Rico.

Equipment for a Chapter.   Each local chapter is expected to provide one of each of the following paraphernalia:

> American flag
> F.F.A. felt banner (3 by 6 feet)(optional)
> ear of yellow corn
> picture of George Washington
> picture of Thomas Jefferson
> owl

gavel and block
secretary's book
treasurer's book
scrapbook
charter (framed)
creed (framed)
purpose of the F.F.A. (framed)
George Washington's profanity order (framed)
F.F.A. manual for each member (optional)
Sentinel's shield of friendship

FIG. 149. F.F.A. chapter officers and some of the chapter paraphernalia.

The room used should be provided with proper seats, heat, and light.

Organizing a Local Chapter. The teacher of vocational agriculture in a new department faces the responsibility as well as the honor of organizing a chapter. He should follow the steps suggested here.

1. Study the F.F.A. manual in detail.
2. Ask the state adviser for information.
3. Secure the approval of local school authorities.
4. Call a meeting for all prospective members to discuss the history, aims, degrees, cost of membership, pins, and chapter goals.
5. Appoint a student committee to recommend on the matter of organizing a local chapter and applying for a chapter.

6. Adopt a constitution and bylaws.

7. Hold an election of officers.

8. Apply for a charter.

9. Secure all paraphernalia.

It is desirable to have the local group meet with a nearby chapter before organizing and then ask that chapter to conduct an installation ceremony later.

Fig. 150. This local chapter of the F.F.A. has constructed a booth where soft drinks are sold on the school grounds.

Fig. 151. Many chapter problems are solved through the work of committees.   (*Courtesy of R. W. Roberts, Arkansas.*)

Financing a Local Chapter.   Teachers find that money is essential for the success of a local chapter.   Funds are needed for educational tours, banquets, recreational facilities, a reference library, contests, chapter proj-

ects, and agricultural trips.   The school will often furnish part of the necessary money, but most chapters desire to raise additional amounts.   The
following plans have been used by chapters for this purpose:

A. Dues and assessments for members
B. Production of agricultural products for the market
　　1. Ornamental plants
　　2. Fresh vegetables
　　3. Vegetable plants
　　4. Fruit trees
　　5. Purebred pigs
　　6. Purebred cattle
　　7. Eggs
　　8. Poultry for meat
　　9. Farm seeds
　　10. Farm crops
C. Selling activities
　　1. Community soliciting type
　　　a. Magazine subscription
　　　b. Christmas cards
　　　c. Books
　　2. Store or merchant type in classroom
　　　a. Candy
　　　b. Cold drinks
　　　c. School supplies
　　　d. Ice cream
　　　e. Fruit juices
　　3. Concession type at special events
　　　a. Booth at local fair or festival
　　　b. Booth at athletic events
　　　c. Special items at athletic games (peanuts and balloons)
　　4. Order type in classroom
　　　a. Fertilizers
　　　b. Seeds
　　　c. Feeds
　　5. Roadside stands
　　　a. Citrus and other fruits
　　　b. Fruit products (jellies and jams)
　　　c. Nuts
　　　d. Vegetables
　　　e. Honey
　　　f. Poultry and eggs

6. Miscellaneous activities
  a. Cutting and selling firewood
  b. Buying, reconditioning, and selling used products
7. Salvaged items
  a. Scrap metals
  b. Rags
  c. Wastepaper
8. Prepared food
  a. Plates at a fish supper
  b. Plates at a political or other rally
9. Chances
  a. Raffle of turkeys, hogs, and guns
  b. Turkey shoot
D. Community service for pay
  1. Landscaping school grounds
  2. Landscaping city parks
E. Working for individuals for pay
  1. Canning fruits and vegetables
  2. Harvesting crops
  3. Planting lawns
  4. Landscaping home grounds
  5. Custom plowing with a tractor
  6. Grading and packing fruits and vegetables
  7. Constructing farm buildings
F. Construction (portable or permanent)
  1. Making and selling mineral boxes
  2. Constructing playground equipment
  3. Building a bicycle shed for the school
  4. Building signposts for civic organizations
G. Sponsoring recreational activities
  1. Holding a program for a "hillbilly" band
  2. Assisting in holding a rodeo
  3. Assisting in holding a fair
  4. Holding a fiddling contest
H. Financing projects
    Loaning of chapter funds to boys and charging interest
I. Winning premium money
  1. Exhibits at fairs
  2. Chapter contests
  3. Livestock prize money on chapter animals

Chapter Program of Work.   Each chapter is expected to prepare a program of work every year.   Most advisers see that committees are appointed to work on each division of the program and then have the divisions adopted by the chapter. The boys on each committee will need supervision from the adviser and chapter officers.

The following activities will give some idea of a desirable chapter program of work:

Supervised Practice

GOAL SET	WAYS AND MEANS
1. Average of two productive enterprises per member.	1. By setting up long-time supervised farming programs.
2. All members with balanced long-time programs based on the type of farming each boy wishes to enter.	2. By balanced long-time programs based on ideal programs of the type each boy wishes.
3. Continuation projects to be carried by 100 percent of the members.	3. Through aid from the local civic clubs.
4. Use of 10 improved practices per boy.	4. Through supplementary farm jobs, improvement projects, and the setting up of standards for the production of enterprises.
5. Average of 10 farm skills to be learned by members.	5. Through the operation of the chapter-leased farm, skills will be taught.
6. 100 percent of the projects to be owned by the members.	6. Through loans by the bank and the individual finances of the boys.
7. Operation of a plot on the school-leased farm.	7. Through arrangements with city commissioners who own the school-leased farm.
8. A 15 percent increase over community yield to be made.	8. By setting up enterprise standards involving improved practices in production.
9. One project tour to be made.	9. By the chapter financing the tour.
10. At least 50 percent of the members to conduct livestock projects.	10. With the cooperation of the banks and livestock farmers.
11. Six months' farm-placement experience each year for those unable to have a supervised farming program.	11. By the chapter maintaining a list of farms where members may get placement experience.

Cooperative Activities

GOAL SET	WAYS AND MEANS

1. Buying activities:
  a. Seed.
  b. Fertilizer.
  c. Crop supplies and equipment.
  d. Feed.
  e. Baby chicks.
	1. By making arrangements with business houses to give special discounts to members when making group purchases.

2. Selling activities:
  a. Meat and livestock products.
  b. General truck products.
  c. Poultry and egg products.
  d. Plants, vegetables, ornamentals, and flowers.
	2. Through local business houses, chapter sales, and women's clubs.

3. Production activities:
   a. Vegetable-plant beds.
   b. Ornamentals and shrubs.
   c. Citrus nursery.
   d. Annual flowering plants.
   e. Trees for windbreaks.
4. Service activities:
   a. Purebred livestock and poultry.
   b. Farm shop.
   c. Soil testing.
   d. Farm tools and equipment.
   e. Project enterprises financed.
   f. Beef and pork butchering.
   g. F.F.A. bulletin library.

3. Through chapter land laboratory plot and chapter farm.

4. Through chapter equipment and cooperative financing by civic clubs and chapter funds. Meat will be butchered by members.

Community Service

GOAL SET

WAYS AND MEANS

1. Farm practice improvement activities:
   a. Winter lawns.
   b. Cover crops.
   c. Pork produced for home use.
   d. Farm windbreaks.
   e. Improved production practices.
   f. Live-at-home program.
   g. Fair exhibit (at least 80 percent of the members to take part).
   h. Construction of a community building for young people.

1. These activities will be encouraged through demonstration on the chapter farm and home-project work. Fair exhibits will also be used.

2. Conservation activities:
   a. Soil and wind erosion.
   b. Reforestation.
   c. Bird breeding ground.
   d. Forest-fire prevention.
   e. School forest.
   f. Soil-improvement crops.
   g. Draining and tiling.
   h. Soil-conservation education.

2. Australian pines will be used as windbreaks. Reforestation will be promoted by an actual demonstration. Have a meeting with a specialist to explain the program. Cooperate with the specialist in explaining the provisions of the soil-conservation program to farmers. The chapter farm will participate by signing a soil-conservation agreement.

3. Beautification activities:
   a. High school.
   b. Chapter building.
   c. Local parks.
   d. Chapter farms.

3. Continue the upkeep and expansion of a beautification program of the high school, the chapter grounds, a roadside market, chapter farm, and parks.

4. General activities:
   a. County fair.
   b. Radio and television programs.
   c. County poultry association.
   d. State fair.
   e. P.T.A. program.
   f. High school assembly program.

4. The chapter will have charge of an entire building at the county fair, will present one radio and one television program, and will give a program before the poultry producers association, before the high school, and before civic clubs.

Leadership Activities

GOAL SET	WAYS AND MEANS
1. State convention.	1. Two delegates and 10 percent of the members will attend the state convention.
2. National convention.	2. A representative will be sent to the national convention.
3. Chapter represented in the following contests: *a.* Judging contest. *b.* Quartet contest. *c.* Harmonica contest. *d.* Public speaking. *e.* Chapter contest. *f.* Essay contest. *g.* Parliamentary procedure. *h.* Swimming contest.	3. Every member will enter at least one local contest. The chapter will select those who win for later competition with other chapters.
4. Chapter members to be active in holding leadership positions in national, state, district, and local F.F.A. groups, and represent school and community on teams.	4. Chapter members encouraged to obtain all leadership positions possible.
5. Green Hand degree, Chapter Farmer degree, State Farmer degree, American Farmer degree, 20 percent increase in membership.	5. All members apply for the advanced degrees as they become eligible. Increase in membership will be encouraged through training, study, contest, and leadership activities.
6. Parent-and-son banquet to be held.	6. An arrangement is made with school officials to hold a parent-and-son banquet to bring about a closer relationship between parents, son, and the agricultural program.
7. One member to be sent to state forestry camp.	7. The camp will be sponsored by the state forest service.

Earnings and Savings

GOAL SET	WAYS AND MEANS
1. A net profit of $500 for the chapter treasury to be earned.	1. Chapter funds will be earned by selling space in special editions of papers and by winnings at a fair, a barn dance, and a Negro minstrel.
2. Each member to earn an average labor income of $200 in his supervised farming program.	2. The income is to be earned through a wise choice of projects and sufficient scope and balance in the supervised farming program.
3. Each member to invest an average of $300 in his supervised farming program.	3. Members are to be encouraged to invest in livestock, land, feed, seeds, and equipment.
4. Establishment of a thrift bank.	4. Savings are to be encouraged through a chapter thrift bank.

Conduct of Meetings

GOAL SET	WAYS AND MEANS
1. One regular meeting to be held on the second and fourth Monday night of each month.	1. Make and post a calendar of meetings and announce each meeting.
2. Meetings to last an average of 60 minutes.	2. Stress the importance of starting and closing on time and plan programs for 60 minutes.
3. Average attendance aim to be 90 percent of the members.	3. Stimulate attendance through interesting and educational programs.
4. One guest to be present at each meeting.	4. Invite guest from civic and business organizations.
5. Each officer and committee chairman to own and use an F.F.A. manual.	5. Buy manuals from chapter funds.
6. Chapter room to be equipped with all paraphernalia.	6. Appoint a standing committee to see that the paraphernalia is in place and that the chapter room is in order.
7. Chapter officers to memorize their part of the ritual.	7. Ask officers to learn their parts.
8. All meetings to be conducted strictly in accordance with the rules of parliamentary procedure.	8. See that each member has the parliamentary-procedure book "Helps in Mastering Parliamentary Procedure."
9. Opening and closing ceremonies to be used.	9. Place responsibility with the president.
10. Secretary and treasurer to use official books.	10. Purchase with chapter funds.
11. Reporter to keep all the news articles about the chapter.	11. Have monthly report at meetings.
12. Refreshments to be served at 50 percent of the meetings.	12. Finance from chapter funds.
13. Entertainment to be given at 50 percent of the meetings.	13. Furnish by the members.

Scholarship

GOAL SET	WAYS AND MEANS
1. School work to be passed by all members.	1. Stress the importance of high school work in obtaining State Farmer and American Farmer degrees.
2. At least 85 percent of the members to maintain an average of 80 percent in all high school work.	2. Make check and encourage interest through awards.
	3. Encourage members to work for national and state foundation awards

Recreation

GOAL SET	WAYS AND MEANS
1. Activities: *a.* Christmas party. *b.* Trip to state fair. *c.* Fishing trip. *d.* Home economics party. *e.* Wiener roast.	1. Stress this part of the program to increase membership and hold interest in chapter activities. To be financed by a recreation fund paid to treasurer by the members.
2. An average participation by 90 percent of the members in recreational activities.	2. Have a variety of the events that will stimulate participation.

A wall chart needs to be posted showing the program of work prepared by each committee and approved by the chapter. As each goal is accomplished, it is to be recorded on the chart. This serves to encourage each committee to complete agreed-upon goals. Near the end of the school year each committee should list recommendations to assist the same committee for the coming school year. Such recommendations will aid each committee to profit from the experience of the same committee in the past. Many chapters encourage each committee to set up only a few goals which can be accomplished. It is discouraging to committee members when impossible and extremely lengthy goals that time does not permit to be completed are set up and adopted.

Fig. 152. F.F.A. members learn practical parliamentary procedure through firsthand experience and competition. (*Courtesy of R. L. Morgan, Oregon.*)

F.F.A. Contests. Future Farmers enjoy participating in worth-while contests. The boys should be familiarized with the various contests early in the year and be permitted to plan their participation in them. Chapter members should be represented in every important contest. The adviser should see that the entry from his chapter is well prepared. Even though it is valuable to take part in contests, too much class time should not be used while preparing for any one contest.

Banquets. Most chapters hold at least one banquet a year. The size of the chapter and the available facilities in the community usually determine the kind of banquet it shall be.   If the chapter is large, it may be necessary to hold a father-and-son banquet.   If there is room, the banquet should preferably be a parent-and-son-banquet occasion.

It is usually best to hold the banquet at the school.   The school cafeteria, the auditorium, or even the agricultural classroom may be used.   In some schools the home economics classes prepare and serve the meal.   If such arrangements cannot be made, it may become necessary to hold the banquet in a restaurant, hotel, or community hall.

Banquets have proved to be extremely valuable for F.F.A. chapters. Parents, school officials, and other interested persons have an opportunity to see what the boys can do and to hear of their accomplishments.

FIG. 153. F.F.A. chapter parent-and-son banquets are popular over the entire country. (*California State Bureau of Agricultural Education.*)

The date for the banquet should be set well in advance.   This will give chapter members adequate time to make the necessary preparation.   It is good practice to invite the main speaker early so that he can arrange to be present.

Chapter members can be the most useful in preparing for a banquet by dividing them into committees.   The following committees will prove helpful:

Time and place	Menu	Decoration	Finance
Invitations	Food and equipment	Cleanup	Checkroom
Program	Reception		

The adviser should meet with each of the committees and assist them. Committees should report at regular and special chapter meetings.   The reports should then be voted upon.

Invitations may be mimeographed, typed, written on cards in longhand, or printed. The invitation committee should prepare carefully a list of people who should be invited to the banquet. The following are usually invited as special guests:

    School principal
    County superintendent of schools
    School trustees
    County school-board members
    County agricultural agent
    Representatives from organizations who have helped the F.F.A.
    Representatives of service clubs, P.T.A., and churches
    Cooperative businessmen and farmers
    State leaders in agricultural education
    Nearby teachers of vocational agriculture
    Nearby state or national F.F.A. officers
    Local members of the state legislature
    Others who have served the F.F.A.

There are many ways to word invitations. The invitation form shown below is a good one to use.

The_____Chapter
of the
FUTURE FARMERS OF AMERICA
Cordially invites you to attend
Their
PARENT—AND—SON BANQUET
at the High School Cafeteria
Friday evening, February 27
at 7:30 o'clock
John Smith, Secretary

The program committee should meet with the adviser several weeks before the date for the banquet and plan the program. It is a good practice to review the banquet programs of previous years and to study a few from other chapters. The total banquet program, including time for eating, should not be longer than two hours. This will make it necessary to time each part on the program if the time objective is to be achieved. The main speaker should certainly be told the amount of time he is to speak. In order to serve to best advantage, a banquet program should inform the public of the accomplishments of the individual members and the chapter. A few boys should participate on the program. There are numerous topics appropriate to the occasion which they may discuss. It is unfair to the boys, to the school, and to the adviser to permit boys to appear on the program without adequate coaching. The adviser should review what each boy will say and coach him until he can perform it well. There are numerous ways in which a program may be organized. The program shown below illustrates a number of student participations.

PROGRAM

		Minutes
1. "My Country 'Tis of Thee"	Group	3
2. Grace	Reverend Jones	2
3. Banquet		45
4. Opening ceremony	Chapter officers	5
5. Welcome address	Charles Smith	3
6. Response	Mr. H. E. George	4
7. "Hail the F.F.A."	Chapter quartet	3
8. My Supervised-farming Program	Billy Reese	3
9. How I Became Established in Farming	Henry C. Boyd (former member)	3
10. Accomplishments of Our Chapter	Harold Holland	4
11. Remarks and introduction of guests	Adviser	8
12. Introduction of speaker	Chairman of program committee	5
13. Address	Guest speaker	25
14. Closing ceremony	Chapter officers	2
		115

The main speaker should not be introduced until the meal is completed. Complete quietness should prevail while speeches are being made.

Most chapters prepare a program folder to be placed by each plate which may also serve as a place card. These folders are well worth the effort necessary to make them. Printed program folders are most attractive and may be printed locally at small cost.

The front cover usually contains the F.F.A. emblem, the name and date of the banquet, and frequently the F.F.A. motto. The second page contains the menu and the third page the program. The fourth, or back page, may contain the names of chapter officers or members, F.F.A. objectives, words for songs being sung, or other important timely material.

The menu committee should confer with the teacher of home economics. She will be able to give excellent advice on menu planning. Two or three menus should be planned for the chapter to select from. Menus are usually listed as shown below.

MENU

Fruit Cocktail

Frozen Vegetable Salad

Baked Chicken with Dressing   Candied Yams

String Beans   Mixed Pickles

Hot Rolls   Coffee or Milk

Strawberry Shortcake

Mints

It may be necessary to collect from the homes in the community some tableware and equipment to use at the banquet. If this is done, it must be carefully marked so that it may be correctly returned.

The decoration committee should get suggestions from the home economics department. A number of recommendations should be made. From these the chapter should select the scheme that is to be used. Cultivated and wild flowers, fruit, clippings from vines and shrubs, leaves, grain sheaves, paper, and other items may be used for decoration. Every chapter has so much material available that all banquet rooms should be made attractive by proper decoration. The committee should not overlook the use of the F.F.A. banner and appropriate chapter paraphernalia.

The finance committee should start planning early in the year how to finance the banquet. The plans should be made, approved, and put into operation so that the banquet may be completely paid for as soon as it is held. The banquet may be financed by money from various sources, such as cooperative projects, assessments, sale of products, or furnishing products for the banquet.

A reception committee should be on hand at the banquet to greet the guests and to help them into the building if it is dark outside. If necessary, the committee should be equipped with flashlights. Guests may be taken to the agriculture room or some other place where their wraps are checked, and they may be seated if they so desire. The committee should help guests find their places in the banquet hall. The committee should also function after the banquet is over.

A cleanup committee should return borrowed articles and make the rooms used for the banquet ready for school the next day.

Barbecues. Chapters often desire to hold a barbecue at some period of the year. To hold one successfully, the chapter has to do careful planning. The following committees and their duties are given as a suggestion:

1. General arrangements
   Secure the grounds, dig the pit, secure the wood, and prepare publicity.
2. Food
   Purchase meat and other foods.
3. Cooking
   Prepare and cook the food.
4. Serving
   Secure utensils for serving, cut meat in serving pieces, and serve plates as people come by in cafeteria style.
5. Program
   Plan whatever program is desired for the barbecue.

6. Invitation and transportation

Extend invitations to selected guests and plan for suitable transportation if any is needed.

7. Follow-up

Clean grounds and return any borrowed articles.

Desirable meats for a barbecue are beef, pork, lamb, kid, and fish. As a rule, each boy will eat from ¾ to 1 pound of meat. For 100 boys it is best to plan for at least 75 pounds of dressed meat.

It is best to cook meat for a barbecue long enough for it to get done to the bone. The meat can be cut in pieces about four inches thick, which will greatly reduce the length of the cooking time.

A *barbecue sauce* can be prepared from the following ingredients to make enough for 100 pounds of meat:

Juice from 2 dozen lemons	One tablespoon of chili powder
Two pounds of butter	Two tablespoons of paprika
One to two tablespoons of Worcestershire sauce	Three tablespoons of black pepper
One tablespoon of Tabasco sauce	Three tablespoons of table salt

Melt the butter and add all the other ingredients. Keep the sauce warm and apply it to the meat as you turn it in cooking. Use a cloth mop on the end of a stick to apply the sauce.

One pint of vinegar may be substituted for the lemon juice and any one of the other ingredients may be omitted if you do not like it.

FIG. 154. A camping trip is often a reward for outstanding chapter work. (*Courtesy of A. W. Tenney, Washington, D.C.*)

Camps and Tours. Camps and educational tours are very valuable to members if they are properly conducted. Plans have to be made for financing camps and tours. Such money usually comes from chapter funds and is awarded to members who reach specified goals of accomplishment.

It is essential that the teacher and students be protected by insurance throughout the camping trip or tour, which includes the use of automobiles or busses for transportation.

Definite plans should be made ahead of time for all tours. Boys should know what clothes to wear, how much money to carry, how people from home could reach them with an emergency message, and approximately the hour and date of arrival at home.

On tours that have been planned, there is little need for allowing the boys to separate and go as they please.

Chapter Topics and Programs. It has been said that a good program for a chapter meeting should provide for something instructional, recreational, social, and inspirational. Topics may be selected that will stress each of these objectives. The teacher has the responsibility of approving the topics for the various meetings of the year.

Since most boys are provided with a four-year course of study in vocational agriculture, a four-year rotation of basic F.F.A. topics for meetings may be desirable. Such a planned program of topics would prevent unnecessary duplication and would hold the interest of all members.

Fig. 155. Many chapters honor outstanding citizens with the Honorary Chapter Farmer degree. (*Courtesy of E. M. Juergenson, California.*)

Many of the suggested topics for chapter meetings could be placed in any grouping of the program. The chapter may desire to modify the sequence at any time.

It is also understood that the program committee may design different types of activities for the same topic. Or in other words, topics may be presented in many different ways. Certain topics probably should be repeated annually.

GROUPING 1

History of the F.F.A.

Duties of F.F.A. Officers

The F.F.A. Emblem

The American Eagle

The Owl

The Plow

The Rising Sun

Table Etiquette

How to Make Dates

Thanksgiving

Christmas

Friendship

Selecting Foods to Eat

Controlling Human Diseases

Magic

Hobbies

Wiener Roast

Chicken Fry

The F.F.A. Banquet

Famous Farmers

Fire Prevention

Safety

Music

Improving Study Habits

Improving Personality Traits

Camping Trip

Educational Tour

The Chapter Program of Work

Making the Chapter Report

Parliamentary Procedure

Financing a Chapter

Community Service

Public Speaking

Initiation for Green Hand Degree

The American Flag

First Aid

FIG. 156. The F.F.A. chapter offers an opportunity to sponsor the right type of recreational activities for young people. (*Future Farmers of America chapter, Chowchilla, California.*)

GROUPING 2

Election of Officers	Party for Future Homemakers
Installation of Officers	Selection of Reading Materials
Current Events	Farm Safety
Prospect Night	String Music
State Flag	Camping Trips
State History	Educational Tours
Crop and Livestock Insurance	Initiation for Green Hand Degree
Personal Investments	Initiation for Chapter Farmer Degree
Introductions for People	Chapter Athletics
Independence Day	The Rural Library
Washington's Birthday	The State F.F.A. Convention
National F.F.A. Week	The Forestry Training Camp
National School Week	Public Speaking
Chicken Pilau	Parliamentary Procedure
Peanut Boiling	The Chapter Program of Work
Negro Minstrel	The Chapter Report for the Year

FIG. 157. National F.F.A. officers visit President Eisenhower. (*National Future Farmers of America Office.*)

GROUPING 3

The State Farmer Degree

Fire Insurance

Lincoln's Birthday

Jefferson's Birthday

The Use of Public Taxes

Bond Issues

National F.F.A. Week

Fish Fry

Steak Fry

School Plays

Election of Officers

Installation of Officers

F.F.A. Banquet

Future Homemakers of America

Family Budgets

Star Farmers

The Social Security Act

Radio Publicity

Newspaper Publicity

Law Enforcement

Enacting Laws

Community History

The Problem of Tariff

Famous Scientists

Public Speaking

Parliamentary Procedure

Chapter Program of Work

Chapter Report for the Year

FIG. 158. A state F.F.A. convention in session.   (*Florida Association of Future Farmers of America.*)

GROUPING 4

American Farmer Degree
Automobile Insurance
Selecting Clothes for Social Affairs
Arbor Day
Memorial Day
Making Wills
National F.F.A. Week
County Health Units
Barbecue
Picnic
Candy Pulling
Chapter Debate
F.F.A. Banquet
Military Heroes
Farming in Other Lands
Protecting Wild Game

Public Speaking
Parliamentary Procedure
Patent Laws
Copyright Laws
Camping Trips
Educational Tours
Registering and Voting
Former-members Night
The National F.F.A. Foundation
The State F.F.A. Camp
Health and Accident Insurance
Facts of Human Inheritance
Rural Appreciation
F.F.A. Chapter Program of Work
F.F.A. Annual Report

FIG. 159. The National F.F.A. Convention in session at Kansas City, Missouri. (*National Future Farmers of America Office.*)

Boys should be given assistance in learning how to use a topic and plan a program for a meeting. The program must be prepared in advance to give due notice to all people who participate. It is well to consider the time involved for each item on the program. To illustrate the above points, a suggested chapter program follows:

TOPIC: First Aid

		Minutes
1. Opening ceremony	Officers	3
2. Reading of minutes	Secretary	2
3. Business	Members	5
4. Group song	Members	3
5. First-aid demonstration		
a. How to lift and carry an injured person	Selected members	5
b. Artificial respiration	Selected members	5
6. Music	F.F.A. string band	5
7. How to use bandages	Registered nurse	30
8. Closing ceremony	Officers	2
9. Refreshments	Members and visitors	

New Farmers of America

The New Farmers of America (N.F.A.) was started at the suggestion of the late Dr. H. O. Sargent, Federal Agent, Agricultural Education for Special Groups, Office of Education, Washington, D.C. The suggestion was made to Professor G. W. Owens, Virginia State College, who wrote the constitution and bylaws for the organization. The New Farmers of Virginia held their first state meeting in May, 1927.

The New Farmers were first known by the various states in which chapters were located; however, in 1935 these states formed the national organization of New Farmers of America for Negro farm boys who were students in vocational agriculture. In many respects, the N.F.A. national organization has features and activities that are similar to the F.F.A. The constitution and bylaws of this organization may be found in a publication called the "N.F.A. Guide."

State associations are to be found in Alabama, Arkansas, Delaware, Florida, Georgia, Kentucky, Louisiana, Maryland, Mississippi, Missouri, North Carolina, Oklahoma, South Carolina, Tennessee, Texas, West Virginia, and Virginia.

Objectives of the N.F.A. The N.F.A. has many worthy aims, or objectives. Those stated in the national N.F.A. constitution are

1. To develop competent, aggressive, agricultural, and rural leadership.

2. To encourage intelligent choice of farming occupations.

3. To encourage members in the development of individual farming programs.

4. To encourage members to improve the home, the farm, and surroundings.
5. To participate in worthy undertakings for the improvement of agriculture.
6. To practice and encourage thrift.
7. To develop character, train for useful citizenship, and foster patriotism.
8. To participate in cooperative effort.
9. To provide and encourage the development of organized rural recreational activities.

FIG. 160. National N.F.A. officers meet with United States Commissioner of Education. (*National New Farmers of America Office.*)

10. To strengthen the confidence of farm boys and young men in themselves and their work.
11. To encourage improvement in scholarship.
12. To create and nurture a love of country life.

Membership and Degrees. Membership is limited to Negro farm boys who are above fourteen and not over twenty-five years of age and who are regularly enrolled in vocational agriculture.

The constitution makes provision for associate membership after the period of active membership and for honorary membership. Collegiate membership is limited to college trainees who are preparing to teach vocational agriculture.

The degrees of active membership are based upon achievement and are as follows: (1) Farm Hand, (2) Improved Farmer, (3) Modern Farmer, and (4) Superior Farmer.   Minimum qualifications for each of these degrees are stated in the "N.F.A. Guide" for New Farmers of America.

The N.F.A. Emblem.   The N.F.A. emblem is made of five different divisions or symbols: (1) the plow, representing tillage of the soil, the basis of modern agriculture; (2) the owl, representing wisdom; (3) the rising sun, representing progress; (4) an open boll of cotton with two leaves attached at its base, representing important economic agricultural interests of many members; and (5) an American eagle with shield, arrows, and olive branch, representing the wide scope of the organization.

The American eagle is located at the top of the cross section of the boll of cotton.   The rising sun is in the center with the owl seated on the plow just beneath it.

Farm Hands are entitled to wear the regulation bronze emblem degree pin; the Improved Farmers, the silver pin; the Modern Farmers, the gold emblem charm; and the Superior Farmers, the gold emblem key.

N.F.A. Colors.   The official colors of the N.F.A. are black and gold. These colors are used for the uniforms, banners, and caps.   It is also suggested that they be used for decorations for banquets, floats in parades, booths in fairs, and similar places.

N.F.A. Chapter Equipment.   Each local chapter is expected to display all official paraphernalia at every meeting.   The following list has been approved:

An American flag	A gavel and block
A picture of the rising sun or an N.F.A. banner	An official secretary's book
	An official treasurer's book
A plow (miniature)	A scrapbook
Bolls of cotton	A charter for the chapter
A picture of Dr. H. O. Sargent	An N.F.A. flag
A picture of Booker T. Washington	A straight stick of native
An owl	wood

N.F.A. Creed.   Members are encouraged to learn and to practice the following creed:

I believe in the dignity of farm work and that I shall prosper in proportion as I learn to put knowledge and skill into the occupations of farming.

I believe that the farm boy who learns to produce better crops and better livestock and who learns to improve and beautify his home surroundings will find joy and success in meeting the challenging situations as they arise in his daily living.

I believe that rural organizations should develop their leaders from within; that the boys in the rural communities should look forward to positions of leadership in the civic, social, and public life surrounding them.

I believe that the life of service is the life that counts; that happiness endures to mankind when it comes from having helped lift the burdens of others.

I believe in the practice of cooperation in agriculture; that it will aid in bringing to the man lowest down a wealth of giving as well as receiving.

I believe that each farm boy bears the responsibility for finding and developing his talents to the end that the life of his people may thereby be enriched so that happiness and contentment will come to all.

National N.F.A. Day.   April 5 has been adopted as National N.F.A. Day in honor of the life and service of Booker T. Washington.   Each local chapter is expected to have a special program on that day which centers around outstanding local achievements and on phases of the life of Booker T. Washington.

A national N.F.A. broadcast is given annually by the national organization on that day.   Many local chapters also give broadcast programs. Many chapters have a program during the day to which the public is invited.

Chapter Officers.   The type of officers selected for any chapter usually influences the achievements for the year.   It is important, therefore, that due consideration be given to the qualifications of members selected for the various offices.   Before the time for the election of officers, the teacher may profitably spend some periods in teaching the duties of every officer in the N.F.A.   In general, the duties of the officers are as follows:

THE PRESIDENT

1. Presides over the meetings of the chapter.
2. Calls special meetings of the chapter when the need arises.
3. Appoints members on various committees.
4. Acts as an ex officio member of each committee.
5. Conducts meetings according to the best-known parliamentary procedure.
6. Suggests to committees and to the chapter any needed service in the community.
7. Represents the chapter and speaks on any occasion when the opportunity affords itself.
8. Coordinates the work of all committees, keeps harmony among the members, and inspires all to work for the good of the chapter.
9. Checks on the progress being made by chapter members.
10. Sees that the reports of the chapter are submitted to the proper authorities on the date specified.

THE VICE-PRESIDENT

1. Acts as president if he is absent.
2. Assists the president with his duties.

3. Takes general charge of committee work.
4. Is familiar with the duties of all officers, especially of the president.

THE SECRETARY

1. Keeps the minutes of each meeting.
2. Has the order of business ready at each meeting for the president.
3. Attends to all official correspondence.
4. Notifies members of special meetings.
5. Assists the president by counting and recording a rising vote.
6. Collects all dues and assessments.
7. Assists in preparing all chapter reports.
8. Calls the meeting to order in the absence of both the president and the vice-president.
9. Keeps all the permanent records of the chapter.
10. Reads the minutes and all communications at each meeting.
11. Has on hand for each meeting the following:
    a. Copy of the official "N.F.A. Guide."
    b. Copy of the local constitution and bylaws.
    c. Copy of the local program of work.
    d. Copy of the state program of work.
    e. Copy of the national program of work.
    f. List of the various chapter committees with the membership thereof.
    g. Reports of any committees.
    h. A copy of the official secretary's book containing the minutes of previous meetings.

THE TREASURER

1. Receives all dues and assessments from the secretary and acts as chapter custodian of funds.
2. Pays all bills authorized by the chapter.
3. Pays state and national dues of each chapter member.
4. Assists in preparing the chapter budget.
5. Assists in suggesting ways of financing chapter activities.
6. Keeps an accurate list of all members.
7. Acts as the leader in the chapter for systematic saving—individual and chapter thrift.
8. Tries to increase the chapter's financial standing.
9. Serves as thrift-bank treasurer unless the chapter designates another member.
10. Makes a financial report to the chapter at regular intervals.

THE REPORTER

1. Collects and classifies chapter news.
2. Prepares news notes and articles for publication.

3. Sends news items to the state reporter.
4. Furnishes the local newspaper with a cut or a mat of the N.F.A. emblem.
5. Files clippings of all news articles.
6. Assists the chapter historian in his work.
7. Assists in maintaining a chapter bulletin board or a chapter display case.
8. Furnishes the officers and members all available materials for the chapter-accomplishment report.
9. Assists in planning chapter exhibits at local or state fairs.
10. Assists in giving radio programs over local stations.

The Watchman

1. Sees that all paraphernalia and equipment items are properly arranged for a meeting.
2. Takes care of the paraphernalia after the close of each meeting.
3. Attends at the door during a meeting.
4. Greets all visitors.
5. Takes charge of candidates during initiation.
6. Checks the heat, light, and ventilation features of the room before each meeting.
7. Assists in entertainment features.
8. Assists in preparing and in serving refreshments.

The Parliamentarian

1. Assists in training the officers of the chapter to follow parliamentary procedure.
2. Rules on points of parliamentary procedure in question at any meeting.
3. Keeps in his possession for reference:
   a. A copy of the "N.F.A. Guide."
   b. A standard publication on parliamentary procedure.
   c. A copy of the local constitution and bylaws.

The Historian

1. Keeps an accurate history of the organization on a local, state, and national level.
2. Compiles material for the chapter scrapbook.
3. Makes reports of historical interest from time to time, especially for the benefit of new members.

The Chaplain

Plans for and conducts all ceremonies of a religious nature.

Song Leader and Cheerleader

1. Teaches chapter members to participate in giving appropriate N.F.A. songs and yells.

2. Is responsible for having music at specified meetings.

Chapter Program of Work.   The chapter program of work is prepared annually for the purpose of giving members leadership training and of furnishing worthy goals for participation activities.   It is well to divide the

FIG. 161. N.F.A. chapter exhibit at an agricultural fair.   (*Courtesy of J. N. Taylor, Florida.*)

members of the chapter into committees to prepare the program.   Items suggested by each committee are discussed and approved by majority votes before they are added to the program.   The adviser should check and approve all work of the committees; otherwise the members may include items that would be of no value in a training program.   The chapter program of work suggested for the F.F.A. may serve as a guide for preparing an N.F.A. chapter program.

N.F.A. Banquets.   It is necessary in a training program to furnish various types of participation experiences.   The N.F.A. annual banquet, given for parents and friends, is of untold value to the boys in furnishing them leadership experiences of the highest order.   The recommendations previously given for an F.F.A. banquet could be followed in planning and in conducting a banquet.

N.F.A. Contests and Awards.   Each state has a number of contests and awards, used chiefly as an educational device to stimulate the learning of worth-while information and skills. The exact type of contests in each state varies from year to year. In general, the contests cover such things as

1. Livestock judging (beef cattle, dairy cattle, hogs, horses and mules, sheep, and poultry)
2. Livestock products judging (dairy products and eggs)
3. Farm-crops judging (corn and other grains, cotton, peanuts, etc.)
4. Vegetable judging (individual vegetables or complete exhibits at fairs)
5. Fruit judging (individual fruits or mixed exhibits at fairs)
6. Quartet and quiz contests
7. Essay writing on stated topics
8. Public speaking
9. Athletic contests
10. Parliamentary procedure
11. Music (vocal and instrumental)
12. Supervised farming
13. Chapter contests
14. H. O. Sargent award
15. Superior Farmer award
16. Dairy Farming award
17. Farm Mechanics award
18. Farm Electrification award
19. Farm and Home Improvement award
20. Soil and Water Management award

Each teacher is expected to give his students the necessary preparation to compete in the contests and awards. To win a contest should be the aim of every teacher; however, the educational value to the students is usually of greater value than the mere fact of winning.

F.F.A. Foundation

The Future Farmers of America Foundation was incorporated under the laws of the District of Columbia on March 29, 1944. Bylaws were adopted by the board of trustees at a special meeting in Kansas City, Missouri, October 7, 1944.

The foundation was established to provide business, industrial, civic, farm, and service organizations and individuals with an opportunity to cooperate in furthering the programs and activities of the F.F.A. and the N.F.A.

The foundation annually provides, on a nationwide basis, prizes and financial awards to deserving members of the F.F.A. and N.F.A. who have achieved distinction in connection with their supervised farming programs, scholarship, citizenship, and rural leadership.

Foundation funds are administered by a board of trustees that is composed of fifteen members, nine of whom are state leaders in agricultural education, elected at regional conferences to represent the various states.   Six members are from the staff of the Agricultural Education Branch of the Office of Education, Federal Security Agency.   An advisory committee, which meets each year with the board of trustees, is composed of one representative from each of the donors to the foundation.

The donors have a sponsoring committee, the function of which is to promote additional interest and participation in the foundation by the donors and potential donors.

Young Farmers of America

Local chapters and state associations known as "Young Farmers of America" are being formed in many parts of the United States.   Membership is limited to young men who are out of school, who are regularly enrolled in and attending a young-farmer class, and who have a satisfactory supervised farming program in operation.   The success of such an organization could prove as valuable an educational aid as the F.F.A. and N.F.A. have already done.

Objectives.   State and local aims or purposes may not be exactly the same; however, the constitutions adopted by several states do contain many similar provisions.   The following purposes are stated in the constitution of one such state organization:[1]

1. Aid and interest out-of-school young farmers through a systematic and organized educational program to become established satisfactorily in farming occupations of their own.

2. Cooperate with all agencies and organizations whose objectives are the improvement of the economic, educational, and social conditions of farm life.

3. Develop abilities in parliamentary procedure, conduct of meetings, public speaking, and other rural leadership activities.

4. Provide wholesome social and recreational activities.

5. Keep informed on measures affecting the welfare of farmers on local, state, national, and international levels.

6. Keep the membership informed of desirable farm placement opportunities either on a rental, lease, or purchase basis.

7. Inform and acquaint members with rural services provided by other agencies and organizations working in the area.

8. Plan and render worth-while community services based on the needs of the community.

9. Develop organization consciousness through cooperative group action in all phases of the program and through cooperation with established farm organizations.

10. Promote, plan, and improve farm family living.

Membership.   Membership is limited to young men who are farming and who are out of school.   The minimum age limit is usually sixteen, and

[1] Constitution of the South Carolina Association of Young Farmers of America.

the upper age limit follows the custom of the state for members of young-farmer classes. To be a member in good standing a young man must be farming, attend meetings of his local chapter, attend a young-farmer class, and pay his annual dues.

The constitutions also provide for the election of honorary members at both the local and state levels.

Fig. 162. Learning to participate in a public meeting. (*California State Bureau of Agricultural Education.*)

Paraphernalia. Paraphernalia for Young Farmers of America is adopted on a state basis. This includes colors, emblems, banners, and chapter equipment.

Program of Work. Each state and local chapter of Young Farmers of America is expected to plan an annual program of work. The following is a sample local program of work:

1. Encourage a live-at-home program to include:
   a. Year-round garden.
   b. Establishment and care of adequate home orchards.
   c. Preservation of meats, vegetables, and fruits.
   d. Provisions for sufficient meats, eggs, and milk for the family use.
2. Encourage farm ownership by making available information concerning sources of credit.
3. Sponsor a recreational program for farm families.
4. Encourage cooperative activities and cooperate with all agencies whose purposes are to improve farm-family standards of living.
5. Encourage diversified farming in compliance with good soil-building practices.

6. Improve production of field crops through the following practices:
   a. Secure and produce certified seed.
   b. Encourage cleaning, treating, and testing seed.
   c. Study and use approved fertilizer practices.
   d. Practice insect and disease control.
7. Encourage livestock-improvement programs.
8. Sponsor safety programs in connection with accidents in the home and in the use of farm machinery.
9. Sponsor extension of rural electrification, telephones, and farm-to-market roads.
10. Encourage home beautification, landscaping, and improvement of buildings.
11. Cooperate with local schools in their lunchroom programs.
12. Encourage more farm boys in high school to enroll in vocational agriculture.
13. Promote conservation of natural resources within the state.

Certainly no area of vocational agriculture at the present time needs more sound thinking and attention than the Young Farmer program. Teachers do well to remember that it is the old "part-time" idea incorporating certain essential economic and social advantages. There is still a lack of uniformity in thinking throughout the country. Conceptions of the scope and plan of Young Farmer organizations still vary considerably. However, one point is very clear—this program, if successful and continuing, will have to be developed and maintained as an educational program with further establishment in farming always the "core."

SELECTED REFERENCES

Cook, G. C., and L. J. Phipps, "A Handbook on Teaching Vocational Agriculture," The Interstate, Danville, Ill., 1952.

Future Farmer Chapter's Program of Work (work chart), The Chapter Supply Company, Danville, Ill.

The Future Farmers of America Foundation, Incorporated, U.S. Office of Education, Bulletins 1 and 2.

Hamlin, H. M., "Agricultural Education in Community Schools," The Interstate, Danville, Ill., 1949.

Judson, L. S., "Public Speaking for Future Farmers," The Interstate, Danville, Ill., 1943.

N.F.A. Guide for New Farmers of America, New Farmers of America publication in Cooperation with the U.S. Office of Education, 1952.

Nichols, M., "Young Farmers," The Interstate, Danville, Ill., 1952.

Noblin, E. Y., The F.F.A. Chapter, Its Organization and Activities, Bulletin 14, Virginia Polytechnic Institute, Blacksburg, Va.

Official Manual for Future Farmers, National Office of the Future Farmers of America, U.S. Office of Education, 1952.

PURKEY, D. R., "Winning F.F.A. Speeches," The Interstate, Danville, Ill., 1951.

ROGERS, C. E., "Reporting F.F.A. News," The Iowa State College Press, Ames, Iowa, 1941.

ROSS, W. A., "Forward F.F.A.," The French-Bray Printing Company, Baltimore, 1939.

STEWART, W. F., Helps in Mastering Parliamentary Procedure, Ohio State University, Columbus, Ohio.

TENNEY, A. W., "Practical Activities for Future Farmer Chapters," The Interstate, Danville, Ill., 1941.

———, Programs for Future Farmer Chapter Meetings, The Interstate, Danville, Ill., 1938.

17. Keeping Records and Making Reports

A LL TEACHERS of agriculture have to keep the records required of classroom teachers in a given school. In addition, there are reports that have to be made to the state office, and records must be kept for use in making them.

Attendance Records. Each state usually has some type of adopted school register for the purpose of keeping attendance records. Each section of students is recorded alphabetically in the register. Definite checks or symbols are made daily to indicate students who are absent or tardy. In most high schools the individual teacher has to report all absences to the office at either the opening or closing of the period.

Fig. 163. There is no substitute for a good set of records on a worth-while undertaking. (*Courtesy of J. K. Coggin, North Carolina.*)

Space is also available in most registers for recording school marks made by students on written or oral tests.

School Marks, or Grades. School marks, or grades, are usually sent to parents each quarter or oftener. Progressive teachers often question the value of school marks.   Few teachers believe that they know how to grade written papers with any degree of accuracy.

Agricultural teachers do have several methods of determining the grade to give a student.   Written or oral tests may be given at any time.   Probably the best way to judge the growth of a student is to observe the work he has done at home on his supervised farming program and in the farm-mechanics shop.   Can he do the job satisfactorily as a beginner?   The answer to this question is an important evaluation method.

FIG. 164. Checking cost accounts on a poultry project.   (*Courtesy of J. K. Coggin, North Carolina.*)

School marks, if given at all, should be based upon tests (classwork), farm-mechanics jobs, supervised farming work, and leadership activities in the Future Farmer organization.

Monthly Reports.   Most states require teachers of agriculture to submit a monthly report of their activities.   The exact information called for varies from state to state.   As a general rule, the following items are required in the report.

1. What has been taught.
2. Visits made to pupils for supervising their farming programs.
3. Visits made to perform community service.
4. Community meetings held or attended.
5. F.F.A. or N.F.A. meetings.
6. Miscellaneous activities.
7. Mileage traveled.
8. Equipment and reference materials obtained.

There is usually a definite day of the month for the monthly report to arrive at the state office.

Preliminary Report on Supervised Farming. The teacher is expected to report to the state office the supervised farming program of each student. The exact form of the report varies. The usual items found on the preliminary report are

1. Names of the students
2. Age or grade of the students
3. Scope of each enterprise in the supervised farming program
4. List of all improvement projects
5. List of all supplementary farm jobs to be learned by each student

A definite date is usually set when these reports are due in the state office.

Final Report on Supervised Farming. At the close of the farming year—usually the end of the calendar year—a final report has to be made giving all the results of each student's supervised farming work. The items usually included on the final report of supervised farming are

1. Names of all students
2. Name and scope of all productive projects
3. Yield of each productive project
4. Cost of production of each productive project
5. Receipts of each productive project
6. List of improved practices completed by adult farmers
7. List of improvement projects completed
8. List of supplementary farm practices completed by each student
9. Labor income or net profit made by each student

The final reports are valuable as records for analysis in teaching.

F.F.A. Reports. The agricultural teacher, as adviser, is responsible for seeing that his local F.F.A. chapter makes the reports requested by the national organization. These reports include the program of the chapter for the year and the accomplishments of the various chapter items at the close of the year.

The secretary of the F.F.A. chapter keeps a record of all items of business and the treasurer keeps a financial record. The reporter is expected to keep a scrapbook of all publicity items, such as articles, photographs, and radio programs.

Record of Students and Former Students. Record blanks for students and follow-up records for former students are available from many state offices. It is suggested that one side of the blank be used for a student while he is in school and the opposite side after he has completed or left high school. The side of the blank used for former students gives a record by years of their farming status.   The blanks are filed alphabetically for all students who are attending classes and for all former students.

In a sense, no student should ever be considered a former student because a boy will need to continue to attend young-farmer and adult-farmer classes. He is only a former student of the high school class in vocational agriculture.

Daily Diary.   Most teachers find it necessary to keep a day-to-day record of all of their activities in order to have the information needed for all reports. The daily diary may be made in various forms, usually in a loose-leaf note-book.   It may be of a size that will fit easily into the pocket of his car.   In

FIG. 165. Going over the F.F.A. chapter records with the state adviser. (*Courtesy of T. L. Faulkner, Alabama.*)

general, the daily diary should include provisions for everything the teacher does in his work.   It is also good to record future appointments in the daily diary.

No teacher can expect to make reports at the end of the month from memory.   If he tries to do so, many of his accomplishments will be omitted.

Filing System for Teachers.   Teachers of agriculture are expected to file a copy of all reports submitted to the state office and to file many additional types of information needed in their teaching.   In order to do this, he needs a four-drawer steel filing cabinet.   In addition, he needs to follow a definite system of filing as recommended in his state.   (See Appendix XI, page 377, for a suggested plan to follow.)

Because each state has slightly different types of records and report forms, it is suggested that a teacher write his state supervisor of vocational agriculture for a complete set of state reports and that he secure local reports from his high school principal or county superintendent.

18. Planning Summer Work and Professional Improvement

FARMING ACTIVITIES are being conducted every month of the year. Hence teachers of vocational agriculture are employed on a 12 months' basis. In many areas the crop-growing season comes during the summer months when school is not in session.

People in general, and other teachers in particular, often wonder why teachers of vocational agriculture have to do schoolwork for the summer. The following activities give some idea of the work that may be done during the period when the high school is not in session:

1. Organize and teach young-farmer classes.
2. Organize and teach adult-farmer classes.
3. Supervise food conservation plants (canning, dehydrating, and quick-freezing).
4. Supervise the farming programs of all students.
5. Render community service to groups and to individuals.
6. Act as adviser of the local F.F.A. or N.F.A. chapter.
7. Revise the course of study in vocational agriculture.
8. Prepare an annual program of work.
9. Prepare teaching plans for jobs to be taught.
10. Visit prospective students for guidance purposes.
11. Prepare visual aids (charts, maps, and graphs).
12. Take pictures for use in teaching.
13. Continue a public information program.
14. Collect samples of seeds, insects, and plant diseases.
15. Order all needed illustrative materials.
16. Order all needed reference materials.
17. File reference materials.
18. Revise materials in the filing cabinet.
19. Order any needed farm-mechanics tools.
20. Order supplies for the farm-mechanics shop.
21. Order any needed equipment and supplies for the classroom and laboratory.

22. Conduct project tours.

23. Conduct educational tours.

24. Supervise the school land laboratory or farm.

25. Take delegates and members to the F.F.A. or N.F.A. state convention.

26. Attend the state conference for teachers of vocational agriculture.

27. Attend summer school for professional and technical improvement.

28. Prepare various reports as required.

29. Assist students in securing placement in farming.

30. Take an approved vacation.

FIG. 166. Work on a school farm is at its height during the summer months and offers an excellent opportunity for practical instruction, both individual and group. (*Courtesy of J. A. Taft, Massachusetts.*)

The Problem of a Vacation.   Various states have specific regulations governing the problem of vacations for all people who are employed on a 12 months' basis.   In general, most states allow at least two weeks during the year for a vacation.   In some cases, the teacher is also granted 15 days during the year for sick leave.

Additional time, but not to exceed four weeks including vacation and summer conference, is sometimes granted a teacher who desires to attend summer school for professional improvement.

Vacation plans are usually made with the local school authorities and then approved by the state supervisor.   If the teacher follows this plan of procedure, he can expect any reasonable request to be granted.

Summer Teaching.   Teachers of vocational agriculture often do some of their best teaching on the farms.   Much of the cultivation of crops, the control of insect and disease pests, the harvesting of crops, servicing farm machinery, and the marketing of crops can be taught best when students face these problems.   Teachers need to keep in constant touch with each student during the summer.   Teaching opportunities are available practically every day that students are out of school.

It is also possible for the teacher to conduct classes during the summer for young and adult farmers.   If he does not actually conduct the classes during the summer, he may complete preliminary plans for classes to be held the following fall or winter.

Fig. 167. The teacher is responsible for keeping a close check on the student's supervised farming programs during the summer months.   (*Courtesy of G. P. Couper, California.*)

Visiting Prospective Students for Guidance Purposes.   Few rural boys know about the opportunities in the various fields of service in agriculture. No teacher can give the best help in guidance problems until he understands the home and home farm of the boy.   In order for any person to succeed in farming, he should enjoy it as a way of life.   If he is unhappy in the country, the chances are that he will be a poor student for the teacher of vocational agriculture.

Farming requires people of different abilities.   Students of less ability may be taught some of the skills in agriculture, and with a knowledge of the skills they may be able to earn a living as a worker for other people.   The teacher would seldom be able to train such a person to become a successful farm owner and manager.

Students with high levels of intelligence are needed for managing large corporations or individual farms.   With the various problems of finance, market prices, labor, weather conditions, disease and insect pests, soil conservation, and farm mechanization facing a farm manager, he needs to be a person of high mental ability.

The problem of whether or not the student can obtain land and capital for his supervised farming program is vital to the teacher. When students desire to register for vocational agriculture, the teacher may do well to advise some of them to take other high school subjects.

The teacher of agriculture will also have an opportunity to assist the boy and his parents in deciding the elective courses to take that will correlate with agriculture.

Fig. 168. Plant-teaching specimens of various kinds can be collected best during the summer months.

Placement of Students. To place students in farming, a teacher needs to prepare a list of the names of farmers who want unskilled labor, skilled labor, farm operators, or farm managers. He also needs to know the farms in the community that are for rent and those that are for sale. The teacher is eager to get each student placed in the best situation, and the summer months offer a splendid opportunity to work on the problem.

Follow-up of Students. Teachers are charged with the responsibility of keeping a current record of former students. Follow-up records are recommended by the Division of Vocational Education, U.S. Office of Education, and are required by many states. Information obtained from the records often assists the teacher in revising his course of study. Follow-up records make a connecting link between the school and each former student.

Checking Physical Facilities. It is very necessary that the equipment for the classroom, laboratory, and farm-mechanics shop be inventoried each summer. Copies of the inventory should be given to the school principal and to the state supervisor. Any replacement or additional equipment needed should be ordered in time for it to be ready for use when school begins.

The problem of checking supplies is also an important responsibility. Supplies can usually be secured at a discount if they are all purchased at one time.

Reference materials need to be obtained each year and properly filed.

Collecting Samples. The community has a wealth of teaching materials that may be collected during the summer. Sample specimens of diseased plants, weeds and weed seeds, farm-crop plants and seeds, and insect specimens are available during the summer. Samples collected should be properly preserved and mounted for use in teaching.

General Recommendations for Summer Work. A few general recommendations to teachers include the following:

1. Keep active in your community during the summer.
2. Keep as busy with your work during the summer months as you do during the time that school is in session.
3. Have everything in your department ready for teaching the first day of school.
4. Take time to visit any new farm people who may have moved into the area.
5. Keep in proper condition any crops or animals produced at the school land laboratory or farm.
6. Send all reports to the proper officials at the date they are due.

Professional and Technical Improvement. Teachers of vocational agriculture are working in a dynamic, changing field. New discoveries are being made each year in technical phases of agriculture. Methods of teaching, methods of preparing the course of study, plans for supervising farming programs of students, methods of publicity, and various types of community service are constantly changing. In fact, all people who are in any professional service work must try to keep up with new facts as well as changes in methods of performing specific tasks. In most states additional salary is given to teachers who have completed work for graduate degrees. Many teachers feel the need of further preparation and are stimulated by the reward of additional salary.

Methods of Technical Improvement. A teacher does not have the time to review all technical subject matter. He can use what time he does have to advantage in the following ways:

FIG. 169. Helping the chapter executive committee with its accomplishment report. (*Courtesy of D. C. Aebischer, Wisconsin.*)

1. Review only the kinds of materials that apply to the local farming types.
2. Review magazines that tend to digest agricultural facts.
3. Use experiment station reports that give a summary of the work done for the year.
4. Keep on the mailing list to receive new bulletins and review those obtained before they are placed in the library.
5. Take advantage of the help of the subject matter specialist in recommending new materials.
6. Check agricultural magazines each month to discover new information.
7. Order and review technical materials recommended by the supervisory staff.
8. Review at least two new books each year.
9. Attend conferences where technical information is to be discussed.
10. Visit the agricultural experiment station and good farms where improved practices are being followed.
11. Listen to radio programs and watch television programs pertaining to agriculture.
12. Take additional on-campus and off-campus courses in technical agriculture. This may be done for technical growth with no regard for graduate credit, or a graduate program may be followed which contains an opportunity for needed technical and professional growth.

Fig. 170. Many state associations of the F.F.A. hold state meetings during the summer months.

Methods of Professional Improvement. Teachers have an opportunity for selecting many different plans to follow for maintaining professional growth. They may choose any one or any combination of the following plans:

1. Review professional books as they apply to agricultural education, vocational guidance, secondary school curriculum, and methods of teaching.
2. Read available professional magazines and bulletins.
3. Take professional graduate courses.
4. Visit other teachers who are doing exceptional work.
5. Attend educational conferences.
6. Use the help of local and state supervisors.

Professional Books. Many professional books came from the press each year. The supervisory staff and the teacher-training staff often prepare recommended lists. It is a good practice to follow to add at least two new professional books to the library each year.

The teacher will be interested in professional books from the following related fields as well as his own field:

1. Agricultural education
2. Vocational education
3. Vocational guidance
4. Secondary school curriculum

5. Methods of teaching in the high school
6. Rural sociology
7. Extracurricular activities
8. Educational psychology
9. Evaluation procedures in education
10. History and philosophy of education

Professional Organizations. Teachers gain valuable experiences from joining and participating in the programs of professional organizations. A teacher will do well to consider each of the following:

1. The American Vocational Association
2. The State Vocational Education Association
3. The State and National Agricultural Teachers Associations
4. The State Teachers Association
5. The National Education Association

The value of membership in these organizations is manifold. Among these values are the following:

1. Professional improvement comes from participating in professional problems and from reading the magazines and reports of these organizations.
2. Teachers receive professional help from other people who have similar problems.
3. Teachers become aware of problems of a local, state, or national nature that they may not otherwise know.
4. Educational organizations have often furnished the leadership in securing needed improvements in school legislation and in more adequate school appropriations.

Professional Magazines. Specific professional organizations publish magazines and mail them to members. For example, the American Vocational Association publishes the *American Vocational Journal* and many state education associations usually publish a monthly journal.

Agricultural teachers should not fail to subscribe for *The Agricultural Education Magazine*. If the teacher is interested, he may subscribe for, or read in the school library, many other valuable magazines.

Professional Bulletins. Professional bulletins are often valuable to teachers. They are usually secured from the following sources:

1. The state department of education
2. From various colleges and universities
3. From reports of educational surveys or research studies made by foundations

4. From reports of professional organizations

5. From bulletins published by the U.S. Office of Education

Professional Conferences. Most states hold a conference each year for all the agricultural teachers. The objective of such a state conference is for both technical and professional improvement. A teacher gains many valuable suggestions from the conference program and through exchanging ideas with other teachers.

Fɪɢ. 171. Summer recreational programs of students require teacher supervision.

Often district or area conferences are held in the fall, winter, and spring. The programs are usually centered around local problems as well as problems of the state as a whole.

The real value of professional conferences is:

1. To give new information and skills.

2. To give inspiration.

3. To give an opportunity to discuss problems.

4. To unify the program on a broad basis and yet give an opportunity for individual variations.

Graduate Work. Graduate work must follow standards adopted by the institution offering the degree. It is true that many graduate programs may be so planned that a teacher may attempt to solve practically any problem he has in his work. Problem courses are common in agricultural education.

Another plan being followed by colleges in their graduate programs is to offer summer workshops. In the workshops some consideration is usually given to practically any problem a teacher may face.

Graduate courses of both a technical and professional nature are given away from the college campus in some states.

Because agricultural teachers are employed for 12 months each year, they often find it difficult to attend a regular session of summer school. Short courses given on a three weeks' basis seem to be most suitable.

Institutions are also offering graduate courses for commuting teachers. The classes are held at night or on Saturdays. Those teachers who live in driving distance have an opportunity to attend.

Visiting Other Departments. Teachers may profit by taking a few days each year to visit some of the most successful departments in the state. The state supervisory staff will be glad to suggest the departments to visit. No matter what department the teacher may visit, he can usually find a few good things being accomplished. Many schools allow two or more days for such visitation purposes.

Many states rotate the place where the district or area conference is held, and thus the teachers can observe each year the physical facilities of several departments.

In-service Training. In addition to the assistance given at conferences, each state has a plan of in-service training. Those individuals assisting in the program may be called "assistant state supervisors," "district, or area, supervisors," "county supervisors," or "itinerant teacher trainers."

The program used usually gives a teacher the following assistance:

1. District or group conferences
2. Individual visits to assist teachers with their problems
3. Special field trips to visit other teachers
4. Service letters and other professional and technical aids
5. Personal conferences
6. Personal correspondence
7. Technical training

Local Professional Help. Any beginning teacher has available the help of the principal of the high school, the superintendent of schools, and experienced teachers in the school system. Counties and school districts may also have a general supervisor of instruction. These individuals may know little about the program of the agricultural teacher, but they often know community needs, how to deal with people in that area, and how to secure results in teaching.

It is expected that the teacher of agriculture will use local help in strengthening his program, that he will attend faculty meetings where local school problems are discussed, and that he will assist in making any community study the school faculty may undertake. Because he is constantly in touch with all the farm people, he can often make a contribution in helping adjust the high school curriculum to the actual needs of students.

Professional and technical improvement never ends. In professional improvement the teacher will receive many more ideas for changes than he can put into practice. Certain devices or procedures may get excellent results when used by a specific teacher and prove a failure when tried by another teacher. Any teacher must keep an open mind and be willing to

Fig. 172. Local farmers need to be visited and assisted during the summer.   (*U.S. Office of Education.*)

consider new ideas. On the other hand, he should analyze new methods thoroughly before he adopts them.

SELECTED REFERENCES

Chisholm, L. L., "Guiding Youth in the Secondary School," American Book Company, New York, 1950.

Cook, G. C., and L. J. Phipps, "A Handbook on Teaching Vocational Agriculture," The Interstate, Danville, Ill., 1952.

Forrester, G., "Methods of Vocational Guidance," D. C. Heath and Company, Boston, rev. 1951.

Guidance Programs for Rural High Schools, U.S. Office of Education, Division of Vocational Education, *Bulletin* 203.

Hamrin, S. A., and C. E. Erickson, "Guidance in the Secondary School," Appleton-Century-Crofts, Inc., New York, 1939.

Jones, A. J., "Principles of Guidance and Pupil Personnel Work," McGraw-Hill Book Company, Inc., New York, 1951.

Myers, G. E., "Principles and Techniques of Vocational Guidance," McGraw-Hill Book Company, Inc., New York, 1941.

Occupational Information and Guidance, U.S. Office of Education, Division of Vocational Education, *Bulletin* 204.

Strang, R., "Educational Guidance, Its Principles and Practice," The Macmillan Company, New York, 1947.

19. Providing School-Community Services

THE TEACHER of agriculture is expected to cooperate with many agencies in the community for the purpose of making desirable improvements. Because of the nature of his work in the area, he is usually familiar with community needs and with the farm families.

Community Service

Groups to Consider. The following list includes a number of typical groups with whom the teacher of agriculture is expected to cooperate in community programs:

1. The Agricultural Extension Service
2. The Farmers Home Administration
3. The Soil Conservation Service
4. American Farm Bureau Federation
5. The National Grange
6. Farmers Educational and Cooperative Union of America
7. The State Cattlemen's Association
8. The State Forestry Association
9. The Production and Marketing Administration
10. The Farm Credit Administration
11. The state and county boards of health
12. The state and county conservation boards
13. The local garden clubs
14. The local civic clubs
15. Veterans organizations
16. Local agricultural cooperatives
17. The local office of the U.S. Employment Service
18. The local P.T.A.
19. Local and state teacher associations
20. Church organizations
2 1. Local fair associations

The agricultural teacher can never take a leading part in all these organizations, but he can often make a substantial contribution to their programs, and in turn, he can get valuable help from many of these organizations. A knowledge of the people of the area and of the local agriculture makes him a key person for many types of community improvement.

School Relationships. The agricultural teacher is employed in the same manner as any other teacher. He is, therefore, responsible to the same administrative authorities that govern all school affairs. He is expected to cooperate with them in the total school program.

Because of the nature of his responsibilities in the community, he should not be given so many little chores at school that any other teacher could do and thereby fail to have the time to perform important community activities.

Community Service. A teacher of agriculture is expected to give the majority of his time to the young and adult students enrolled in his classes. However, he is often called to assist people in the area who are not enrolled in any organized class. The service may be of an emergency nature or it may be in the form of technical advice. It is well for him to assist in all such cases provided he can do so and not neglect his organized teaching program or encroach upon the activities of other professional persons. By performing various types of community service, he can often make lasting friends who are then willing to assist him in connection with problems he may face.

Community Agricultural Program. The agricultural teacher will be interested in improving the farming program in his area. After determining the vital agricultural problems of the community by surveys and personal conferences, he will need to formulate a program that is designed to improve the conditions. Other agricultural agencies and his advisory council should be of help in preparing the program.

The procedure in preparing a five-year agricultural community program would be as follows:

1. Determine the chief agricultural problems of the area. Both studies and farm surveys may be used.
2. Suggest objectives for each year of the program.
3. Have these problems and goals checked by agricultural agencies and by the advisory council.
4. Make plans for having the goal met and recorded.

The five-year community agricultural program shown above is given as an illustration.

The School-Community Food Conservation Program. The chief aim of having a canning plant, a meat-curing plant, or a freezer locker plant is to use it for teaching rural people to provide an adequate home food supply. It is true that people who use these facilities also have to be taught how to

FIVE-YEAR COMMUNITY PROGRAM

Items set up to be accomplished	Objective (number, scope)	Goals (G) and accomplishments (A)									
		1st year		2d year		3d year		4th year		5th year	
		G	A	G	A	G	A	G	A	G	A
1. Rat-proof corncribs......	25 cribs	5	3	5	3	5	0	5	0	5	
2. Winter cover crops......	1,250 acres	200	150	250	200	200	200	200	250	200	
3. Purebred sires..........	5 head	1	3	1	5	1	10	1	10	1	
4. 12 varieties of fruit per farm.................	25 farms	5	0	5	0	5	5	5	5	5	
5. Cooperative market shed.	2 sheds	...	...	2	2						
6. Community peanut sheller	1 sheller	...	...	1	1						
7. Improved permanent pasture...................	5 farms	1	1	1	1	1	1	1	1	1	
8. A 10-bu. increase per acre for corn at a cost of 10 cents per bushel for each added bushel, by proper fertilization.............						100%	60%				
9. Five homes landscaped (complete).............	5 homes	1	1	1	1	1	1	1	2	1	
10. Running water in home*.	5 homes	1	2	1	5	1	15	1	50	1	
11. Electric lights in home*..	10 homes	2	2	2	5	2	195	2	20	2	
12. School fairs.............	5 fairs	1	1	1	1	1	1	1	1	1	
13. Hog shows.............	5 shows	1	1	1	1	1	1	1	1	1	
14. Cooperative hog sales....	10 sales	2	2	2	2	2	50	2	55	2	
15. Farmers raising hogs on sanitation plan..........	100 farmers	20	20	20	20	20	25	20	25	20	
16. Two 3-gal. cows per farm.	250 farms	50	50	50	25	50	25	50	20	50	
17. Screened homes.........	200 homes	40	20	40	25	40	30	40	20	40	
18. Improved method of living* (home conveniences)	50 homes	10	10	10	10	10	150	10	20	10	
19. Farm-wood-lots improvement.................	50 farms	10	5	10	5	10	5	10	5	10	
20. Brood mares............	50 head	10	10	10	5	10	5	10	8	10	
21. 50 purebred hens per farm	50 farms	10	5	10	10	10	10	10	10	10	
22. Farm records kept.......	50 farms	10	3	10	5	10	50	10	50	10	

* The Rural Electrification Administration made possible these increases over objectives.

operate the machinery and how to prepare the food properly. Of equal importance, however, is an educational program to teach what foods should be produced and the best methods of production. Each state has plans showing size, arrangement, location of equipment, storage facilities, and other needed items in canning plants or freezer lockers.

As a general rule, the agricultural teacher is responsible for the educational program as it pertains to the production of food. He is usually furnished a person to actually supervise the operation of the canning plant, meat plant, and freezer locker. In canning plants or freezer lockers most schools keep a supply of containers for patrons to use. In the majority of cases, a processing fee is charged to cover the cost of operating the plant. In a few cases, membership fees are the method of financing. An accurate system of record keeping is essential.

Fig. 173. Residents of the community preserving food in the school cannery. (*Vocational Division, Georgia State Department of Education.*)

The School Garden and Lunchroom. In some schools the agricultural department undertakes the responsibility of providing fresh and processed fruits and vegetables for the lunchroom. Because the lunchroom uses many surplus products furnished free by the Federal government, it is often a problem to know ahead of time what will be needed from local sources. It is advisable for the teacher to have a conference with the lunchroom supervisor and make as definite plans as possible.

Some departments of vocational agriculture charge the regular wholesale price for all products furnished the lunchroom. Other departments sell products on the local market and give all surplus products and those that are offgrade to the lunchroom.

It is also possible for the school garden to grow products, in such quantities as are needed, to process for the lunchroom.

Students who grow and process products for the lunchroom feel that they have made a contribution to the school and to a better program of nutrition. However, this part of the training program must not take so much of the time of the teacher and students as to jeopardize a sound instructional program.

Community Health. Many health problems center around the available food for farm families. Other problems are connected with the sanitation of the farm home and grounds.

The teacher of agriculture is anxious to cooperate with local health units in producing clean milk, in the inspection of meats and other food products, in the control of hookworm and other contagious diseases, and in a sound recreational program.

Fɪɢ. 174. An educational exhibit prepared under teacher supervision by students of vocational agriculture. (*Courtesy of T. L. Faulkner, Alabama.*)

Social Relationships. The teacher of agriculture is a definite part of the school and the community and has a share in all social problems. It is well for him to sponsor various social functions for the young people of the area. The nature of these functions will, of course, depend upon what the people of the community need and will approve.

There is usually no question about the approval of parties, banquets, plays, minstrels, and other forms of wholesome entertainment. Dancing, properly chaperoned, will meet the approval of patrons in most schools, but there are a few schools where serious objections may be registered.

Religious Relationships. Most communities prefer a teacher who is affiliated with some church. As a general rule, most school officials care little about the particular denomination of which a person may be a member. The teacher in a rural area is expected, however, to attend the church of his choice.

A leader of young people is in great demand and can easily get involved in more responsibilities than he can perform.   All forms of church activities are important, but the teacher of agriculture must remember that his duties as a teacher take a large part of his time.   He can participate in church activities, however, even if he does not have the time to direct them.

School-Community Agricultural Services

Teachers of vocational agriculture in the United States assist in many ways in improving the farming program in their respective communities.   Many of these educational services are performed on the farms either during, before, or after school hours.

Teachers have also learned that they may assist their communities better by maintaining certain educational services at the school plant.   Among these educational services found in the various states are

1. The school canning plant
2. The school freezer locker
3. The school feed and feed-mixing mill
4. The school fence-post treating plant
5. The school fertilizer-mixing plant
6. The school sawmill
7. The school farm-mechanics shop

The School Canning Plant.   The question often arises over the advisability of the school maintaining a canning plant.   It is true that the school furnishes the physical equipment for this purpose and that it requires public funds, but the school thereby can conduct an educational program that would not be possible without the canning plant.   The main reasons for having a canning plant at the school are

1. It provides the physical facilities necessary as a basis for an educational program for improving the diet of farm people.
2. It provides an opportunity for the school to can products to be used in the lunchroom.
3. It helps improve the program of both the agricultural and home economics teachers in teaching farm-family living.
4. It provides better food products to the farm families and reduces the percentage of spoilage.
5. It saves time for the farm families in their food processing.
6. It develops a better relationship between the school and the farm families.
7. It makes possible a greater variety of foods in the diets of the people.
8. It encourages farm families to grow more food to be conserved.
9. It provides an opportunity for each member of the family to participate in conserving food.

Financing the Cannery.   Many different plans have been used to purchase the plant and equipment for canning and to pay operating and maintenance costs.   The common methods that have been used to obtain the plant and the equipment are

1. Funds from Federal emergency programs
2. Funds furnished by the regular school authorities
3. Personal donations, money, and labor
4. Membership fees
5. Funds raised by having plays, games, picture shows, dinners, and food sales

The best method is to induce the school authorities to finance the canning plant in the same way other school equipment is purchased.

In operating the school cannery, there is a need for fuel, lights, and water as well as repair costs.   There must be people employed to operate the plant and to keep proper records.   Communities operate the plants by the following plans:

1. A fee is charged for all cans processed.   A common rate is 3 to 4 cents per can for No. 2 cans and 5 cents for No. 10 cans.
2. A membership fee is charged per family.
3. The school furnishes all operating costs.
4. The school purchases cans at wholesale and sells them at retail to patrons.

Problems of the Teacher in Operating Canneries.   The teacher of agriculture is responsible for an educational program in his community.   He does not have the time to operate a school cannery.   His main problems are

1. To see that skilled people are employed to operate the plant.
2. To see that an educational program is available to instruct farm families what to plant for canning as well as to teach them the skills and technical facts needed in canning.
3. To see that the canning plant is operated at the time of the year when it can be used economically.
4. To encourage low-income families, who need to use it, to avail themselves of the opportunity.
5. To see that the proper amount of food to be canned is brought each day.
6. To see that supplies are available and that equipment is repaired or replaced when needed.
7. To see that the cannery is kept clean.

The Physical Plant for a Cannery.   Many states have floor plans available for school authorities who desire to establish a cannery.   The plans always include a list of the major items of equipment. In general, the physical plant should follow these suggestions:

1. The plant should be a rectangular building of the same general material as the total school plant. Locate the building on the school ground where plenty of parking space is available. The size of the building will depend upon the volume of canning to be done each day. The minimum size is usually 30 by 60 feet.
2. Provide concrete floors with drainage facilities.
3. Provide ample windows for light and ventilation. Exhaust fans are essential for necessary ventilation during the summer months.
4. Provide sanitary facilities—screened windows and doors and toilet and laboratory facilities.
5. A storage room for coal (if used) and supplies is essential.
6. The boiler must be ample in size to furnish the needed steam and hot water.
7. Arrange the equipment in line and in the order of its use:
   a. Preparation equipment—tables, sinks, pea shellers, corn cutters, and blanching vats.
   b. Preheating, filling, exhausting, and sealing equipment.
   c. Processing equipment—retorts and cooling vats.

The School Freezer Locker. Many educational and other problems of operating a school freezer-locker plant are the same as the ones already discussed for a cannery. The educational program is fully as important.

The building and equipment must be secured by some approved method, and the cost of operation is another problem. As a general rule, freezer-locker units are rented to school patrons on an annual basis. The rent charged should be enough to cover all operating costs, repairs, replacements, and a reasonable amount on the investment. The teacher must have some person who knows how to operate the freezer-locker plant and how to keep the proper records.

The freezer-locker plant should have the following facilities:

1. A preparation room
2. A cold-storage room
3. A room for the freezer-locker units
4. A reception room and office
5. A storage room for supplies
6. A meat-curing room
7. A room for smoking meats

The School Feed and Feed-mixing Mill. In areas where grains are economically produced, farmers often need to grind feed for livestock and poultry.   The community may not have a feed mill where it can have the grains ground and mixed.   The agricultural teacher, in order to encourage the production of better livestock, may sponsor the establishment of a feed and feed-mixing mill.   The mill has to be operated on stated days each month or each week and a toll charged to take care of the costs of operation.

Fig. 175. A school fence-post treating plant in operation.   (*Courtesy of T. L. Faulkner, Alabama.*)

The School Fence-post Treating Plant.   The railway companies of the United States have learned to treat crossties before they are placed in the roadbed.   The same idea has been tried for treating fence posts.   With the proper methods of treating posts, farmers may expect them to last for 20 years or more.

The facilities of a post treating plant include a boiler for heating and a concrete tank and cover.   A fee must be charged per post to cover the operating cost.

There is a necessity for the teacher to schedule days for operating the plant. Posts of the desired size should be cut at the proper time and peeled.   Farmers have to be given instruction in all these points.

The School Fertilizer-mixing Plant.   In a few communities the school has provided the physical facilities for mixing commercial fertilizers.   Where the farmer furnishes his own labor, he can usually save money by mixing his own fertilizers.   The main purpose, however, is to obtain special mixtures that the farmer may want for specific crops.

As in all other cases, the school must schedule the days of operating the plant and must charge enough fees to pay actual operating costs.

The School Sawmill.   A few agricultural teachers have secured portable sawmills for sawing lumber for farmers.   The lumber is available for building farm structures and for the framework of country homes.   The timber is secured from the farm wood lot and the farmer furnishes his own labor.   The school usually has to employ some person who can operate the saw.

The School Farm-mechanics Shop.   Farmers are taught to perform many of the skills in connection with the repair of farm machinery and other farm-mechanics jobs.   This may be done in organized class instruction, or individually.

Many agricultural teachers schedule certain days each week for the farmer

FIG. 176. A special drier for removing moisture from seed corn.   (*Courtesy of G. P. Deyoe, Illinois.*)

to come for instruction.   At other times when a specific farmer has an emergency job, he is often allowed to use the shop for making the necessary repairs.

Community Services in General.   The agricultural teacher should adopt certain general principles to apply to all community services performed by or in his department at the school.   In general, these principles are as follows:

1. No physical equipment should be purchased to perform at school the services for adults that are being adequately performed by private industry.
2. School-community services should be kept strictly on an educational basis.
3. Each person should at least pay for supplies and for operating costs.
4. No materials should be made or repaired at the school to be sold by the person on the market.
5. Provisions should be made for safety devices, but the school should not be held responsible for accidents when patrons are performing services for themselves.
6. Records should be made and kept of all services performed by farm people at the school plant.   This includes records on receipts and expenditures.

Agricultural Fairs

The agricultural teacher is expected to cooperate with existing fair officials and to take a leadership role in establishing and conducting a community fair.

On a small scale the local F.F.A. chapter may organize and conduct a fair. Members may show their own products, or they may extend an invitation to the local chapter of the Future Homemakers of America to assist.   The invitation may be extended to all departments of the school.

Fig. 177. A temporary farmers' market being operated in a booth at an agricultural fair. (*Courtesy of G. P. Couper, California.*)

The following list includes a few of the most important values of a community fair:

1. The educational values of the exhibits should help improve the agriculture and the farm-family living of the area.
2. Students who participate receive educational values when they prepare and manage an exhibit.
3. The people of the community are better able to judge the accomplishments of the school.
4. Interest should be created in getting more prospective students to enroll in vocational agriculture.
5. Fairs provide an opportunity for desirable social relationships.
6. Fairs provide an opportunity for many desirable demonstrations to be given to farmers.
7. Pride of ownership is strengthened by winning a prize at a fair.

How to Plan a Fair.   A fair must be planned far in advance of the date of the opening.   If the agricultural teacher desires to hold a community fair for the first time he should follow these steps:

1. Secure the approval of the local school officials.
2. Ask the local F.F.A. chapter to approve and participate in the fair.
3. Secure the interest and help of all the school students.
4. Secure the help of all allied agricultural professional workers in the area.
5. Develop a sound plan of financing the fair.
6. Call a public meeting of all interested people for the purpose of selecting officials, appointing committees, assigning responsibilities, and making final plans.

Officers for a Community Fair.   In order to place responsibility where it should fall, a community-fair organization will need the following officers:

1. President
2. Vice-president
3. Secretary
4. Treasurer
5. Department superintendents
   a. Animal husbandry
   b. Farm crops
   c. Horticulture
   d. Home economics
   e. Elementary school
   f. Junior high school
   g. Senior high school

Fig. 178. High-quality beef produced by Future Farmers and exhibited at the Grand National Junior Show.   (*California State Bureau of Agricultural Education.*)

    h. Vocational agriculture
    i. Special exhibits
6. Board of directors
    a. One professional agricultural worker
    b. One farmer
    c. One businessman
    d. One teacher
    e. At least two high school students
    f. One homemaker

The board of directors would meet with the other officers to determine policies and make major decisions.

Time and Length of a Fair.   Fairs are usually held at the season of the year when crops and animals are at their best for exhibition purposes.   As a general rule, the time coincides with the harvest season and that varies considerably.

Samples of field crops may be stored for a considerable period of time. Fruit and vegetable exhibits must be made at the time of harvest unless specimens are preserved in some way.

FIG. 179. Local chapter exhibit at a community fair.

Community fairs usually continue from one to three days, the average being two days. Some form of entertainment should be provided, especially for the night program.

Financing the Fair. The amount of money needed for a community fair will depend upon its size, whether or not cash prizes are awarded, and the extent of the decorations. A minimum amount of money will be needed if prizes are just ribbons.

There are various methods in use for securing the money needed for holding a fair.

1. Making a personal solicitation of businessmen and farmers for cash donations
2. Printing a fair catalogue and selling advertisement space to business firms
3. Selling concession space at the fair or operating concessions
4. Having donations made by the local chamber of commerce or agricultural organizations
5. Raising money by means of school plays and minstrels
6. Asking the county or school to provide a certain amount of funds for use in operating a fair

Program for the Fair. Time should be allowed for all visitors to see the various exhibits. Experience has shown, however, that other attractions are needed to draw a big crowd. Among the added attractions may be

1. Athletic games and contests
2. School plays, minstrels, and judging contests
3. Motion pictures
4. Style shows
5. Cakewalks and dances
6. Rodeo
7. Musical entertainment (vocal and instrumental)
8. Livestock auction sales
9. Addresses by outstanding men or women
10. Demonstrations by specialists in the field of agriculture or homemaking
11. Parades

Preparing an Exhibit. People who prepare exhibits will do well to consider the following suggestions:

1. Exhibits should teach something.
2. Displays must be arranged properly.
3. All items need to be labeled.
4. Action of any kind attracts people.
5. One idea can be better shown in an exhibit than a number of facts.

Fig. 180. A winning chapter flock of sheep. (*Courtesy of R. L. Morgan, Oregon.*)

328 TEACHING VOCATIONAL AGRICULTURE

6. Only the products of the best quality available should be displayed.
7. Each entry needs to be uniform as to size, color, and shape.
8. An attractive background for the exhibit needs to be set up.
9. All identifications and statements are to be neatly lettered.
10. All exhibits that must be held for the fair should be carefully stored.
11. Hays and grains cured and stored in a dark storage place will retain a
better color than if cured in the sun.

County or District Fairs. In many areas the agricultural teacher will find a county or district fair already in operation. The main thing he needs to do in that case is to cooperate with the officials and see that exhibits are properly prepared. In some cases, he will need to get the fair officials to modify their premium list to take care of his students and their needs. Work may also be needed to provide the proper type of agricultural judging contests.

SELECTED REFERENCES

Community Canning Centers, U.S. Department of Agriculture, *Miscellaneous Publication* 544, rev. 1946.

Community Food Conservation Centers, U.S. Department of Agriculture, Bureau of Home Economics, *Miscellaneous Publication* 472.

COOK, G. C., and L. J. PHIPPS, "A Handbook on Teaching Vocational Agriculture," The Interstate, Danville, Ill., 1952.

DUNCAN, A. O., "Food Processing," Turner E. Smith & Co., Atlanta, Ga., rev. 1951.

Future Farmers News, *Bulletin* 9, Agricultural and Mechanical College of Texas, College Station, Tex.

HAMLIN, H. M., "Agricultural Education in Community Schools," The Interstate, Danville, Ill., 1949.

School-Community Canning Plants, *Special Bulletin* 14, University of Georgia, Athens, Ga.

20. Establishing and Maintaining Good Public Relations

FUNDS for the support of any form of public education come essentially from taxation. In the support of vocational agriculture the Federal, state, and county government each has a share. Individual citizens and school officials of the county need to be kept well informed in order that they may answer intelligently questions that are asked constantly concerning the

FIG. 181. The local F.F.A. chapter entered a float in the local Pioneer Day Parade. (*California State Bureau of Agricultural Education.*)

program. Members of the state board for vocational education and members of the state legislature need to know the program in order to be in a position to recommend and to appropriate funds. Members of the Congress also need to be kept informed as to what is being accomplished in order to give their support. Every agricultural teacher, therefore, owes it to himself and to the further development of the program of which he is an integral part, to keep his local people well informed concerning the needs and the accomplishments of his department.

The agricultural teacher commonly uses the following mediums to secure favorable publicity:

1. Articles in the newspaper
2. Exhibits of products produced by students
3. Demonstrations
4. Project tours
5. Agricultural demonstrations
6. Project markers for student work
7. Community fair
8. Radio and TV programs
9. Talks before various organizations
10. Vacation tours

Newspaper Stories.   The teacher will find that he can keep the local people well informed concerning the needs and the accomplishments of his department by preparing regularly both news and feature stories of its activities and those of his students for publication in the local press.   News articles tell of important recent events.   The first paragraph or lead of a news story should contain the answer to who, where, when, what, how, and why.   The body of the story gives the details of the facts that were briefly given in the lead.

Feature stories are less limited to time than news stories.   Many feature stories give a summary of results which may cover a period of several years. In a feature story the writer is allowed to express his own opinion if he cares to do so.   As a rule, feature stories have one or more pictures to help emphasize important points.   The teacher should keep in the background but liberally use the names of students and patrons in all articles prepared.

SAMPLE FEATURE STORY

Accomplishments of Local F.F.A. Chapter

The annual accomplishment report of Ridgeway Chapter, Future Farmers of America, recently released by John Smith, Chapter Reporter, shows why it was judged the best chapter in the state for the year and received the honor of representing the State Association at the National F.F.A. Convention.

Furthermore, its president, Claude Johnson, was elected president of the F.F.A. State Association and two members, Claude Johnson and Monroe Bell, applied for and received State Farmer degrees.   The past year's accomplishment record was unquestionably the best the Ridgeway Chapter, chartered in 1933, has ever enjoyed.

The 75 members including boys from fourteen to nineteen years of age carried out during the year a total of 160 productive enterprises and 109 farm-improvement projects. Continuation projects in the long-time farmer training program totaled 76 and supplementary farm practices 519.   Individuals averaged 10 improved crop-growing practices each and learned new farm skills including the mixing of sprays, budding fruit trees, driving tractors, and the like.   Every member owned his supervised farming program and kept complete, neat, and accurate records.

In order to stimulate better supervised programs among the members as well as furnish the basic means of financing the F.F.A. treasury, the chapter rented 10 acres of muck land from the school farm on which two crops of beans were grown.   From this collective project 2,229 hampers of beans were harvested with gross receipts amounting to $2,185.25 and a net profit of $750.23.   Three hundred fryers raised in the chapter's battery broiler plant yielded 545 pounds and returned a net profit of $72.50.   Cutting and selling wood netted $13.75, and F.F.A. sponsored shows and parties netted $89.20, making a total of $925.68 net earnings which went into the chapter treasury during the year.

The 75 members on their individual supervised farming projects made a net return of $10,377, or an average of $138.36 per member.   Each member's average investment in individual projects totaled $97 and averaged savings for the year of $31.   Buying and selling was carried on for the most part on a cooperative basis in order to allow each member the benefit of the best prices obtainable.

The chapter's community service program, which was not designed for profit, included a nursery where 4,500 ornamental plants and shrubs were propagated from cuttings, 1,000 seedling fruit trees were planted for budding next year, and 500 cocus plumosis palms were started.   These are to be potted and later set out in a permanent place.   All nursery products were or will be given away when ready for community beautification.

Among the other numerous community services rendered by the chapter during the year were surveys of farm-practice improvement in celery and lima bean growing; an educational exhibit at the fair; the growing of a soil-improvement cover crop for public demonstration; fertilizer demonstrations for educational purposes; demonstrations of the approved methods of raising fryers in batteries; working with volunteer firemen and learning how to operate fire-fighting equipment; securing data and preparing charts on the conservation of soils; the conducting of a school-beautification program; collecting and repairing toys to be given to underprivileged children at Christmas; cooperation with schools, clubs, and civic organizations by appearing on or presenting programs when requested; a donation of $10 for food to underprivileged families; the decoration of schools and churches with specimen plants belonging to the chapter; and a donation of two large potted palms to the First Baptist Church.

The chapter sponsored a local "Boys Town" which gave members an insight into the functioning of municipal government, and all members participated in leadership activities both in school and community affairs.   Members held 68 offices in various school and community organizations, 30 of which were class or club offices in the school.   All members were active in recreational activities, participating in 12 various types of recreation. Chapter meetings were held twice each month plus three called meetings, all of which were conducted under strict parliamentary procedure.   An average scholastic grade of 85 was maintained by members throughout the school term.

Preparations for another big year of accomplishments by the F.F.A. chapter are already under way.   Eighty percent of the members will hold Future Farmer degrees and 20 percent or less, Green Hand degrees.   In addition, three members will be State Farmers, holders of the highest F.F.A. degree in the state, and one will be an American Farmer, the highest F.F.A. degree in the nation.

SAMPLE NEWS STORY
Winner in National Public Speaking Contest

R. L. Jones of Carrollton, Alabama, won national honors in Kansas City, Missouri, when he placed first in the National F.F.A. Public Speaking Contest featured at the national convention of Future Farmers of America, October 18 to 25.

An outstanding member of the Carrollton F.F.A. Chapter, Carrollton, Alabama, young Jones earned the right to represent all other Southern states in the national competition when he won the Regional Contest held September 5 at Benton, Louisiana. He took State Honors in Auburn this summer and defeated opponents from Georgia and Florida in the Tri-State competition late in July.

In his prize-winning address, "The Soil: A National Heritage," Jones appeals to the individual farmer to accept his responsibility in conserving the soil. Emphasizing the place of soil conservation in the national defense program, he asserts, "While it is necessary to defend the American way of life, it is also necessary to defend the American means of making a living."

R. L., who is eighteen years of age, graduated from Carrollton High School in May after completing four years of vocational agriculture. He is an active F.F.A. member and has served as an officer in the local organization for two years. He holds the Future Farmer degree. For four years he carried out supervised projects including cotton, corn, potatoes, livestock, and poultry. He owns 3 cows, 6 hogs, and 50 pullets. Jones is active in community organizations, school clubs, and other young people's organizations. He won the medal of achievement his senior year in high school and ranked in the upper fourth of his class scholastically.

Jones entered the F.F.A. Public Speaking Contest four years ago and continued to enter them until he received the national honors. At the first public speaking contest four years ago, he was not able to express himself satisfactorily. Realizing his handicap, Jones strove very hard to overcome this handicap. He kept entering the speaking contest each year, with his eye on the state winner. By hard work, persistence, and true determination, he surpassed his dream by winning the State, Tri-State, Southern Regional, and National F.F.A. Public Speaking Contests.

This is the first time an Alabama boy has won the title of National F.F.A. Public Speaker.

How to Get Copy Ready for the Press. The agricultural teacher will need to set a definite time each week for getting his copy to the press. In getting the copy ready for the editor, he may use the following methods:

1. He may write the articles himself and expect to have them rewritten by the rewrite man.

2. He may assign certain students to write the articles and then correct them himself.

3. He may cooperate with the teacher of English and have students write articles as a part of their English work.

4. He may get certain farmers who are members of his evening class to tell of their accomplishments. Often he will need to change the articles in certain respects.

5. He may ask the secretary of any local agricultural organization to furnish him material.

6. He may get a banker to write a few articles on the use of farm credit as it relates to Future Farmers.

7. He may get the editor or a reporter from the newspaper to be present at specific programs, tours, or demonstrations.

FIG. 182. Teacher demonstrating the use of a six-row cotton duster to farmers of the community. (*Vocational Division, Georgia State Department of Education.*)

The Type of Material to Publish. It is a good idea for the agricultural teacher to plan a definite program of seasonal topics for the year.   In addition to the planned program, news items will be available from month to month.   The teacher will find that the following topics will be worth considering in planning his publicity program for the year:

1. The Annual Program of Work
2. The Accomplishment Report
3. The Program for the Local F.F.A. Chapter
4. Results of Supervised Farming Programs
5. School Enrollment in All Types of Classes
6. Improved Practices Being Followed by Evening-class Members
7. Demonstrations Being Conducted in the Community
8. Summary of Farm Surveys
9. Reports of Community Cooperative Efforts
10. Trips, or Tours, Made by Students
11. Prizes, or Awards, Won by Students
12. Former Students Who Are Farming
13. Father-and-Son or Parent-and-Son Banquets
14. Community Recreational Activities
15. Conservation of Natural Resources as It Relates to F.F.A. Activities

Exhibits for Publicity Purposes. The teacher will find that the proper type of exhibit is rather a difficult problem.   He does not want to simply stress the production of desirable agricultural products, but he wants to stress

also the educational values that a student receives in such production.   This
dual purpose is not always easy to show in an exhibit.

In making an exhibit, the teacher will want to select agricultural products
with the same degree of perfection that any other exhibitor follows.   He will
also want to make charts, graphs, and placards in order to tell of the educational value of the program.   Contrast exhibits showing before and after

FIG. 183. An attractive display catches and holds the attention of fairgoers.

results are excellent.   Exhibits may be used to advantage at such places as
the following:

1. In display cases at the high school
2. In a booth at a community or county fair
3. In a local bank window
4. In a window at the local chamber of commerce

Demonstrations.   The teacher may use two different types of demonstrations.   In the first place, he may conduct fertilizer, cover-crop, and forestry
demonstrations on the school-farm or land-laboratory plot or on some farm
in the community.   If conducted in the proper manner, such demonstrations
should be of much value in making apparent to the public certain facts.   In
the second place, the teacher may use agricultural students to give demon-

strations of specific farm skills and practices.   Demonstrations of this nature
may be given at the following places:

1. At chapel or school-assembly exercises
2. At public picnics
3. At civic clubs
4. At community or county fairs

Fig. 184. A local F.F.A. chapter assists in purchasing and distributing an improved
variety of oatseed.   (*Courtesy of M. J. Peterson, Minnesota.*)

The following list indicates examples of demonstrations that may be given
by students:

1. Culling hens
2. Budding fruit trees
3. Grafting fruit trees
4. Treating farm seeds
5. Mixing commercial fertilizers
6. Mixing feeds
7. Grading fruits or vegetables
8. Packing fruits or vegetables
9. Treating hens for lice
10. Potting house plants
11. Preparing soil for potted plants
12. Repairing farm machinery
13. Grading and culling livestock

Project Tours.   One very good method of securing publicity is to arrange
for a project tour.   The tour should be conducted at a time when the work of
each boy will be at its best.   In addition to the members of his class, the
teacher should invite the following:

1. The editor of the local newspaper
2. The secretary of the local chamber of commerce
3. The county agricultural agent
4. The high school principal
5. The county superintendent of education
6. Members of the local board of school trustees
7. Local businessmen and farmers

It is probably a good plan to serve refreshments at the last visit made on the tour.   For the refreshments try to arrange to have something which has been grown by one of the boys.   The editor of the local newspaper will usually be glad to give good publicity to what he sees on the trip.

Project Markers.   An agricultural teacher may secure project markers for each of his students.   If the project markers are well located, the public will be able to compare what agriculturally trained boys are doing with what they see accomplished by the average farmer.   On the other hand, project markers will give unfavorable publicity if teachers are careless about the type of projects they approve, or if they fail to see that each job is properly performed.

The Community Fair.   The teacher of agriculture should be willing to cooperate in holding a community fair each year.   It is doubtful, however, if he should try to find time to conduct a community fair on his own responsibility.   With the help and cooperation from farmers and from businessmen, it will be observed that a community fair gives his department favorable publicity and also aids in improving the agriculture of the area.

Fig. 185. Teachers of vocational agriculture in training receive instruction on preparing and presenting radio programs.   (*Courtesy of C. G. Howard, New Mexico.*)

Radio and Television Programs.   Such programs may be used to advantage for giving publicity to the agricultural program.   Again if careful thought is not given to the contents of each program, the teacher may easily draw adverse publicity.   If the teacher desires to use this method of publicity, he should be certain to observe the following recommendations:

1. Have a conference with the officials of the broadcasting station far in advance of the desired date.   In many cases, programs are prepared weekly, and, in some cases, they are prepared monthly.   Schedule your program.
2. Plan to give short programs—not over 15 minutes.
3. Vary the program.   Use music, songs, plays, skits, interviews, talks, and news flashes to give variety.
4. Use only good talent.
5. Practice the script several times before going to the station and at least one time at the station.
6. See that all materials necessary for making the desired sound effects are available before the time of the program.
7. Make copies of the complete script for each program and submit one copy to the announcer several days in advance.
8. Try not to rattle the script during the program.
9. Speak in your natural voice and not too rapidly.
10. Use facts, but if they would reflect on the reputation of any person, group, or community, avoid using them.

Talks or Addresses.   The agricultural teacher will usually have the opportunity to speak before civic clubs, agricultural organizations, and school organizations.   It is not the purpose here to discuss the technique of public speaking.   The teacher, however, may profit by studying books on that subject.

Many times the teacher will be asked for a talk and will have no previous notice.   He may be asked just a day or two ahead of a scheduled meeting. It is wise for him to prepare several talks and have them available for any emergency.   Properly prepared talks may be modified to fit any local situation.   The following topics should be useful if they are well developed by the teacher:

1. Objectives of the F.F.A.
2. Supervised Farming Programs
3. Placement of Boys in Farming
4. Correlating Teaching and Practice
5. Our Out-of-school Rural Youth
6. The Purpose of an Adult Class in Vocational Agriculture

7. A Report of a Trip, or Tour
8. The Program of Vocational Education Being Promoted by the Federal
Government

Educational Tours.   Many agricultural teachers conduct educational
tours during the summer months.

Articles concerning the plans for the tour make good publicity items.
Pictures and articles about the completed trip also make good publicity.

SELECTED REFERENCES

How to Prepare and Display Extension Exhibits, U.S. Department of
Agriculture, *Department Circular* 385.

PATTERSON, CHOATE, and BRUNNER, "The School in American Society,"
International Textbook Company, Scranton, Pa., 1936.

Promoting Vocational Education in Agriculture, U.S. Office of Education,
Division of Vocational Education, *Bulletin* 97.

ROGERS, C. E., "Reporting F.F.A. News," The Iowa State College Press,
Ames, Iowa, 1941.

TENNEY, A. W., "Practical Activities for Future Farmer Chapters," The
Interstate, Danville, Ill., 1941.

————, "Programs for Future Farmer Chapter Meetings," The Interstate,
Danville, Ill., 1938.

The White House Conference on Rural Education, National Education
Association, Washington, D.C., 1944.

WOFFORD, K. V., "Modern Education in the Small Rural School," The
Macmillan Company, New York, 1938.

21. Evaluating the Vocational Agricultural Program

A
S ALREADY explained, each agricultural teacher is expected to prepare a program of work for the year. Some states require a five-year
program of work. This program is based on student needs and upon specific
community needs. The teacher is also expected to prepare a course of study
based, in general, on the needs of those who farm in the local area.

FIG. 186. The goal of every true farmer is a high-producing, well-kept farm and an
attractive farm home.

In preparing the course of study and the annual program of work, the
teacher should keep in mind the chief objectives of agricultural education as
stated in the text of the Smith-Hughes Act which reads: "That the controlling
purpose of such education shall be to fit for useful employment."[1] He also
is expected to consider the objectives as stated in *Monograph* 21 of the U.S.
Office of Education:[2]

[1] Smith-Hughes Act, sec. 10, 1917.

[2] Educational Objectives in Vocational Agriculture, U.S. Office of Education, Division
of Vocational Education, *Monograph* 21, 1940.

1. To make a beginning and advance in farming.
2. To produce farm commodities efficiently.
3. To market farm products advantageously.
4. To conserve soil and other natural resources.
5. To manage a farm business efficiently.
6. To maintain a favorable environment.

The teacher should be interested in continually evaluating all phases of his program in light of the objectives he has used. The objectives may be short-time aims or may cover a long period of time. There will be group or community objectives as well as individual objectives.

In any type of evaluation the teacher often has no way of determining the exact part of community or individual growth which is due primarily or

Fig. 187. Progressive farmers must use power machinery efficiently. (*Courtesy of T. L. Faulkner, Alabama.*)

entirely to the vocational agriculture program. He must remember that the agricultural press and various other agencies conduct educational programs which also exert a strong influence in many communities.

Individual Student Evaluation. In terms of his objectives, the teacher may evaluate the work of a given student, utilizing any or all of the following means:

1. By checking management efficiency on the farm
2. By checking leadership activities in the F.F.A. or N.F.A.

3. By testing skills on the job

4. By written or oral tests on certain phases of subject matter

In giving written or oral tests, the teacher is usually more interested in knowing whether or not a student can apply technical facts in solving problems than he is in knowing whether or not a student has retained pure memory facts.   Over a period of years in a school, the teacher may design objective tests that will have some degree of accuracy.   Standardized tests, on a

Fig. 188. This vocationally trained young farmer has established a new farm home.

national basis, have very little general use because of wide differences in practices and in farm enterprises.   For example, in the extreme Southern areas of this country, farmers plant strawberries in the field in the early fall and harvest the fruit the following winter and spring, plowing under the plants by March or April.   In other areas, strawberry plants are set in the field in the spring and may occupy the land for two or three years.   A question on the time to transplant strawberries in the field, therefore, would not bring forth the same answer in all states.   Hundreds of other examples could be given to illustrate this point.

There are many outlines for evaluating the supervised farming program of a student. Efficiency factors are usually found in the average project record book, and farm-management survey blanks often contain analyses.

The growth of a student can be estimated to some extent by the advancement he makes in the F.F.A. or N.F.A. Any boy who has been awarded the American Farmer or Superior Farmer degree has shown marked progress and real growth.

FIG. 189. Training in a chosen farming occupation is the basis for a successful home and eventual economic security.

Evaluating the Total Program. In evaluating a total program of vocational agriculture, there are several phases that may well be studied; included are

1. The physical facilities in use
2. The course of study being followed
3. The quality of the classroom, shop, and field instruction being given by the teacher
4. The quality or standards being followed by each student in his own farming program

5. The percentage of former students who are satisfactorily established in farming
6. The percentage of farm boys and farmers being reached by organized instruction
7. The quality of the promotional activities of the teacher
8. The reports and activities of the advisory council

Most states have evaluative criteria for studying physical equipment—buildings, tools, equipment, and supplies. Where available, these criteria are usually more adapted to local needs than an outline that is general.

Fig. 190. The most valuable contribution to any nation's welfare is trained, industrious, self-supporting farm citizens. (*Courtesy of A. W. Tenney, Washington, D.C.*)

A National Standards Committee on Vocational Agriculture[3] has suggested a number of items to consider in the evaluation of a local program.

The teacher should be interested in making a continuous evaluation of his complete program. Others who may help make such evaluations include:

1. Local school administrators and supervisors
2. The supervisory staff from the state department of education
3. The teacher-training staff
4. Special evaluations made by experts often secured from other states
5. The advisory council for the local department of vocational agriculture

[3] Evaluative Criteria for Vocational Education in Agriculture, National Committee on Standards for Vocational Education in Agriculture, U.S. Office of Education, Division of Vocational Education, *Bulletin* 240.

All evaluation should be made with only one objective in mind—to constantly improve the instruction being given to the farm boys and farmers of America.

SELECTED REFERENCES

Cook, G. C., and L. J. Phipps, "A Handbook on Teaching Vocational Agriculture," The Interstate, Danville, Ill., 1952.

Deyoe, G. P., "Supervised Farming in Vocational Agriculture," The Interstate, Danville, Ill., 1947.

Directing Vocational Agriculture Day-school Students in Developing Their Farming Programs, U.S. Office of Education, Division of Vocational Education, *Bulletin* 225, Agriculture Series 56, 1944.

Educational Objectives in Vocational Education in Agriculture, U.S. Office of Education, Division of Vocational Education, *Monograph* 21, 1940.

Evaluative Criteria for Vocational Education in Agriculture, National Committee on Standards for Vocational Education in Agriculture, U.S. Office of Education, Division of Vocational Education, *Bulletin* 240.

Hamlin, H. M., "Agricultural Education in Community Schools," The Interstate, Danville, Ill., 1949.

Appendix I

The National Vocational Education Act (Smith-Hughes)

Public Law 347, Sixty-fourth Congress, Senate Bill 703

Section 1. An Act to provide for the promotion of vocational education; to provide for cooperation with the States in the promotion of such education in agriculture and the trades and industries; to provide for cooperation with the States in the preparation of teachers of vocational subjects; and to appropriate money and regulate its expenditure.

Be it enacted by the Senate and House of Representatives of the United States of America in Congress assembled, That there is hereby annually appropriated out of any money in the Treasury not otherwise appropriated, the sums provided in sections two, three, and four of this Act, to be paid to the respective States for the purpose of cooperating with the States in paying the salaries of teachers, supervisors, and directors of agricultural subjects, and teachers of trade, home economics, and industrial subjects, and the sum provided for in section seven for the use of the Federal Board for Vocational Education for the administration of this Act and for the purpose of making studies and investigations, and reports to aid in the organization and conduct of vocational education, which sums shall be expended as hereinafter provided.

Section 2. That for the purpose of cooperating with the States in paying the salaries of teachers, supervisors, or directors of agricultural subjects there is hereby appropriated for the use of the States, subject to the provisions of this Act, for the fiscal year ending June thirtieth, nineteen hundred and eighteen, the sum of $500,000; for the fiscal year ending June thirtieth, nineteen hundred and nineteen, the sum of $750,000; for the fiscal year ending June thirtieth, nineteen hundred and twenty, the sum of $1,000,000; for the fiscal year ending June thirtieth, nineteen hundred and twenty-one, the sum of $1,250,000; for the fiscal year ending June thirtieth, nineteen hundred and twenty-two, the sum of $1,500,000; for the fiscal year ending June thirtieth, nineteen hundred and twenty-three, the sum of $1,750,000; for the fiscal year ending June thirtieth, nineteen hundred and twenty-four, the sum of

$2,000,000; for the fiscal year ending June thirtieth, nineteen hundred and twenty-five, the sum of $2,500,000; for the fiscal year ending June thirtieth, nineteen hundred and twenty-six, and annually thereafter, the sum of $3,000,000. Said sums shall be allotted to the States in the proportion which their rural population bears to the total rural population in the United States, not including outlying possessions, according to the last preceding United States census. Provided, ...

Section 3. That for the purpose of cooperating with the States in paying the salaries of teachers of trade, home economics, and industrial subjects there is hereby appropriated for the use of the States, for the fiscal year ending June thirtieth, nineteen hundred and eighteen, the sum of $500,000; for the fiscal year ending June thirtieth, nineteen hundred and nineteen, the sum of $750,000; for the fiscal year ending June thirtieth, nineteen hundred and twenty, the sum of $1,000,000; for the fiscal year ending June thirtieth, nineteen hundred and twenty-one, the sum of $1,250,000; for the fiscal year ending June thirtieth, nineteen hundred and twenty-two, the sum of $1,500,-000; for the fiscal year ending June thirtieth, nineteen hundred and twenty-three, the sum of $1,750,000; for the fiscal year ending June thirtieth, nineteen hundred and twenty-four, the sum of $2,000,000; for the fiscal year ending June thirtieth, nineteen hundred and twenty-five, the sum of $2,500,-000; for the fiscal year ending June thirtieth, nineteen hundred and twenty-six and annually thereafter, the sum of $3,000,000. Said sums shall be allotted to the States in the proportion which their urban population bears to the total urban population in the United States, not including outlying possessions, according to the last preceding United States census. Provided, ...

That not more than twenty per centum of the money appropriated under this Act for the payment of salaries of teachers of trade, home economics, and industrial subjects, for any year, shall be expended for the salaries of teachers of home economics subjects.

Section 4. That for the purpose of cooperating with the States in preparing teachers, supervisors, and directors of agricultural subjects and teachers of trade and industrial and home economics subjects there is hereby appropriated for the use of the States for the fiscal year ending June thirtieth, nineteen hundred and eighteen, the sum of $500,000; for the fiscal year ending June thirtieth, nineteen hundred and nineteen, the sum of $700,000; for the fiscal year ending June thirtieth, nineteen hundred and twenty, the sum of $900,000; for the fiscal year ending June thirtieth, nineteen hundred and twenty-one, and annually thereafter, the sum of $1,000,000. Said sums shall be allotted to the States in the proportion which their population bears to the total population of the United States, not including outlying possessions, according to the last preceding United States census. Provided,

. . . .

Section 5. That in order to secure the benefits of the appropriations provided for in sections two, three, and four of this Act, any State shall through the legislative authority thereof, accept the provisions of this Act and designate and create a State board, consisting of not less than three members, and having all necessary power to cooperate, as herein provided, with the Federal Board for Vocational Education in the administration of the provisions of this Act. The State board of education, or other board having charge of the administration of public education in the State, or any State board having charge of the administration of any kind of vocational education in the State may, if the State so elects, be designated as the State board, for the purposes of this Act.

In any State the legislature of which does not meet in nineteen hundred and seventeen, if the governor of that State, so far as he is authorized to do so, shall accept the provisions of this Act and designate or create a State board of not less than three members to act in cooperation with the Federal Board for Vocational Education, the Federal Board shall recognize such local board for the purposes of this Act until the legislature of such State meets in due course and has been in session sixty days.

Any State may accept the benefits of any one or more of the respective funds herein appropriated, and it may defer the acceptance of the benefits of any one or more of such funds, and shall be required to meet only the conditions relative to the fund or funds the benefits of which it has accepted. Provided, That after June thirtieth, nineteen hundred and twenty, no State shall receive any appropriation for salaries of teachers, supervisors, or directors of agricultural subjects, until it shall have taken advantage of at least the minimum amount appropriated for the training of teachers, supervisors, or directors of agricultural subjects, as provided for in this Act, and that after said date no State shall receive any appropriation for the salaries of teachers of trade, home economics, and industrial subjects until it shall have taken advantage of at least the minimum amount appropriated for the training of teachers of trade, home economics, and industrial subjects, as provided for in this Act.

Section 6. That a Federal Board for Vocational Education[1] is hereby created, to consist of the Secretary of Agriculture, the Secretary of Commerce, the Secretary of Labor, the United States Commissioner of Education, and three citizens of the United States to be appointed by the President, by, and with the advice and consent of the Senate. One of said three citizens shall be a representative of the manufacturing and commercial interests, one a representative of the agricultural interests, and one a representative of labor. The Board shall elect annually one of its members as chairman. In the

[1] The duties of the Federal Board for Vocational Education were, by Executive order in 1933, transferred to the U.S. Office of Education.

first instance, one of the citizen members shall be appointed for one year, one for two years, and one for three years, and thereafter for three years each. The members of the Board other than the members of the Cabinet and the United States Commissioner of Education shall receive a salary of $5,000 per annum.

The Board shall have power to cooperate with State boards in carrying out the provisions of this Act. It shall be the duty of the Federal Board for Vocational Education to make, or cause to have made, studies, investigations, and reports, with particular reference to their use in aiding the States in the establishment of vocational schools and classes and in giving instruction in agriculture, trades, and industries, commerce and commercial pursuits, and home economics. Such studies, investigations, and reports shall include agriculture and agricultural processes and requirements upon agricultural workers; trades, industries, and apprenticeships, trade and industrial processes and pursuits; commerce and commercial pursuits and requirements upon commercial workers; home management, domestic science, and the study of related facts and principles; and problems of administration of vocational schools and of courses of study and instruction in vocational subjects.

When the Board deems it advisable such studies, investigations, and reports concerning agriculture, for the purposes of agricultural education, may be made in cooperation with or through the Department of Agriculture; such studies, investigations, and reports, concerning trades and industries for the purposes of trades and reports concerning commerce and commercial pursuits, for the purposes of commercial education, may be made in cooperation with or through the Department of Commerce; such studies, investigations, and reports concerning the administration of vocational schools, courses of study, and instruction in vocational subjects may be made in cooperation with or through the Bureau of Education [now Office of Education].

The Commissioner of Education may make such recommendations to the Board relative to the administration of this Act as he may from time to time deem advisable. It shall be the duty of the Chairman of the Board to carry out the rules, regulations, and decisions which the Board may adopt. The Federal Board for Vocational Education shall have power to employ such assistants as may be necessary to carry out the provisions of this Act.

Section 7. That there is hereby appropriated to the Federal Board for Vocational Education the sum of $200,000 annually, to be available from and after the passage of this Act, for the purpose of making or cooperating in making the studies, investigations, and reports provided for in section six of this Act, and for the purpose of paying the salaries of the officers, the assistants, and such office and other expenses as the Board may deem necessary to the execution and administration of this Act.

Section 8. That in order to secure the benefits of the appropriation for any purpose specified in this Act, the State board shall prepare plans, showing the kinds of vocational education for which it is proposed that the appropriation shall be used; the kinds of schools and equipment; courses of study; methods of instruction; qualifications of teachers; and, in the case of agricultural subjects the qualifications of supervisors or directors; plans for training of teachers; and, in case of agricultural subjects, plans for the supervision of agricultural education, as provided for in section ten. Such plans shall be submitted by the State board to the Federal Board for Vocational Education, and if the Federal Board finds the same to be in conformity with the provisions and purposes of this Act, the same shall be approved. The State board shall make an annual report to the Federal Board for Vocational Education, on or before September first of each year, and on the work done in the State and the receipts and expenditures of money under the provisions of this Act.

Section 9. That the appropriation for the salaries of teachers, supervisors, or directors of agricultural subjects and teachers of trade, home economics, and industrial subjects shall be devoted exclusively to the payment of salaries of such teachers, supervisors, or directors having the minimum qualifications set up for the State by the State board, with the approval of the Federal Board for Vocational Education. The cost of instruction supplementary to the instruction in agriculture and in trade, home economics, and industrial subjects provided for in this Act, necessary to build a well-rounded course of training, shall be borne by the State and local communities, and no part of the cost thereof shall be borne out of the appropriations herein made. The moneys expended under the provisions of this Act, in cooperation with the States, for the salaries of teachers, supervisors, or directors of agricultural subjects, or for the salaries of teachers of trade, home economics, and industrial subjects shall be conditioned that for each dollar of Federal money expended for such salaries the State or local community, or both, shall expend an equal amount for such salaries; and that appropriations for the training of teachers of vocational subjects, as herein provided, shall be conditioned that such money be expended for maintenance of such training and for each dollar of Federal money so expended for maintenance, the State or local community or both shall expend an equal amount for the maintenance of such training.

Section 10. That any State may use the appropriations for agricultural purposes, or any part thereof allotted to it, under the provisions of this Act, for the salaries of teachers, supervisors, or directors of agricultural subjects, either for the salaries of teachers of such subjects in schools or classes or for the salaries of supervisors or directors of such subjects under a plan of supervision for the State to be set up by the State board, with the approval of the Federal Board for Vocational Education. That in order to receive the benefits of such appropriations for the salaries of teachers, supervisors, or directors of agricultural education that such education shall be that which is under public supervision or control; that the controlling purpose of such education shall be to fit for useful employment; that such education shall be of less than college grade and be designated to meet the needs of persons over fourteen years of age who have entered upon or who are preparing to enter upon the work of the farm or of the farm home; that the State or local community, or both, shall provide the necessary plant and equipment determined upon by the State board, with the approval of the Federal Board for Vocational Education, as the minimum requirement for such education in schools and classes in the State; that the amount expended for the maintenance of such education in any school or class receiving the benefit of such appropriation shall not be less annually than the amount fixed by the State board, with the approval of the Federal Board as the minimum for such schools or classes in the State; that such schools shall provide for directed or supervised practice in agriculture, either on a farm provided for by the school or other farm, for at least six months per year; that the teachers, supervisors, or directors of agricultural subjects shall have at least the minimum qualifications determined for the State by the State board, with the approval of the Federal Board for Vocational Education.

Section 11. That in order to receive the benefits of the appropriation for the salaries of teachers of trade, home economics, and industrial subjects the State board of any State shall provide in its plans for trade, home economics, and industrial education that such education shall be given in schools or classes under public supervision or control; that the controlling purpose of such education shall be to fit for useful employment; that such education shall be of less than college grade and shall be designed to meet the needs of persons over fourteen years of age who are preparing for a trade or industrial pursuit or who have entered upon the work of a trade or industrial pursuit; that the State or local community, or both, shall provide the necessary plant and equipment determined upon by the State board, with the approval of the Federal Board for Vocational Education, as the minimum requirement in such State for education for any given trade or industrial pursuit; that the total amount expended for the maintenance of such education in any school or class receiving the benefit of such appropriation shall be not less annually than the amount fixed by the State board, with the approval of the Federal Board, as the minimum for such schools or classes in the State; that such schools or classes giving instruction to persons who have not entered upon employment shall require that at least half of the time of such instruction be given to practical work on a useful or productive basis, such instruction to extend over not less than nine months per year and not less than thirty hours per week; that at least one-third of the sum appropriated to any State for the salaries of teachers of trade, home economics, and industrial subjects shall, if expended, be applied to part-time schools or classes for workers over fourteen years of age who have entered upon employment, and such subjects in a part-time school or class may mean any subject to enlarge the civic or vocational intelligence of such workers over fourteen and less then eighteen years of age; that such part-time schools or classes shall provide for not less than one hundred and forty-four hours of classroom instruction per year; that evening industrial schools shall fix the age of sixteen years as a minimum entrance requirement and shall confine instruction to that which is supplemental to the daily employment; that the teachers of any trade or industrial subject in any State shall have at least the minimum qualifications for teachers of such subject determined upon for such State by the State board, with the approval of the Federal Board for Vocational Education. Provided, That for cities and towns of less than twenty-five thousand population, according to the last preceding United States census, the State board, with the approval of the Federal Board for Vocational Education, may modify the conditions as to the length of course and hours of instruction per week for schools and classes giving instruction to those who have not entered upon employment, in order to meet the particular needs of such cities and towns.

Section 12. That in order for any State to receive the benefits of the appropriation in this Act for the training of teachers, supervisors, or directors of agricultural subjects, or of teachers of trade, industrial, or home economics subjects, the State board of such State shall provide in its plan for such training that the same shall be carried out under the supervision of the State board; that such training shall be given in schools or classes under public supervision or control; that such training shall be given only to persons who have had adequate vocational experience or contact in the line of work for which they are preparing themselves as teachers, supervisors, or directors, or who are acquiring such experience or contact as a part of their training; and that the State board, with the approval of the Federal Board, shall establish minimum requirements for such experience or contact for teachers, supervisors, or directors of agricultural subjects and for teachers of trade, industrial, and home economics subjects; that no more than sixty per centum nor less than twenty per centum of the money appropriated under this Act for the training of teachers of vocational subjects to any State for any year shall be expended for any one of the following purposes: For the preparation of teachers, supervisors, or directors of agricultural subjects, or the preparation of teachers of trade and industrial subjects, or the preparation of teachers of home economics subjects.

Section 13. That in order to secure the benefits of the appropriations for the salaries of teachers, supervisors, or directors of agricultural subjects, or for the salaries of teachers of trade, home economics, and industrial subjects, or for the training of teachers as herein provided, any State shall, through the legislative authority thereof, appoint as custodian for said appropriations its State treasurer, who shall receive and provide for the proper custody and disbursements of all money paid to the State from said appropriations.

Section 14. That the Federal Board for Vocational Education shall annually ascertain whether the several States are using, or are prepared to use, the money received by them in accordance with the provisions of this Act. On or before the first day of January of each year the Federal Board for Vocational Education shall certify to the Secretary of the Treasury each State which has accepted the provisions of this Act and compiled therewith, certifying the amounts which each State is entitled to receive under the provisions of this Act. Upon such certification the Secretary of the Treasury shall pay quarterly to the custodian for vocational education of each State the moneys to which it is entitled under the provisions of this Act. The moneys so received by the custodian for vocational education for any State shall be paid out on the requisition of the State board as reimbursement for expenditures already incurred to such schools as are approved by said State board and are entitled to receive such moneys under the provisions of this Act.

Section 15. That whenever any portion of the fund annually allotted to any State has not been expended for the purpose provided for in this Act, a sum equal to such portion shall be deducted by the Federal Board from the next succeeding annual allotment from such fund to such State.

Section 16. That the Federal Board for Vocational Education may withhold the allotment of moneys to any State whenever it shall be determined that such moneys are not being expended for the purposes and under the conditions of this Act.

If any allotment is withheld from any State, the State board of such State may appeal to the Congress of the United States, and if the Congress shall not direct such sum to be paid, it shall be covered into the Treasury.

Section 17. That if any portion of the moneys received by the custodian for vocational education of any State under this Act, for any given purpose named in this Act, shall, by any action or contingency, be diminished or lost, it shall be replaced by such State, and until so replaced no subsequent appropriation for such education shall be paid to such State. No portion of any moneys appropriated under this Act for the benefit of the States shall be applied, directly or indirectly, to the purchase, erection, preservation, or repair of any building or buildings or equipment, or for the purchase or rental of lands, or for the support of any religious or privately owned or conducted school or college.

Section 18. That the Federal Board for Vocational Education shall make an annual report to Congress, on or before December first, on the administration of this Act and shall include in such report the reports made by the State boards on the administration of this Act by each State and the expenditure of the money allowed to each State.

Approved, February 23, 1917, by President Woodrow Wilson.

Public Law 35, Sixty-eighth Congress (House Bill 4121) extended the provisions of the Smith-Hughes Act to the territory of Hawaii. Under the provisions of this Act Hawaii received $30,000 annually. Approved, March 10, 1924.

Public Law 791, Seventy-first Congress (Senate Bill 5139) extended the provisions of the Smith-Hughes Act to Puerto Rico. Under the provisions of this Act Puerto Rico receives $105,000 annually. Approved, March 3, 1931.

Appendix II

The George-Barden Act

Public Law 586, Seventy-ninth Congress, Chapter 725, Second Session, Senate Bill 619

To amend the Act of June 8, 1936, relating to vocational education, so as to provide for the further development of vocational education in the several States and Territories.

Be it enacted by the Senate and House of Representatives of the United States of America in Congress assembled, That the Act approved June 8, 1936, entitled "An Act to provide for the further development of vocational education in the several States and Territories" (49 Stat. 1488, ch. 541), is amended to read as follows:

Short Title

Section 1. This Act may be cited as the "Vocational Education Act of 1946."

Definitions

Section 2. As used in this Act—

    (1) the term "States and Territories" means the several States, the Territories of Alaska and Hawaii, the island of Puerto Rico, and the District of Columbia;

    (2) the terms "State plan" and "State board" shall have the meaning which said terms have in the Smith-Hughes Vocational Education Act; and

    (3) the term "Smith-Hughes Vocational Education Act" means the Act approved February 23, 1917 (39 Stat. 929, ch. 114).

Authorization for Appropriations for Vocational Education

Section 3. (*a*) For the purpose of assisting the several States and Territories in the further development of vocational education, there is authorized to be appropriated for the fiscal year beginning July 1, 1946, and annually thereafter—

(1) $10,000,000 for vocational education in agriculture, including supervision by the vocational agriculture teachers of the activities, related to vocational education in agriculture, of the Future Farmers of America and the New Farmers of America, to be apportioned for expenditure in the several States and Territories in the proportion that their farm population bears to the total farm population of the States and Territories, according to the last preceding United States census;

(2) $8,000,000 for vocational education in home economics, to be apportioned for expenditure in the several States and Territories in the proportion that their rural population bears to the total rural population of the States and Territories, according to the last preceding United States census;

(3) $8,000,000 for vocational education in trades and industry, to be apportioned for expenditure in the several States and Territories in the proportion that their nonfarm population bears to the total nonfarm population of the States and Territories, according to the last preceding United States census;

(4) $2,500,000 for vocational education in distributive occupations, to be apportioned for expenditure in the several States and Territories in the proportion that their total population bears to the total population of the States and Territories, according to the last preceding United States census.

(b) The funds appropriated under authority of paragraphs (1) to (4), inclusive, of subsection (a) of this section may be used for assisting the several States and Territories, for the purposes therein specified, in the maintenance of adequate programs of administration, supervision, and teacher-training; for salaries and necessary travel expenses of teachers, teacher-trainers, vocational counselors, supervisors and directors of vocational education and vocational guidance; for securing necessary educational information and data as a basis for the proper development of programs of vocational education and vocational guidance; for training and work-experience training programs for out-of-school youths; for training programs for apprentices; for purchase or rent of equipment and supplies for vocational instruction: Provided, That all expenditures for the purposes as set forth in this section shall be made in accordance with the State plan for vocational education.

(c) Notwithstanding the provisions of subsection (a), the amount to be available for expenditure in any State or Territory shall be not less, for any fiscal year, than $40,000 each for vocational education in agriculture, in home economics, and in trades and industry; $15,000 for vocational education in distributive occupations and there is hereby authorized to be appropriated for the fiscal year beginning July 1, 1946, and annually thereafter, such additional sums as may be needed for the purpose of providing such minimum amounts.

Requirements as to Matching of Funds

Section 4. The several States and Territories, in order to receive the benefits of this Act, shall be required to match by State and local funds or both 100 per centum of the appropriations made under authority of section 3.

Making of Payments

Section 5. The Secretary of the Treasury, through the Fiscal Service of the Treasury Department, shall, upon the certification of the United States Commissioner of Education, pay, in equal semiannual payments, on the first day of July and January of each year, to the custodian for vocational education of each State and Territory designated in the Smith-Hughes Vocational Education Act, the moneys to which the State or Territory is entitled under the provisions of his Act.

Availability of Funds for Salary and Expenses of State Directors

Section 6. Funds appropriated under authority of section 3 shall be available, on a prorated basis determined by the State board, for the salary and necessary travel expenses of a State director of vocational education selected by the State board, in accordance with the requirements of the State plan, on the basis of his technical and professional qualifications including experience in vocational education.

Applicability of Smith-Hughes Vocational Education Act

Section 7. The appropriations made under authority of this Act shall be in addition to, and shall be subject to the same conditions and limitations as, the appropriations made to carry out the Smith-Hughes Vocational Education Act; except that (1) the appropriations made under authority of this Act for home economics shall be subject to the conditions and limitations applicable to the appropriation for agricultural purposes under the Smith-Hughes Vocational Education Act, with the exception of that part of section 10 thereof which requires directed or supervised practice for at least six months per year; (2) such moneys as are provided under authority of this Act for trade and industrial subjects, and public and other service occupations, may be expended for part-time classes operated for less than one hundred and forty-four hours per year; (3) the provisions of section 11 of the Smith-Hughes Vocational Education Act, requiring at least one-third of the sum appropriated to any State to be expanded for part-time schools or classes shall be held to include any part-time day-school classes for workers sixteen years of age and over, and evening-school classes for workers sixteen years of age and over; (4) the appropriations made by this Act for distributive occupational subjects shall be limited to part-time and evening schools as provided in the Smith-Hughes Vocational Education Act, for trade, home economics, and industrial subjects and is qualified by the provisions of this section; (5) preemployment schools and classes organized for persons over eighteen years of age or who have left the full-time school may be operated for less than nine months per year and less than thirty hours per week and without the requirement that a minimum of 50 per centum of the time must be given to shop work on a useful or productive basis; and (6) the appropriations available under section 9 of this Act shall be available for expenses of attendance at meetings of educational associations and other organizations and for expenses of conferees called to meet in the District of Columbia or elsewhere, which, in the opinion of the Commissioner, are necessary for the efficient discharge of the provisions of this Act.

Restrictions and Conditions

Section 8. (*a*) No part of the appropriations made under authority of this Act shall be expended in industrial-plant training programs, except such industrial-plant training be bona fide vocational training, and not a device to utilize the services of vocational trainees for private profit.

(*b*) After June 30, 1951; not more than 10 per centum of the amount appropriated for each of the purposes specified in section 3 (*a*) shall be used for the purchase or acquisition of equipment.

Appropriations for Office of Education

Section 9. For the purpose of carrying out the provisions of this Act there is hereby authorized to be appropriated to the Office of Education, Federal Security Agency, for vocational education, for the fiscal year beginning July 1, 1937, and annually thereafter the sum of $350,000, to be expended for the same purposes and in the same manner as provided in section 7 of the Smith-Hughes Vocational Education Act, as amended October 6, 1917.

Approved August 1, 1946.

Appendix III

Equipment for the Classroom and Laboratory

Soils

1 farm level
1 soil-testing outfit for acid, lime, nitrogen, phosphorus, potash
1 vial of blue litmus paper
1 vial of red litmus paper
1 soil thermometer
1 soil auger
6 250- or 300-cc. beakers
12 test tubes
12 student lamp chimneys
12 tin cans for soil samples
1 set of soil sieves
1 package of assorted corks
1 package of filter paper
1 lb. assorted glass tubing
25 wide-mouth display bottles for soil samples

Animal Husbandry

1 emasculator
1 electric clipmaster
1 veterinary thermometer
1 tattoo earmarker
1 clipper for needle teeth of pigs
1 set of butchering equipment
1 hoof clipper
1 hoof rasp
1 hog-cholera vaccination outfit
1 hog holder
1 castrating and spaying knife
1 cattle dehorner
1 hog ringer
1 mouth speculum
1 posting set
1 hog bit and capsule gun for worming

Dairy Husbandry

1 Babcock milk tester, 12 or 24 bottles
5 acid measures, 17.5 cc.
5 pipettes, milk
6 cream test bottles
1 pair of dairy scales
1 lactometer
1 hydrometer
12 milk sample jars
2 milk sample dippers

358

6 skim-milk test bottles
1 Harvard trip balance scales
  with weights
5 test-tube brushes
24 whole-milk test bottles
2 4½-in. dividers

1 aluminum strip cup
1 milk-fever outfit
1 cattle trocar
1 churn for making butter
1 electric ice-cream churn

Poultry

1 egg scale
1 caponizing set
1 egg candler
1 poultry toe punch
1 band applicator
1 fowl catcher

1 poultry-killing knife
1 worming outfit
1 incubator (if desired for
  demonstration)
1 brooder (can build locally)
2 exhibition crates

Fruit Crops

1 tree pruner
1 lopping shears
1 hedge-pruning shears
1 tree caliper
12 hand shears

12 budding knives
1 plant setter for trees
1 tool for cleft grafting
1 spraying outfit
1 dust gun

Vegetable Crops

1 germinator
5 tripod magnifiers
5 seed flats (made in shop)
1 machine for treating seeds
  with dust
6 hoes
6 potato diggers

2 garden rakes
2 hand push plows (not needed
  if tractor is available)
1 garden tractor
2 shovels
2 spades
1 50-ft. water hose

Visual Aids

1 16-mm. sound-film machine
1 curtain for motion pictures
1 slide and filmstrip machine

1 opaque projector (Balopticon)
1 camera

Miscellaneous

1 compound microscope
1 pencil sharpener
1 paper punch
1 stapler machine

1 typewriter
1 outfit for binding bulletins
2 steel filing cases
1 letter and package scale

Appendix IV
Supplies for the
Classroom and Laboratory

Soils

Samples of the local soil types
Samples of fertilizer materials

Chemicals for refill of soil-
testing outfit

Animal Husbandry

Livestock-judging cards
Colored pictures and charts
of breeds
Diseased specimens
Preserved external parasites
Preserved internal parasites
Supply of eartags

Cattle covers
Halters for cattle
Hog worm capsules
Disinfectants and dips
Various medicines
Samples of various feeds

Dairy Husbandry

Dichromate tablets for preserving
milk
Disinfectant powders
Sulfuric acid for milk testing

Rennet for use in making cheese
Screwworm killer
Disinfectants and dips
Colored pictures and charts

Poultry

Poultry leg bands
Poultry wing bands
Pictures and charts
Samples of feeds

Judging cards
Medicines and disinfectants
Sample egg crates

360

Fruit Crops

Plant hormone for cuttings
Plant hormone for use in
  transplanting
Grafting wax
Nursery tape for budding
Samples of all spray materials
Samples of all dust materials

Charts and pictures
Exhibit of the different methods
  of grafting
Plant disease specimens
Samples of containers for
  different fruits
Fruit insect specimens

Farm Crops

Farm-crop insect specimens
Disease specimens of crops
Samples of farm-crop seed
Inoculation materials for legumes
Spray and dust materials

Charts and pictures
Grain grade samples
Samples of cotton grades
Collection of weed samples

Vegetable Crops

Samples of all vegetable seeds
Samples of spray and dust materials
Disease specimens
Sample containers for shipping
  various vegetables

Insect specimens
Samples of weed killers
Material for controlling rodents
DDT
Charts and pictures

Visual Aids

Paper for making charts
Lettering outfit for making charts
Lettering pencils and pens
Slides covering all divisions
  of agriculture

Filmstrips covering all divisions
  of agriculture
Motion picture (16-mm.) films
Films for taking pictures

Miscellaneous

Letterhead stationery
Bond paper
Second-sheet paper
Carbon paper

Glue or paste
Paper clips
Stencils
Scotch tape

Gummed labels
Thumbtacks
Insect pins
Erasers

Appendix V
Farm Shop Check List

T HE FOLLOWING list of suggested general equipment and tools for the vocational agriculture school farm-mechanics shop is based on one furnished by the Division of Vocational Education, Agricultural Education Branch, U.S. Office of Education, Washington 25, D.C.

The number in parentheses after each tool or piece of equipment is a suggestion and may need to be increased in some sections of the country to meet specific state or local conditions.

It is recognized that each state may have a list of tools and equipment recommended for farm-mechanics shops. It is also recognized that the need for tools and equipment of a particular nature will vary between states as well as in schools within a state.

Anvils

Blacksmith's, with tool steel facing, 150 or 200 lb. (1)
Guard and sickle (1)

Bars

Crow and tamping, combination, 6 ft., homemade (2)
Pinch, 3- and 4-ft. lengths (2 each)
Wrecking (2)

Brace and Bits

Auger, $\frac{1}{4}$ to $1\frac{1}{4}$ in. by 16th (2 sets)
Countersink (2)
Drill, twist; $\frac{1}{2}$-, $\frac{5}{8}$-, $\frac{3}{4}$-, $\frac{7}{8}$-, 1-, $\frac{1}{2}$-in. shank (1 each)
Expansive, $\frac{7}{8}$ to 3 in. (2)
Screw driver; $\frac{1}{4}$, $\frac{5}{16}$, $\frac{3}{8}$ in. (2 each)

Wood boring, for use in brace, $\frac{1}{4}$ to $\frac{3}{4}$ in. by 16ths (1 set)
Brace, ratchet bit, 10-in. sweep (2)

Cans

Filler, oil; 1, 2, and 4 qt. (1 each)
Crankcase, draining (2)
Gasoline, safety, size optional (1)
Oiler, squirt, assorted sizes (3)
Storage, for solvent (1)
Water (1)

Chisels

Cabinet; shank running through handle; $\frac{1}{4}$, $\frac{1}{2}$, $\frac{3}{4}$, 1, $1\frac{1}{4}$ in. (1 set)
Cold; $\frac{3}{8}$, $\frac{1}{2}$, $\frac{3}{4}$, 1 in. (2 each)
Cold, blacksmith's, handle width at eye $1\frac{1}{2}$ in. (1)
Hot, blacksmith's, handle width at eye $1\frac{1}{2}$ in. (1)

Clamps

Clamp fixtures, for use on ¾-in. pipe (4 sets)
C; 4, 6, 8 in. (1 pair each)
Splicing, 9 in. (1)

Compressors

Air, single stage, automatic, horizontal type (1)

Cutters

Glass (1)
Pipe, capacity ¼ to 2 in. (1)
Die stock and dies, pipe threading, ratchet pipe, capacity ⅛ to ¾ in. (1)
Diestock and dies, pipe threading, ratchet, adjustable, with receding dies, capacity 1 to 2 in. (1)

Drills

Hand, capacity ¼ in. (1)
Electric, heavy duty, ½ in., with bench stand (1)
Post, with 3-jaw key or self-tightening chuck, 2 or more speeds (1)
Star; ¼, ⅜, ½, ⅝, ¾, 1 in. (1 set)

Drivers

Screw, automatic (2)
Screw, shockproof; 4, 6, 8, 12 in. (1 each)
Screw, offset, 6 in. (1)
Screw, short, heavy duty, shockproof (1)

Gauges

Draw, harness maker's (1)
Vacuum (1)

Grinders

Bench, electric, wheel size 6 to 8 in. (2)
Floor, electric, wheel size 12 in., face 1½ to 2 in. (1)
Sickle, electric (1)

Groovers

Concrete worker's (1)
Hand, sheet metal worker's, ¼ to ⅜ in. (1 each)

Guns

Grease, air power to fit grease can (1)
Oil and grease (1)
Zerk, lever type (2)

Hammers

Ball peen, 1 and 2 lb. (2 each)
Claw, curved or straight, 16 oz. (12)
Cross peen, 2½ lb. (4)
Sledge, handle, 6 to 8 lb. (2)

Hatchet

Broad or bench, 4½-in. cutting edge (2)
Shingling (2)

Hoists

Built up, A frame, 3-in. pipe or tubing, with casters; or I beam (1)
Chain, differential, capacity ½ to 1 ton (1)

Knives

Draw, 10 in. (2)
Putty (2)
Saddler's round (1)
Skiving (1)

Levels

Builder's, with telescope (1)
Carpenter's, spirit (2)

Planes

Block, adjustable, 6 in. (2)
Jack, 14 in. (4)
Jointer, 22 in. (1)

Pliers

Combination, side cutting, 8 in. (6)
Diagonal cutting, 8 in. (2)
Lineman's, 8 in. (2)
Long nose, 6 in. (2)

Pullers

Gear, heavy duty (1)
Gear, small, 0 to 3 in. (1)

Punches

Aligning, points $\frac{3}{16}$, $\frac{1}{4}$, $\frac{3}{8}$ in. (1 each)
Belt, revolving head, 4 or 6 tube (1)
Blacksmith's round; handle; $\frac{1}{4}$, $\frac{3}{8}$, $\frac{1}{2}$ in. (1 each)
Center, machinist's, diameter at top of tapered point $\frac{1}{8}$ and $\frac{7}{32}$ in. (1 each)
Leather, hollow, used with hammer, assorted sizes (2 sets)
Pin, machinist's; $\frac{3}{32}$, $\frac{1}{8}$, $\frac{5}{32}$, $\frac{3}{16}$, $\frac{7}{32}$, $\frac{9}{32}$ in. (1)
Sheet metal, with punches $\frac{3}{32}$ to $\frac{1}{4}$ in. by 32ds (1)
Starter (1)
Drift; $\frac{1}{8}$, $\frac{3}{16}$, $\frac{1}{4}$, $\frac{5}{16}$, $\frac{3}{8}$ in. (1 each)

Reamers

Burring, spiral pipe end, $\frac{1}{4}$ to 2 in. (1)

Expansion blade, $\frac{19}{32}$ to $1\frac{11}{32}$ in. (1 set)

Rules

Fourfold, brass bound, 2 ft. (6)
Steel tape, 6 ft. (2)
Zigzag, 6 ft. (4)

Saws

Compass, 12 in. (1)
Crosscut, 8 and 10 point, 26 in. (4)
Hack, adjustable frame (2)
Keyhole, hack, 10 in. (1)
Rip, 5 or 6 point, 26 in. (2)
Tilting arbor or radial, complete with motor, 12 in. (1)

Sets

Nail, assorted sizes (6)
Rivet (3)
Saw, pistol grip (1)

Shovels

Round point, long handle (1)
Round point, short handle (1)
Square point, long handle (2)

Snips

Tinner's, combination pattern, 12-in. length (2)
Tinner's, regular pattern (2)

Squares

Combination, 12 in. (1)
Carpenter's steel, 16- by 24- by $\frac{1}{16}$-in. markings (4)
Carpenter's steel, 8 by 12 in. (2)
Straightedge, wood, homemade (1)

Tongs

Bolt, blacksmith's; $\frac{3}{8}$, $\frac{1}{2}$, $\frac{3}{4}$, by 20 to 24 in. (2 each)

Plowshare, homemade, 24 in. (2)
Straight-lipped, 20 to 24 in. (4)

Torches

Blow, gasoline, capacity 1 qt. (1)
Welder, arc, 150 to 200 amp., a.c.
  or d.c. (1)
Welding, oxyacetylene, with cutting attachment (1)

Vises

Drill press, 6-in. opening (1)
Machinist's, 4-in. jaw (4)
Machinist's, heavy duty, $4\frac{1}{2}$-in.
  jaw (1)
Pipe, $\frac{1}{8}$ to $3\frac{1}{2}$ in. (1)
Saw, $9\frac{1}{2}$-in. jaw (1)
Solid box, blacksmith's, 50 to 100
  lb. (1)
Woodworking, rapid acting, 7-in.
  jaw (4)

Wrenches

Adjustable, open end, 8 in. (4)
Adjustable, open end; 10, 12,
  18 in. (2 each)
Box type, $\frac{5}{16}$ to 1 in. by 16ths
  (1 set)
Box type, combination box and
  open end, $\frac{1}{4}$ to $\frac{3}{4}$ in. by 16ths
  (2 sets)
Flex set; $\frac{3}{8}$, $\frac{1}{2}$, $\frac{5}{8}$, $\frac{3}{4}$ in. (1)
Ignition (1 set)
Monkey, 18 and 21 in. (1 each)
Pipe; 14, 18, 24 in. (1 each)

Socket master, 12 point, $\frac{1}{2}$-in.
  square drive, $\frac{3}{8}$ to $1\frac{1}{8}$ in. by
  32ds (1 set)
Socket, special mechanic's set,
  12 point, $\frac{7}{16}$ to 1 in. by 16ths,
  with ratchet handle (1 set)
Tappet and check nut (1 set)

Miscellaneous

Battery lifter (1)
Bevel, sliding T (1)
Brush, wire (1)
Bolt clipper, 30-in. length (1)
Coppers, soldering, $1\frac{1}{2}$ and 3 lb.
  (1)
Copper, electric soldering (1)
Dividers, wing, 8 or 10 in. (2)
Dresser, emery wheel (1)
Edger, concrete worker's (1)
Fire pot, gasoline (1)
First aid kit (1)
Forge, blacksmith's (1)
Goggles, grinding (6 pairs)
Hafts, awl, assorted sizes (6)
Hardy, blacksmith's, to fit anvil (2)
Helmet, arc welder's (2)
Jack, automotive hydraulic (1)
Jointer for handsaws (1)
Lamp, trouble and cord (1)
Mallet, wood (3)
Oilstone, combination (2)
Nippers, end cut (1)
Plumb bob (1)
Scraper, carbon (1)
Trowel, brick and plasterer's,
  (1 each)

Appendix VI

Agricultural Magazines

Aberdeen-Angus Journal, Webster City, Iowa.
Agricultural Leaders' Digest, Chicago, Ill.
The Agricultural Situation, Bureau of Agricultural Economics, U.S. Department of Agriculture, Washington, D.C.
American Bee Journal, Hamilton, Ill.
The American Brahman, Houston, Tex.
American Farm Youth Magazine, Danville, Ill.
American Fruit Grower, Willoughby, Ohio.
American Poultry Journal, Chicago, Ill.
Ayrshire Digest, Brandon, Vt.
The Belgian Review, Wabash, Ind.
Berkshire News, Springfield, Ill.
Better Crops with Plant Food, The American Potash Institute, Washington, D.C.
Better Farm Equipment and Methods, Midland Publishing Co., St. Louis, Mo.
Better Homes and Gardens, Des Moines, Iowa.
Breeder's Gazette, Spencer, Ind.
Cappers Farmer, Topeka, Kan.
Chester White Journal, Rochester, Ind.
Citrus Leaves, Los Angeles, Calif.
The Citrus Magazine, Tampa, Fla.
Country Gentleman, Curtis Publishing Company, Philadelphia, Pa.
County Agent & Vo-Ag Teacher, Philadelphia, Pa.
Daily Live Stock Reporter, East St. Louis, Mo.
Dairy Farmer, Des Moines, Iowa.
Dixie Farm and Poultry Journal, Nashville, Tenn.
Duroc News, Peoria, Ill.
Electricity on the Farm Magazine, New York, N.Y.
Farm Journal, Philadelphia, Pa.
Farm and Ranch—Southern Agriculturist, Nashville, Tenn.
The Fertilizer Review, National Fertilizer Association, Washington, D.C.
The Florida Cattleman and Livestock Journal, Kissimmee, Fla.

Florida Grower, Tampa, Fla.

Florida Poultry & Dairy Journal, Zephyrhills, Fla.

The Furrow, Deere & Co., Moline, Ill.

The Garden Magazine, Doubleday Page Co., Garden City, N.Y.

Guernsey Breeders' Journal, The American Guernsey Cattle Club, Peterboro, N.H.

Hampshire Herdsman, Peoria, Ill.

Hoard's Dairyman, Fort Atkinson, Wis.

Holstein-Friesian World, Lacona, N.Y.

The Jersey Bulletin, Indianapolis, Ind.

Land Policy Review, Bureau of Agricultural Economics, Washington, D.C.

Leghorn World, Waverly, Iowa.

Market Growers Journal, Akron, Ohio.

National Grange Monthly, Springfield, Mass.

The Poland China World, Galesburg, Ill.

Polled Hereford Magazine, H. J. Herbert, Inc., Montgomery, Ala.

Poultry Tribune, Mount Morris, Ill.

Progressive Farmer, Birmingham, Ala.

Red Polled News, Lincoln, Neb.

Reliable Poultry Journal, Dayton, Ohio.

Rhode Island Red Journal, Waverly, Iowa.

Rural Electrification News, Rural Electrification Administration, U.S. Department of Agriculture, Washington, D.C.

Shorthorn World, Shorthorn World Publishing Co., Aurora, Ill.

Soil Conservation, Soil Conservation Service, U.S. Department of Agriculture, Washington, D.C.

Successful Farming, Des Moines, Iowa.

The Swine World, James J. Doty Publishing Co., Chicago, Ill.

Appendix VII

Companies Publishing Agricultural Books

American Poultry Association, Davenport, Iowa.
Appleton-Century-Crofts, Inc., New York, N.Y.
The Blakiston Company, New York, N.Y.
Brookings Institution, Washington, D.C.
The Bruce Publishing Company, Milwaukee, Wis.
Burgess Publishing Company, Minneapolis, Minn.
College Book Company, Columbus, Ohio
Doubleday & Company, Inc., New York, N.Y.
Ginn & Company, Boston, Mass.
Harper & Brothers, New York, N.Y.
D. C. Heath and Company, Boston, Mass.
Henry Holt and Company, Inc., New York, N.Y.
Houghton Mifflin Company, Boston, Mass.
The Interstate, Danville, Ill.
Lea and Febiger, Philadelphia, Pa.
J. B. Lippincott Company, Philadelphia, Pa.
Longmans, Green & Co., Inc., New York, N.Y.
McGraw-Hill Book Company, Inc., New York, N.Y.
The Macmillan Company, New York, N.Y.
Meredith Publishing Company, Des Moines, Iowa.
W. W. Norton & Company, New York, N.Y.
Orange Judd Publishing Co., Inc., New York, N.Y.
Prentice-Hall, Inc., New York, N.Y.
Rand McNally & Company, Chicago, Ill.
The Ronald Press Company, New York, N.Y.
Charles Scribner's Sons, New York, N.Y.
Turner E. Smith & Co., Atlanta, Ga.
Vanguard Press, New York, N.Y.
The Webb Publishing Company, St. Paul, Minn.
John Wiley & Sons, Inc., New York, N.Y.
Yale University Press, New Haven, Conn.

Appendix VIII

Books for the F.F.A. and Agricultural Library

ALLEN, B., and M. P. BRIGGS, "Behave Yourself!" J. B. Lippincott Company, Philadelphia, 1945.

——— and ———, "If You Please," J. B. Lippincott Company, Philadelphia, 1942.

ANDERSON, A. L., "Introductory Animal Husbandry," The Macmillan Company, New York, 1943.

———, "Swine Enterprises," J. B. Lippincott Company, Philadelphia, 1945.

ANDERSON, H. P., "Your Career in Agriculture," E. P. Dutton & Co., Inc., New York, 1940.

ANGLE, P. M. (editor), "The Lincoln Reader," Rutgers University Press, New Brunswick, N.J., 1947.

BAILARD, V., and H. C. McKOWN, "So You Were Elected," McGraw-Hill Book Company, Inc., New York, 1946.

——— and R. STRANG, "Ways to Improve Your Personality, "McGraw-Hill Book Company, Inc., New York, 1951.

BALCH, W. B., A. S. COLBY, and T. J. TALBERT, "Horticulture Enterprises," J. B. Lippincott Company, Philadelphia, 1949.

BATHURST, E. G., "Your Life in the Country," McGraw-Hill Book Company, Inc., New York, 1948.

BENNETT, H. H., "Elements of Soil Conservation," McGraw-Hill Book Company, Inc., New York, 1947.

BURNHAM, H. A., E. G. JONES, and H. D. REDFORD, "Boys Will Be Men," J. B. Lippincott Company, Philadelphia, 1949.

CARD, L. E., and M. HENDERSON, "Farm Poultry Production," The Interstate, Danville, Ill., 1948.

CARROLL, W. E., and J. L. KRIDER, "Swine Production," McGraw-Hill Book Company, Inc., New York, 1950.

CASE, J. F., "Peace Valley Warrior," The Interstate, Danville, Ill., 1940.

CHAPMAN, P. W., "Efficient Farm Management," Turner E. Smith & Co., Atlanta, Ga., 1948.

————, "The Green Hand," J. B. Lippincott Company, Philadelphia, 1932.

————, "Successful Farming," Turner E. Smith & Co., Atlanta, Ga., 1948.

————, "Your Personality and Your Job," Science Research Associates, Chicago, 1944.

———— and R. W. THOMAS, "Southern Crops," Turner E. Smith & Co., Atlanta, Ga., 1947.

COLLINGS, G. H., "Commercial Fertilizers, Their Sources and Use," 4th ed., The Blakiston Company, New York, 1947.

COOPER, J. B., "Poultry for Home and Market," Turner E. Smith & Co., Atlanta, Ga., 1950.

COPE, C., "Front Porch Farmer," Turner E. Smith & Co., Atlanta, Ga., 1949.

DAVENPORT, E., and A. W. NOLAN, "Agricultural Arts," Garrard Press, Champaign, Ill., 1938.

DETJEN, M. F., and E. W. DETJEN, "Your High School Days," McGraw-Hill Book Company, Inc., New York, 1947.

DEYOE, G. P., "Living on a Little Land," The Interstate, Danville, Ill., 1948.

———— and J. L. KRIDER, "Raising Swine," McGraw-Hill Book Company, Inc., New York, 1952.

DRESSE, M., "How to Get the Job," Science Research Associates, Chicago, 1944.

DRISCOLL, C. B., "Country Jake," The Macmillan Company, New York, 1946.

DUNCAN, A. O., "Food Processing," Turner E. Smith & Co., Atlanta, Ga., 1949.

DYKSTRA, R. R., "Animal Sanitation and Disease Control," The Interstate, Danville., Ill.,1951.

ELLIOTT, C. N., "Conservation of American Resources," Turner E. Smith & Co., Atlanta, Ga., 1940.

FERGUS, E. N., C. Hammonds, and H. ROGERS, "Southern Field Crops Management," J. B. Lippincott Company, Philadelphia, 1944.

FORSTER, G. W., "Farm Organization and Management," Prentice-Hall Inc., New York, 1946.

GARRIGUS, W. P., "Introductory Animal Science," J. B. Lippincott Company, Philadelphia, 1951.

GARRIS, E. W., and G. P. Hoffmann, "Southern Horticulture Enterprises," 3d ed., J. B. Lippincott Company, Philadelphia, 1946.

———— and H. S. WOLFE, "Southern Horticulture Management," J. B. Lippincott Company, Philadelphia, 1949.

GOURLEY, J. H., and F. S. HOWLETT, "Modern Fruit Production," The Macmillan Company, New York, 1941.

GUISE, C. H., "The Management of Farm Woodlands," 2d ed., McGraw-Hill Book Company, Inc., New York, 1950.

GULLICKSON, T. W., "Feeding Dairy Cattle," The Webb Publishing Company, St. Paul, 1943.

GUSTAFSON, A. F., "Using and Managing Soils," McGraw-Hill Book Company, Inc., New York, 1948.

HAMMONDS, C., and R. H. WOODS, "Today's Agriculture," J. B. Lippincott Company, Philadelphia, 1943.

HAMPSON, C. M., "Starting and Managing a Farm," McGraw-Hill Book Company, Inc., New York, 1948.

HENRY, W. H. F., and L. SEELEY, "How to Organize and Conduct a Meeting," Grosset & Dunlap, Inc., New York, 1942.

HOPKINS, J. A., "Elements of Farm Management," Prentice-Hall, Inc., New York, 1947.

HOUGH, E., "The Covered Wagon," Grosset & Dunlap, Inc., New York, 1942.

HUDELSON, R. R., "Farm Management," The Macmillan Company, New York, 1946.

HUMPHREYS, J. A., "Choosing Your Career," Science Research Associates, Chicago, 1944.

HUNT, R. L., "Farm Management in the South," The Interstate, Danville, Ill., 1942.

IVINS, L., and A. WINSHIP, "Fifty Famous Farmers," The Macmillan Company, New York, 1924.

JOHNSON, E. J., and A. H. HOLLENBERG, "Servicing and Maintaining Farm Tractors," McGraw-Hill Book Company, Inc., New York, 1950.

JONES, A. M., "Leisure Time Education," Harper & Brothers, New York, 1946.

JONES, M. M., "Shopwork on the Farm," McGraw-Hill Book Company, Inc., New York, 1945.

JUDKINS, H. F., and M. J. MARK, "The Principles of Dairying," 3d ed., John Wiley & Sons, Inc., New York, 1941.

JUERGENSON, E. M., "Approved Practices in Beef Cattle Production," The Interstate, Danville, Ill., 1951.

JULL, M. A., "Raising Turkeys, Ducks, Geese, Game Birds," McGraw-Hill Book Company, Inc., New York, 1947.

———, "Successful Poultry Management," 2d ed., McGraw-Hill Book Company, Inc., New York, 1951.

KAMMLADE, W. G., "Sheep Science," J. B. Lippincott Company, Philadelphia, 1947.

KILANDER, H. F., "Nutrition for Health," McGraw-Hill Book Company, Inc., New York, 1951.

KING, G. H., "Pastures for the South," The Interstate, Danville, Ill., 1950.

KITSON, H. D., "I Find My Vocation," McGraw-Hill Book Company, Inc., New York, 1947.

KNODT, C. B., "Successful Dairying," McGraw-Hill Book Company, Inc., New York, 1953.

LLOYD-JONES, E., and R. FEDDER, "Coming of Age," McGraw-Hill Book Company, Inc., New York, 1941.

MARSH, H. M., "Building Your Personality," 2d ed., Prentice-Hall, Inc., New York, 1947.

MARTIN, J. H., and W. H. LEONARD, "Principles of Field Crop Production," The Macmillan Company, New York, 1949.

McKOWN, H. C., "A Boy Grows Up," 2d ed., McGraw-Hill Book Company, Inc., New York, 1949.

———, "Home Room Guidance," 2d ed., McGraw-Hill Book Company, Inc., New York, 1946.

METCALF, C. L., and W. F. FLINT, "Destructive and Useful Insects," 3d ed., McGraw-Hill Book Company, Inc., New York, 1951.

MILLAR, E. C., "Fundamentals of Soil Science," John Wiley & Sons, Inc., New York, 1946.

MORRISON, F. B., "Feeds and Feeding," 8th ed., The Morrison Publishing Company, Ithaca, N.Y., 1949.

MYERS, G. E., G. M. LITTLE, and S. ROBINSON, "Planning Your Future," 4th ed., McGraw-Hill Book Company, Inc., New York, 1953.

NOLAN, A. W., "Short Stories for Future Farmers," The Interstate, Danville, Ill., 1936.

PEARSON, H. S., "Success on the Small Farm," McGraw-Hill Book Company, Inc., New York, 1946.

PETERS, W. H., G. P. DEYOE, and W. A. ROSS, "Raising Livestock," 2d ed., McGraw-Hill Book Company, Inc., New York, 1953.

PETERSON, H. (editor), "Great Teachers," Rutgers University Press, New Brunswick, N.J., 1946.

PIERCE, W. G., "Youth Comes of Age," McGraw-Hill Book Company, Inc., New York, 1948.

PRESTON, J. F., "Developing Farm Woodland," McGraw-Hill Book Company, Inc., New York, 1953.

PURKEY, D. R., "Winning F.F.A. Speeches," The Interstate, Danville, Ill., 1951.

RATHER, H. C., and C. M. HARRISON, "Field Crops," 2d ed., McGraw-Hill Book Company, Inc., New York, 1951.

RAWLINGS, M. K., "The Yearling," Charles Scribner's Sons, New York, 1938.

RICE, J. E., and H. E. BOTSFORD, "Practical Poultry Management," 5th ed., John Wiley & Sons, Inc., New York, 1949.

RICE, V. A., F. N. ANDREWS, and E. J. WARWICK, "Breeding Better Livestock," McGraw-Hill Book Co., Inc., New York, 1953.

ROBERTSON, L. S., and R. H. WOODS, "Farm Management," J. B. Lippincott Company, Philadelphia, 1946.

ROEHL, L. M., "The Farmer's Shop Book," The Bruce Publishing Company, Milwaukee, 1947.

ROSS, W. A., "Forward F.F.A.," The French-Bray Printing Company, Baltimore, 1939.

SCHLESINGER, A. M., "Learning How to Behave," The Macmillan Company, New York, 1946.

SCHMIDT, S., "Shadow over Winding Ranch," Random House, New York, 1940.

SHOEMAKER, J. S., "Vegetable Growing," John Wiley & Sons, Inc., New York, 1947.

SMEDLEY, F., "Home Pork Production," Orange Judd Publishing Co., Inc., New York, 1945.

SOUTHWELL, B. L., J. T. WHEELER, and A. O. DUNCAN, "Swine Production in the South," The Interstate, Danville, Ill., 1940.

"Standard of Perfection," American Poultry Association, Davenport, Iowa, 1945.

STONE, A. A., "Farm Machinery," 3d ed., John Wiley & Sons, Inc., New York, 1942.

STOUT, G. J., "The Home Freezer Handbook," D. Van Nostrand Company, Inc., New York, 1947.

STRATTON, D. C., and H. B. SCHLEMAN, "Your Best Foot Forward," McGraw-Hill Book Company, Inc., New York, 1940.

TENNEY, A. W., "Practical Activities for Future Farmers Chapters," The Interstate, Danville, Ill., 1941.

———, "Programs for Future Farmer Chapter Meetings," The Interstate, Danville, Ill., 1938.

THOMAS, R. H., P. M. REAVES, and C. W. PEGRAM, "Dairy Farming in the South," The Interstate, Danville, Ill., 1944.

TRESSLER, D. K., and C. F. EVERS, "The Freezing and Preservation of Food," Avi Publishing Company, New York, 1947.

TURNER, A. W., and E. J. JOHNSON, "Machines for the Farm, Ranch, and Plantation," McGraw-Hill Book Company, Inc., New York, 1948.

VAUGHN, H. W., "Breeds of Livestock in America," College Book Company, Columbus, Ohio, 1947.

WATTS, R. L., "The Vegetable Growing Business," Orange Judd Publishing Co., Inc., New York, 1946.

WESTVELD, R. H., and R. H. PECK, "Forestry in Farm Management," John Wiley & Sons, Inc., New York, 1941.

WILSON, H. K., "Grain Crops," McGraw-Hill Book Company, Inc., New York, 1948.

WILSTACH, P., "Jefferson and Monticello," Doubleday & Company, Inc., New York, 1925.

WINTERS, L. M., "Introduction to Breeding Farm Animals," John Wiley & Sons, Inc., New York, 1942.

WOLFE, T. K., and M. S. KIPPS, "Production of Field Crops," 4th ed., McGraw-Hill Book Company, Inc., New York, 1953.

WOOLEY, J. C., "Repairing and Constructing Farm Buildings," McGraw-Hill Book Company, Inc., New York, 1952.

WRIGHT, P. H., "So We'll Live," Houghton Mifflin Company, Boston, 1937.

Appendix IX
F.F.A. Supplies

L. G. Balfour Company, Attleboro, Mass. All types of official F.F.A. jewelry, such as pins, keys, medals, rings, plaques, necktie chain clasps, watch fobs, trophy cups, belt buckles, etc.

The Chapter Supply Company, Danville, Ill. Officer drapes, owls, model ears of corn, flags, trophies, and busts of Washington and Jefferson.

Cundy Bettoney Company, Hyde Park, Boston, Mass. Copies of the "F.F.A. March."

Deere & Co., Moline, Ill. Miniature metal plow.

Future Farmers Supply Service, Alexandria, Va. All types of official F.F.A. supplies, such as blankets, bracelets, book ends, billfolds, buttons, caps, coveralls, banners, denims, emblem cuts and cutouts, felt goods, jackets, knives, metal signs, neckties, notebooks, pens, pencils, picnic and banquet supplies, plaques, recordings, shirts, shop coats, stationery and printed materials, and stencils.

St. Louis Button Company, St. Louis, Mo. Badges, buttons, flags, gavels, metal markers, pencil clips, prize ribbons, project markets, etc.

Swift and Company, Chicago 9, Ill. Pictures of Washington and Jefferson.

W. M. Welch Manufacturing Company, Chicago, Ill. Charters for F.F.A. chapters.

Appendix X

N.F.A. Supplies

L. G. Balfour Company, Attleboro, Mass.   Jewelry.

Deere & Co., Moline, Ill.   Miniature plows.

The French-Bray Printing Company, Baltimore 2, Md.   Chapter treasurer and secretary books, printing, and electrotype cuts of N.F.A. emblem.

Prairie View A. & M. College, Department of Agricultural Education, Prairie View, Tex.   Chapter charters.

St. Louis Button Company, St. Louis, Mo.   N.F.A. buttons.

Staunton Novelty Company, Staunton, Va.   Banners, caps, pennants, neckties, monograms, etc.

Dr. W. F. Stewart, Ohio State University, Columbus, Ohio.   "Helps in Mastering Parliamentary Procedure."

Swift and Company, Agricultural Research Department, Chicago 9, Ill. Pictures of Dr. H. O. Sargent and Booker T. Washington.

Appendix XI

Filing System for a Teacher of Vocational Agriculture

Four-drawer Filing Cabinet

Top Drawer.   One set of *A* to *Z* guides, a number of blank guides, and manila letter folders.

1. Official correspondence, *A* to *Z* guides
2. Future Farmers of America
    a. Chapter program of work
    b. Programs for chapter meetings
    c. Chapter contests
    d. Chapter membership list by degrees held
    e. List of officers—national, state, and local
    f. Chapter record of publicity
    g. Secretary and treasurer books
    h. Chapter-accomplishment report
    i. Reference materials
    j. Miscellaneous
3. Reports of the teacher
    a. Blank report forms
    b. Monthly reports
    c. Preliminary reports on supervised farming
    d. Final reports on supervised farming
    e. The teacher's annual program of work
    f. The teacher's accomplishment report
    g. Monthly or quarterly salary vouchers
    h. State newsletters
    i. Inventory of equipment
    j. Miscellaneous

Second Drawer.   One set of *A* to *Z* guides, blank guides, and manila letter folders.

1. Veteran training program in agriculture
    a. Blank forms
    b. Regulations and instructions
    c. Course outlines and teaching materials

377

    d. Reports
    e. Unpaid bills
    f. Paid bills
    g. County advisory committee
  2. Records of students
    a. Folder for each student enrolled, arranged alphabetically
  3. Follow-up records
    a. Follow-up record cards for each former student and a folder for cards by years
    b. Summary cards of follow-up records
    c. Supervised farming records for the past year
    d. Miscellaneous

Third Drawer. Blank guides and letter folders.

  1. Teaching materials
    a. The course of study
    b. Teaching plans
    c. Recommendations of supervisors
    d. Agricultural education bulletins
    e. Miscellaneous teaching aids
  2. Special reference materials
    a. Local farm surveys made
    b. Results of farm-management surveys
    c. Production and Marketing Administration
    d. Soil conservation
    e. Miscellaneous

Fourth Drawer. One set of *A* to *Z* guides, blank guides, and manila letter folders.

  1. General reference materials and catalogues
    a. Agricultural statistics
    b. Book lists and catalogues
    c. Fertilizer materials
    d. Horticulture
    e. Livestock
    f. Forestry
    g. Farm shop
    h. Poultry
    i. School supplies
    j. Visual-aid materials
    k. Miscellaneous
  2. Transfer
    a. Previous year's correspondence
    b. Reports of previous years

Appendix XII

Livestock Breed Associations

Beef and Dual-purpose Cattle

American Aberdeen-Angus Breeders' Association, Union Stock Yards, Chicago 9, Ill.

American Brahman Breeders' Association, Houston 2, Tex.

American Devon Cattle Club, Meredith, N.H.

American Galloway Breeders' Association, Henry, Ill.

American Hereford Association, Kansas City 6, Mo.

American Milking Shorthorn Society, Chicago 9, Ill.

American Polled Hereford Breeders' Association, Kansas City 6, Mo.

American Polled Shorthorn Society, Chicago 9, Ill.

American Shorthorn Breeders' Association, Union Stock Yards, Chicago 9, Ill.

Red Dane Cattle Breeders' Association, Marlette, Mich.

Red Poll Cattle Club of America, Lincoln 3, Neb.

Dairy Cattle

American Guernsey Cattle Club, Peterboro, N.H.

American Jersey Cattle Club, Columbus 15, Ohio.

American Kerry and Dexter Club, Decorah, Iowa.

Ayrshire Breeders' Association, Brandon, Vt.

Brown Swiss Cattle Breeders' Association, Beloit, Wis.

Dutch Belted Cattle Association of America, Anamosa, Iowa.

Holstein-Friesian Association of America, Brattleboro, Vt.

Horses, Jacks, and Ponies

American Hackney Horse Society, Inc., New York, N.Y.

American Quarter Horse Association, Amarillo, Tex.

American Saddle Horse Breeders' Association, Louisville, Ky.

American Shetland Pony Club, South Bend, Ind.

American Shire Horse Association, Des Moines, Iowa.

American Suffolk Horse Association, Clinton, N.J.

Appaloosa Horse Club, Moscow, Idaho.
Arabian Horse Club of America, Chicago 3, Ill.
Belgian Draft Horse Corporation of America, Wabash, Ind.
Cleveland Bay Society of America, White Post, Va.
Clydesdale Breeders' Association of the United States, Clarksburg, W.Va.
The Jockey Club (Thoroughbred), New York 17, N.Y.
Morgan Horse Club, New York 4, N.Y.
Morocco Spotted Horse Association of America, Greenfield, Iowa.
Palomino Horse Association, Reseda, Calif.
Palomino Horse Breeders of America, Mineral Wells, Tex.
Percheron Horse Association of America, Union Stock Yards, Chicago 9, Ill.
Pinto Horse Society, Concord, Calif.
Standard Jack and Jennet Registry of America, Garden City, Kan.
Tennessee Walking Horse Breeders' Association, Lewisburg, Tenn.
United States Trotting Association (Standardbred), Columbus, Ohio.
Welsh Pony Society of America, University of Michigan, Ann Arbor, Mich.

Sheep and Goats

American Cheviot Sheep Society, Oneonta, N.Y.
American Corriedale Association, Columbia, Mo.
American Cotswold Registry Association, Union Stock Yards, Chicago, Ill.
American and Delaine-Merino Association, Marysville, Ohio.
American Hampshire Sheep Association, Detroit 2, Mich.
American Leicester Sheep Registry Association, Cameron, Ill.
American Oxford Down Record Association, Clayton, Ind.
American Rambouillet Sheep Breeders' Association, San Angelo, Tex.
American Romney Sheep Breeders' Association, Oregon State College, Corvallis, Ore.
American Shropshire Registry Association, Lafayette, Ind.
American Southdown Breeders' Association, State College, Pa.
American Suffolk Sheep Society, University of Idaho, Moscow, Idaho.
Black Top and National Delaine-Merino Sheep Breeders' Association, Dexter, Mich.
Columbia Sheep Breeders' Association of America, College Station, Fargo, N.D.
Karakul Fur Sheep Registry, Friendship, Wis.
National Lincoln Sheep Breeders' Association, East Lansing, Mich.
National Suffolk Sheep Association, Middleville, Mich.
Texas Delaine-Merino Record Association, Brady, Tex.
American Angora Goat Breeders' Association, Rocksprings, Tex.
American Goat Society, Mena, Ark.
American Milk Goat Record Association, Ipswich, Mass.

Swine

American Berkshire Association, Springfield, Ill.
American Spotted Poland China Record Association, Moberly, Mo.
American Yorkshire Club, Lafayette, Ind.
Breeders' Chester White Record Association, Des Moines 9, Iowa.
Chester White Swine Record Association, Rochester, Ind.
Hampshire Swine Registry, Peoria, Ill.
Kentucky Red Berkshire Swine Association, Lancaster, Ky.
National Hereford Hog Record Association, Chariton, Iowa.
National Mule Foot Hog Record Association, DeGraff, Ohio.
National Spotted Poland China Record, Indianapolis, Ind.
O.I.C. Swine Association, Brookville, Ohio.
O.I.C. Swine Breeders' Association, Goshen, Ind.
Poland-China Record Association, Galesburg, Ill.
Tamworth Swine Association, Hagerstown, Ind.
United Duroc Record Association, Peoria 3, Ill.

Appendix XIII

Agricultural Colleges, Experiment Stations, and Extension Services

State	Agricultural college	Experiment station	Extension service
Alabama	Auburn	Auburn	Auburn
Arizona	Tucson	Tucson	Tucson
Arkansas	Fayetteville	Fayetteville	Little Rock
California	Berkeley	Berkeley	Berkeley
Colorado	Fort Collins	Fort Collins	Fort Collins
Connecticut	Storrs	Storrs and New Haven	Storrs
Delaware	Newark	Newark	Newark
Florida	Gainesville	Gainesville	Gainesville
Georgia	Athens	Experiment	Athens
Idaho	Moscow	Moscow	Boise
Illinois	Urbana	Urbana	Urbana
Indiana	Lafayette	Lafayette	Lafayette
Iowa	Ames	Ames	Ames
Kansas	Manhattan	Manhattan	Manhattan
Kentucky	Lexington	Lexington	Lexington
Louisiana	Baton Rouge	Baton Rouge	Baton Rouge
Maine	Orono	Orono	Orono
Maryland	College Park	College Park	College Park
Massachusetts	Amherst	Amherst	Amherst
Michigan	East Lansing	East Lansing	East Lansing
Minnesota	University Farm, St. Paul	University Farm, St. Paul	University Farm, St. Paul
Mississippi	State College	State College	State College
Missouri	Columbia	Columbia	Columbia
Montana	Bozeman	Bozeman	Bozeman
Nebraska	Lincoln	Lincoln	Lincoln
Nevada	Reno	Reno	Reno
New Hampshire	Durham	Durham	Durham
New Jersey	New Brunswick	New Brunswick	New Brunswick
New Mexico	State College	State College	State College
New York	Ithaca	Ithaca and Geneva	Ithaca
North Carolina	Raleigh	Raleigh	Raleigh
North Dakota	Fargo	Fargo	Fargo
Ohio	Columbus	Wooster	Columbus
Oklahoma	Stillwater	Stillwater	Stillwater
Oregon	Corvallis	Corvallis	Corvallis
Pennsylvania	State College	State College	State College
Rhode Island	Kingston	Kingston	Kingston
South Carolina	Clemson	Clemson	Clemson
South Dakota	Brookings	Brookings	Brookings
Tennessee	Knoxville	Knoxville	Knoxville
Texas	College Station	College Station	College Station
Utah	Logan	Logan	Logan
Vermont	Burlington	Burlington	Burlington
Virginia	Blacksburg	Blacksburg	Blacksburg
Washington	Pullman	Pullman	Pullman
West Virginia	Morgantown	Morgantown	Morgantown
Wisconsin	Madison	Madison	Madison
Wyoming	Laramie	Laramie	Laramie

Appendix XIV
Correlated List of Visual Aids

THE VISUAL AIDS listed below and on the following pages can be used to supplement the material in this book. For the convenience of its users, they have been grouped under three categories—educational principles, education methods, and vocational agriculture. No attempt has been made to list the many films and other visual aids that can be used in the teaching of agricultural subjects.

Both motion pictures and filmstrips are included in this list, and the character of each one is indicated by the self-explanatory abbreviations "MP" and "FS." Immediately following this identification is the name of the producer; and if the distributor is different from the producer, the name of the distributor follows the name of the producer. Abbreviations are used for the names of producers and distributors, and these abbreviations are identified in a directory of sources at the end of the bibliography. In most instances, the films can be borrowed or rented from local or state 16mm film libraries. (A nationwide list of these local sources is given in *A Directory of 2002 16mm Film Libraries*, available from the Superintendent of Documents, Washington 25, D.C.) Unless otherwise indicated, the motion pictures are 16mm sound black-and-white films. The filmstrips are all 35mm black-and-white and silent. The length of the motion pictures is given in minutes (min), that of the filmstrips in frames (fr).

This bibliography is suggestive only, and film users should examine the latest annual edition and quarterly supplements of *Educational Film Guide*, a catalogue of some 12,000 films published by the H. W. Wilson Company, New York. The *Guide*, a standard reference book, is available in most college and public libraries.

Educational Principles

Assignment: Tomorrow (MP NEA 26min). Shows the importance of the teacher and the public school in preserving the American way of life. Stresses community needs and the role of the teacher in meeting such needs.
Design of American Public Education (MP McGraw 16min).

Compares and contrasts by means of animated cartoons and drawings an "assembly-line" educational system with one geared to meet the needs of today's young people.   Explains the "design" of American education as one devoted to people, not merely to method.

Education for All American Children (FS   NEA   52fr).   Illustrates the major conclusions and recommendations in the 1948 report, with the same title, of the Educational Policies Commission.

Preparation of Teachers (MP   USDS/UWF   20min).   Explains the teacher-training program at Ball State Teachers College, Muncie, Ind., and illustrates how to understand children, provide for individual differences, and develop desirable personality traits in teachers.

Problem of Pupil Adjustment: The Drop-out (MP   McGraw   20min). Shows the characteristics of a high school program which cause students to leave school as soon as possible.

Problem of Pupil Adjustment: The Stay-in (MP   McGraw   19min). Tells how "drop-outs" can be reduced when individual needs are met in a school program that stresses learning in terms of adjustment to everyday living.

The School and the Community (MP   McGraw   14min   color). Illustrates with animated cartoons and drawings the traditional and modern concepts of the relationship between the school and its community. Correlated filmstrip, same title, 31fr, also available.

Teachers for Tomorrow (MP   Wis U   22min).   Tells how prospective teachers are chosen and prepared for a teaching career at the University of Wisconsin.

Teaching (MP   VGF   11min).   Deals briefly with the contributions of teachers, the traits of a good teacher, teaching attractions, educational requirements, and various types of teaching jobs.

Willie and the Mouse (MP   MGM/TFC   11min).   Demonstrates the educational implications of the psychological testing of mice in the laboratory and shows how advances in the understanding of behavior have influenced teaching materials and methods.

Educational Methods

Broader Concept of Method.   Part 1: Developing Pupil Interest (MP   McGraw   13min).   Contrasts a conventional, teacher-dominated lesson and an informal class with teachers and students planning and working together.   Correlated filmstrip, same title, 33fr, also available.

Broader Concept of Method.   Part 2: Teachers and Pupils Planning and Working Together (MP   McGraw   19min).   Shows students learning to work together in class projects with the help and guidance of the teacher.   Correlated filmstrip, same title, 37fr, also available.

Community Resources in Teaching (MP   Iowa   20min).   Shows how the community and its resources and the school and its functions can be integrated.

Introduction to Student Teaching (MP   Ind U   20min).   Portrays the activities of student teachers.   Designed primarily for prospective secondary school teachers.

Maintaining Classroom Discipline (MP   McGraw   15min).   Illustrates two methods of discipline and their results in terms of classroom behavior and student learning.

Teaching-materials Center (MP   Va Ed Dept   12min).   Depicts the values to the classroom teacher of a teaching-materials center, the materials and resources available from a good center, and the organization of such a center.

Vocational Agriculture

The Farmer of Tomorrow (MP   GM   28min   color).   Dramatizes the part the Future Farmers of America play in the lives of many of its members and former members.

The Green Hand (MP   SR/Venard   44min).   Tells the story of a bad boy who was not really so bad but just not interested and how, through the Future Farmers of America and the guidance of his vocational agriculture teacher, he became a good farmer and a good citizen.

Schools and the Community (MP   MOT/McGraw).   Shows how various communities are training their students in the skills by which they will later earn their livelihood, including those of vocational agriculture.

That Inspiring Task (MP   SR/Venard   20min   color).   Pays tribute to the vocational agriculture instructor and the part he plays in inspiring farm boys to remain on the farm and to be better farmers.   Shows many projects and activities of the Future Farmers of America.

Sources of Films Listed

GM—General Motors Corporation, Detroit 2, Mich.

Ind U—Indiana University, Audio-Visual Center, Bloomington, Ind.

Iowa—State University of Iowa, Iowa City, Iowa.

McGraw—McGraw-Hill Book Company, Inc., Text-Film Department, 330 West 42d St., New York 36, N.Y.

MGM—Metro-Goldwyn-Mayer. (Film distributed by Teaching Film Custodians.)

MOT—March of Time.

NEA—National Education Association, 1201 16th St., N.W., Washington, D.C.

SR—Sears Roebuck Foundation, Chicago, Ill.

TFC—Teaching Film Custodians, Inc., 25 West 45th St., New York 18, N.Y.

USDS—U.S. Department of State.   (Films distributed in the United States by United World Films, Inc.)

UWF—United World Films, Inc., 1445 Park Ave., New York 29, N.Y.

Va Ed Dept—Virginia State Department of Education, Richmond, Va.

Venard—The Venard Organization, Peoria 2, Ill.

VGF—Vocational Guidance Films, 215 East Third St., Des Moines, Iowa.

Wis U—University of Wisconsin, Bureau of Visual Instruction, Madison, Wis.

Index

Students, discipline of, 187–189
  enrollment of, 140
  evaluation of, 340–342
  follow-up of, 304
  former, 299–300
  notebooks for, 189–193
  placement services for, 221–222, 303–304
  records of, 297–300
  registering, 146–148
  response of, 175
  in supervised farming, 226–227, 233–235
  transportation of, 165
  visiting, 303–304
Summer teaching, 301–303
Supervised farming, 215–235
  for adult farmers, 261
  cooperative relationships in, 224–226
  jobs in, 122–123
  program planning for, 222–224
  projects in, 216–218, 221
  records of, 227–231
  reports on, 299
  school credit for, 233
  students, establishing in, 233–235
    launching in, 226–227
  teacher's supervision, 231–233
  values of, 218–219
  for young farmers, 246–247
Supervised study method, 158–160
Supplementary farm practice, 218
Supplies, 56–68
  classroom, 63–64, 358–361
  farm mechanics, 66–68, 362–365
  F.F.A., 375
  laboratory, 63–64, 358–361
  N.F.A., 376
Surveys, 94–114
  contribution to living, 106–108
  farm-enterprise, 100–102, 116
  farm-inventory, 94–100, 116
  farm-management, 108
  farm-mechanics, 108–114, 116
  progress and achievement, 102–106

Tables, 56–58
  acidproofing, 57
  classroom, 56
  laboratory, 58
Talks, publicity, 337–338
Teachers, annual program of, 35–43

Teachers, books for, 307–308
  bulletins for, 308–309
  conferences of, 309
  duties of, 22–30
  filing system for, 300, 377–378
  graduate work for, 309–310
  guidance by, 303–305
  in-service training of, 310
  local help for, 310–311
  magazines for, 308
  office of, 50
  opportunities for advancement of, 44–45
  professional and technical improvement of, 305–310
  qualifications of, 30–32
  records kept by, 232, 297–300
  summer activities of, 43, 301–305
  vacations for, 302–303
Teaching methods (see Teaching procedures)
Teaching plans, 178–184
  for adult farmers, 256–258
  for young farmers, 247–249
Teaching procedures, 149–177
  assignment method, 156–158
  conference method, 176–177, 256–259
  demonstrations, 169–171
  discussion method, 171–176
  field trips, 164–169
  four-step, 150–152
  individualized study, 153–156
  laboratory method, 161–164
  project method, 6–7
  supervised study, 158–161
  (See also Course of study)
Teaching program, outline of, 122–129
Teaching schedule, 144–146
Television programs, 337
Tests, performance, 152
Textbooks, agricultural, 69–70, 369–374
Thought questions, 174
Tools, farm shop, 362–365
  inventory of, 110–111
  storing, 67–68
Tours, for adult farmers, 260
  educational, 338
  F.F.A., 279–280
  project, 225
  (See also Field trips)
Type jobs, 127–128

F